NELSON Math GRADE 5

ISBN-13: 978-0-17-682337-5
ISBN-10: 0-17-682337-9

Printed and bound in Canada
3 4 20 19

Cover Design
Trinh Truong

Cover Image
Bowden Images/Getty Images

Illustrations
Page 18, 42, 82, 83, 120: Coin images © 2017 Royal Canadian Mint. All rights reserved.
Page 18 and 38: Canadian banknote images are reproduced with permission from the Bank of Canada.

Contents

REWARD CONTRACT

When you complete a topic in your Nelson Math Workbook, colour in a circle.

My reward will be ...

NOTHING AT ALL!

____

____

START

Patterns in Mathematics

Numeration

Data Management

Addition and Subtraction

Measuring Length and Time

Multiplication and Division

2-D Geometry

Area and Grids

Multiplying Decimals

Dividing Decimals

3-D Geometry and 3-D Measurement

Fractions

Probability

Patterns and Motion in Geometry

FINISH

Name: ______________________ Date: ______________

Parent/Guardian: ______________________________

2-D Patterns

Use models and t-charts to record, extend, and make predictions about number patterns.

Look at design 1 of the capital letter F.
It has been made from 10 dots.

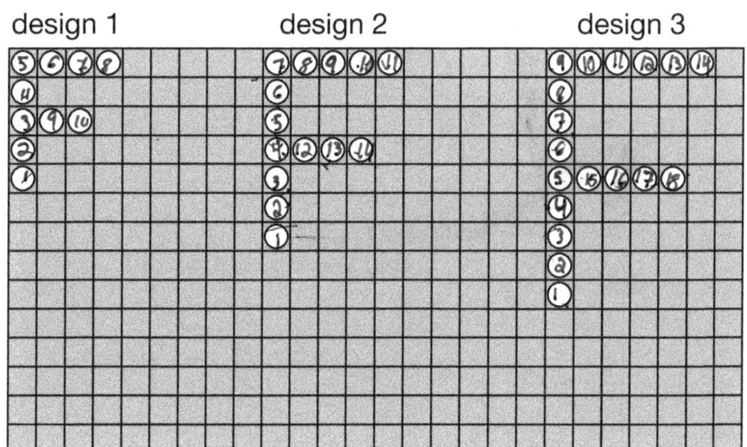

1. How many dots are needed to complete design 4?
22 dots ✓

2. Predict the number of dots needed to complete design 5.
26 dots ✓

3. Draw design 4 and design 5.

4. Complete the t-chart to show the pattern.

Letter design	Number of dots
1	10 ✓
2	14 ✓
3	18 ✓
4	22 ✓
5	26 ✓

design 4 design 5

5. If you had a total of 50 dots, what design number would the letter F be?
Design 9 x11

At-Home Help

A **2-D pattern** has a length and a width.

For example, these shapes form a 2-D pattern.

A **t-chart** has 2 columns. The data in both columns are related.

For example: As the number of songs increases by 1, the number of minutes of practice increases by 15 minutes.

Number of songs	Number of minutes of practice
1	10
2	25
3	40

Patterns in Tables

Create tables to display, predict, and extend patterns.

Apple crisp is a great recipe to make for many different sized groups. The recipe in the chart is complete for one class and partially complete for two classes.

Apple Crisp Recipe

Number of classes	Number of apples	Amount of butter (mL)	Amount of brown sugar (mL)
1	24	150	200
2	48	300	400 ✓
3	72	450 ✓	600 ✓
4	96 ✓	600 ✓	800 ✓
5	120 ✓	750 ✓	900 ✗ 1000

At-Home Help

A **table** usually has two or more columns of data. Each column has its own heading and is related to the other columns.

For example:

Number of times I make the recipe	Number of cups of water	Number of scoops of crystals	Number of people served
1	5	3	4
2			

1. Complete the recipe for all of the classes in the chart.

2. What pattern rules did you use to complete the table?

   +The first number. ✓

3. If you bought 200 apples, what is the greatest number of classes that could have apple crisp? Explain your thinking using numbers.

4. **a)** If one and one half classes wanted apple crisp, explain how you would calculate the amount of each ingredient.

   b) Calculate the amounts. Show your work.

Solve Problems Using Patterns

Identify patterns to solve problems.

1. What pattern could you use to add these numbers? Write a number sentence to show the pattern.

   1 + 2 + 3 + 4 + ... + 37 + 38 + 39 + 40

2. Use a pattern to add these numbers. Show your work.

   15 + 25 + 35 + 45 + 55 + 65 + 75 + 85

At-Home Help

Pairing numbers can help you find sums more easily. Try to find pairs that add up to the same number.

For example, to add

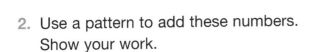

1 + 3 + 5 + 7 + 9 + 11

notice that 1 + 11, 3 + 9, and 5 + 7 all add up to 12.

sum = (1 + 11) + (3 + 9) + (5 + 7)
= 12 + 12 + 12
= 36

3. Glynis is stacking boxes of candles for a store display.

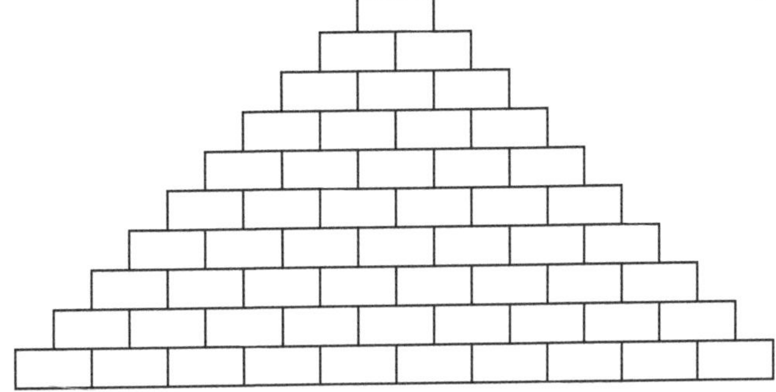

a) Make a plan that uses a pattern to find the number of boxes in the stack. Use number sentences and words.

b) Use your plan to find the total number of boxes in the stack.

c) How many boxes would there be in a stack that has 16 boxes in the bottom row? Explain your answer using number sentences and words.

3-D Patterns

Create a 3-D pattern and make predictions about its growth.

Look at the stack of boxes in Question 3 on page 3.

1. Determine how each stack is made from the one before. Then complete the table to show how many layers of boxes there will be if there are 210 boxes in total.

Number of layers	Number of new boxes	Total number of boxes
1	1	1
2	2	2 + 1 = 3
3	3	3 + 3 = 6
4		

2. Explain what pattern you used to calculate your answer.

____

____

At-Home Help

A **3-D pattern** has a length, a width, and a height.

For example, these cubes form a 3-D pattern.

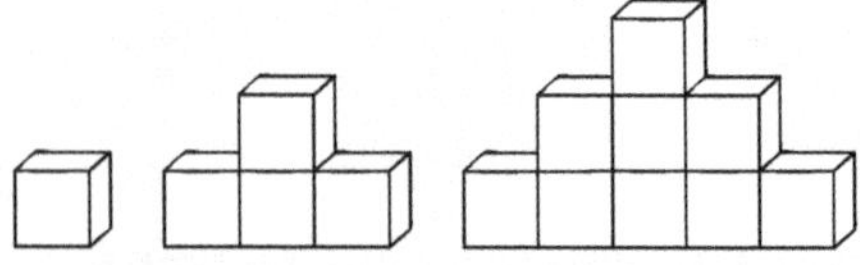

Organizing numbers in a table helps you see patterns.

For example:

Number of layers	Number of new boxes	Total number of boxes
1	1	1
2	3	3 + 1 = 4
3	5	5 + 4 = 9
4	7	7 + 9 = 16

total number of boxes
= number of new boxes
+ total number of boxes
in the line above

Number Patterns in Spreadsheets

Create and identify patterns in spreadsheets.

Yoshi is starting a new spreadsheet for a school sale of used equipment that includes small beanbags, medium hula hoops, and large basketballs.

	A	B	C	D
1	Sports equipment sale prices			
2	Number of items	Small	Medium	Large
3	1	$1.20	$2.40	$4.40
4	2	$2.40	$4.80	$8.80
5	3	$3.60	$7.20	$13.20
6	4	$4.80	$9.60	$17.60
7	5			
8	6			
9	7			
10	8			

At-Home Help

Spreadsheets are columns of data that are related. Each number in a spreadsheet has its own cell. To extend the numbers in a column, use one or more operations.

For example:
cost of 3 red shirts in cell
B5 = B3 + B4, or B5 = B3 × A5
total cost in cell D3 = B3 + C3

	A	B	C	D
1	Shirt prices			
2	Number of shirts	Red	Green	Total cost
3	1	$10.00	$15.00	$25.00
4	2	$20.00	$30.00	$50.00
5	3	$30.00	$45.00	$75.00

1. Complete the spreadsheet.
2. Write a pattern rule for column B by looking at the numbers in that column. Then write a pattern rule for columns C and D.

____

____

____

3. Calculate the total cost. Show your work.

   a) 6 small items and total cost

   b) 3 small items, 2 medium items, and 7 large items and total cost

   c) 10 items of each size and total cost

4. How can you get the answer in cell C5 from other cells?

Test Yourself

Circle the correct answer.

Use the table to answer Questions 1 and 2.

Number of teams	Number of players
1	4
2	8
3	16
4	32
5	64

1. What is the pattern in the second column of the table?

   A. The numbers increase by 4.
   B. The numbers double.
   C. The numbers increase by 3.
   D. The numbers increase by 2.

2. How many players would there be if there were 7 teams?

   A. 256 **B.** 212 **C.** 128 **D.** 246

3. Which table shows column 1 increasing by multiplying by 3 and column 2 doubling?

A.

1	8
3	10
9	12
12	14

B.

1	4
3	8
6	16
12	32

C.

1	2
2	6
4	18
8	54

D.

1	1
3	2
9	4
27	8

4. What are the next 2 numbers in this pattern?

   29, 30, 32, 35, 39, 44, ______, ______

   A. 50 and 55 **B.** 49 and 55 **C.** 50 and 57 **D.** 49 and 57

Test Yourself Page 2

5. Soccer teams go through a lot of equipment in one season. What numbers would complete the last row of this table?

Number of teams	Number of soccer nets	Number of soccer balls
1	2	5
3	6	15
5	10	25
?	?	?

A. 7, 14, 30 **B.** 7, 14, 35 **C.** 6, 15, 30 **D.** 7, 15, 35

6. What will be the number of Xs in design 4 and design 7?

design 1

```
XXX
X X
```

design 2

```
XXXX
X  X
X  X
```

design 3

```
XXXXX
X   X
X   X
X   X
```

A. 19 and 13 **B.** 23 and 14 **C.** 14 and 23 **D.** 13 and 19

Use this spreadsheet to answer Questions 7 and 8.

	A	B	C	D
1	Cost of Cans			
2	Number of Cans	Small	Medium	Large
3	1	$0.50	$2.00	$3.25
4	2	$1.00	$4.00	$6.50
5	3	$1.50	$6.00	$9.75

7. What would be the total cost of 4 cans of each size?

A. $22.50 **B.** $24.00 **C.** $23.50 **D.** $23.00

8. What is the pattern rule for column C?

A. Start at $2.00 and add $0.50 to each number going down column C.

B. Start at $2.00 and add $2.00 to each number going down column C.

C. Start at $2.00 and add $3.25 to each number going down column C.

D. Start at $2.00 and add $1.00 to each number going down column C.

Estimating 50 Thousand

Use numbers you know to estimate 50 thousand objects.

1. Make a list of items in your home that you can count to 100.

____

____

____

2. Choose one item from your list. Count 2 sets of 100 and put them in a pile.

3. How many of those piles would make a quantity of 1000 items? Show your work.

4. How many piles of 1000 would make a quantity of 50 thousand items? Show your work.

At-Home Help

To estimate 50 thousand, use familiar objects in smaller quantities.

For example: Use 100 nickels. Put them in a pile in a shoebox. About how many piles of 100 will fill the shoebox?

This answer can be used to estimate the number of boxes needed for 10 thousand nickels.

This new answer can be used to estimate the number of boxes needed for 50 thousand nickels.

5. Estimate what 50 thousand of those items would look like. How would you describe it to a friend?

____

____

____

6. Use another way to estimate 50 thousand of the same item. Describe your method in detail.

____

____

7. Choose another item from your list. Estimate what 50 thousand of these items would look like.

____

____

Reading and Writing Numbers

Read, write, and model five-digit numbers.

1. A file on your computer is 15 827 bytes long.

   a) Write this number in words.

   ____

   b) Write this number in expanded form.

   ____

   c) Draw a representation of 15 827 using base ten blocks.

Ten thousands	Thousands	Hundreds	Tens	Ones

At-Home Help

Numbers can be represented in different ways.

For example, sixteen thousand eight hundred fifty-four is

16 854 in **standard form**,

10 000 + 6000 + 800 + 50 + 4 in **expanded form**, and

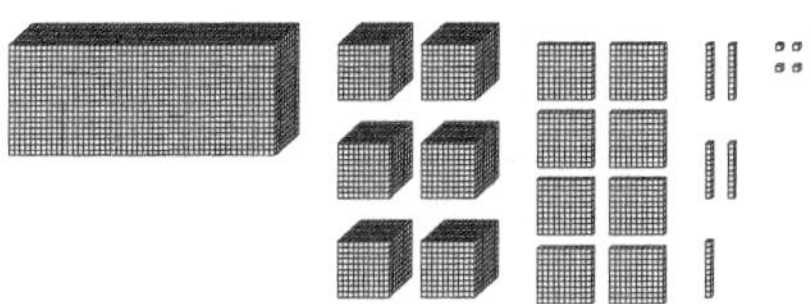

using base ten blocks

2. Write each number in words and in expanded form.

   a) 35 247 ______________________________

   ____

   b) 40 409 ______________________________

   ____

   c) 10 000 more than 50 030 ______________________________

   ____

   d) 1000 less than 70 007 ______________________________

   ____

3. Write each number in standard form.

   a) fifty thousand eleven ____________ **b)** 50 000 + 8000 + 60 + 3 ____________

Renaming Numbers

Rename numbers with up to five digits.

Suppose an ice cream company created the largest milkshake ever made. The company made a milkshake that would fill 24 382 one-litre containers.

1. Find five different combinations of full containers that would hold this milkshake. Show your work and record your answers in the table below.

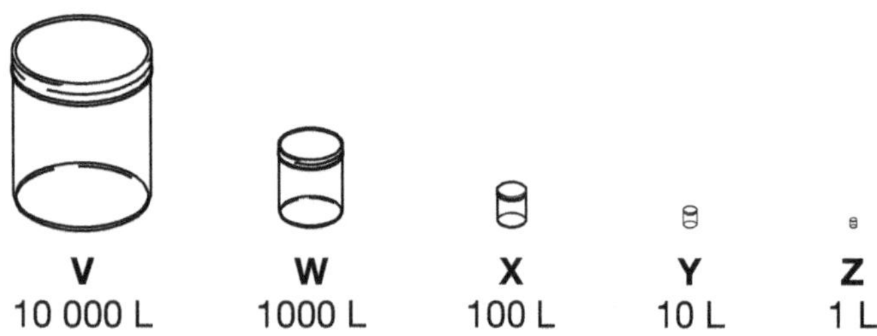

At-Home Help

Numbers can be named many different ways.

For example, 22 712 can be named

- 2 ten thousands 2 thousands 7 hundreds 1 ten 2 ones
- 22 thousands 7 hundreds 12 ones
- 227 hundreds 12 ones
- 2 ten thousands 27 hundreds 1 ten 2 ones
- 22 thousands 71 tens 2 ones

... and many more combinations of thousands, hundreds, tens, and ones.

Container V 10 000 L	Container W 1000 L	Container X 100 L	Container Y 10 L	Container Z 1 L
2	4	3	8	2

2. Draw 2 representations of 24 382 using base ten blocks.

Ten thousands	Thousands	Hundreds	Tens	Ones

Comparing and Ordering Numbers

Compare and order numbers with up to five digits.

1.

Blue Jays' opponents	Average attendance in Toronto	Average attendance at opponent's stadium
Orioles	20 572	27 955
Devil Rays	20 459	9048
Expos	31 571	12 782
Yankees	27 205	33 916
Angels	20 106	41 088

a) Which teams had a greater attendance when in their home stadium?

____

b) Show the attendance of three games on the number line.

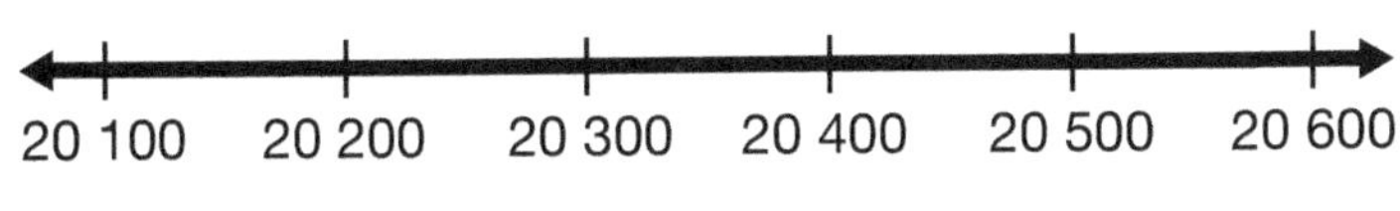

At-Home Help

When comparing and ordering numbers up to five digits, compare the digits in this order:

- ten thousand
- thousand
- hundred
- ten
- one

You can also compare and order numbers by their positions on a number line.

Inequality signs < and > show that one number is greater than another.

For example, 8 > 5 is read "eight is greater than five."

5 < 8 is read "five is less than eight."

2. Complete each number sentence using < or >.

a) 20 899 ____ 20 100 **c)** 45 072 ____ 47 072 **e)** 90 000 ____ 89 999

b) 3687 ____ 3675 **d)** 24 531 ____ 23 154 **f)** 19 560 ____ 20 650

3. Order each group of numbers from greatest to least using inequality signs.

a) 14 532 8927 41 536 50 001

____

b) 67 013 6713 67 130 67 103

____

Rounding Numbers

Round numbers to the nearest ten thousand, thousand, and hundred.

A doughnut machine has a counter to record the number of doughnuts made in a day. Yesterday the count was 36 471.

1. Round the number of doughnuts to the nearest hundred. Explain your answer.

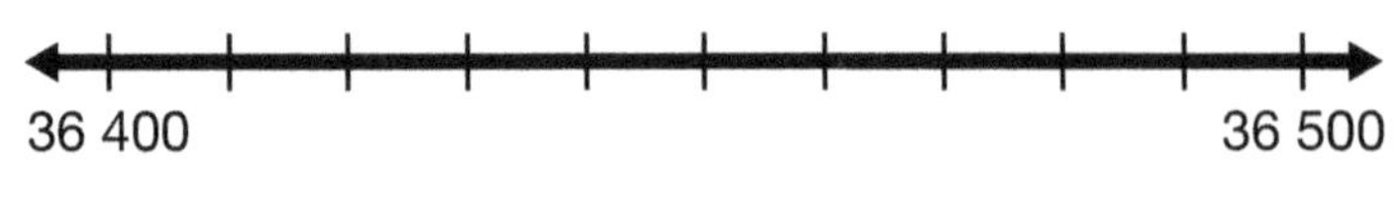

____

At-Home Help

Numbers can be **rounded** to the nearest hundred, thousand, and ten thousand.

For example, 85 354 rounded

- to the nearest hundred is 85 400
- to the nearest thousand is 85 000
- to the nearest ten thousand is 90 000

A number line helps with rounding.

2. Round the number of doughnuts to the nearest thousand. Explain your answer.

____

3. Use the number line to round the number of doughnuts to the nearest ten thousand. Explain your answer.

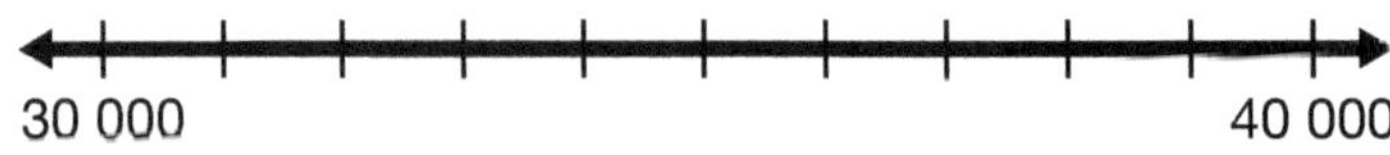

____

4. Round each number to the nearest hundred, thousand, and ten thousand.

a) 45 632 **b)** 60 119 **c)** 75 456

Communicate About Numbers in the Media

Evaluate the use of numbers in the media.

Gen is doing a science project on Canada geese. She found this information on a Web page.

The Canada goose is well known for its V-shaped migratory flight pattern and characteristic honk.

There are 11 geographical species, some with populations well over a million, and some with barely over one thousand.

In 1991 there were 63 581 Canada geese in the United Kingdom.

The largest goose is the giant, with a wingspan of more than 2 m and a mass under 10 kg. The smallest is the so-called "cackling" goose, which has a mass of only 1–2 kg.

Between 1983 and 2000, the size of the urban wintering flock in Wichita grew from 1623 birds to over 15 000!

At-Home Help

Numbers are reported in the media to give information. These are some guidelines for reporting numbers.

- When reporting a large number, use a rounded number instead of an exact number.
- When rounding, round to the most appropriate place value.
- Use ranges so that a reader can tell the difference between least and greatest values.

Communication Checklist

☑ Did you explain your thinking?
☑ Did you use math language?
☑ Did you include the right amount of detail?

1. What numbers on the Web page do you find confusing?

___

___

___

___

2. Are all the numbers described in the same way?

___

3. Do you agree with how the numbers 1623 and 15 000 are represented?

___

___

4. Where would you like to see a range given?

___

Decimal Hundredths

Read, write, and represent decimal hundredths.

1. In gym class, students practised long jump in the sandpit. Paige recorded her friends' jumps in a chart.

Long jump distances	
Sean	1.27 m
Dan	0.96 m
Lisa	1.36 m

At-Home Help

The number 1.35 is read "one and thirty-five hundredths."

This number can be represented on a metre stick number line.

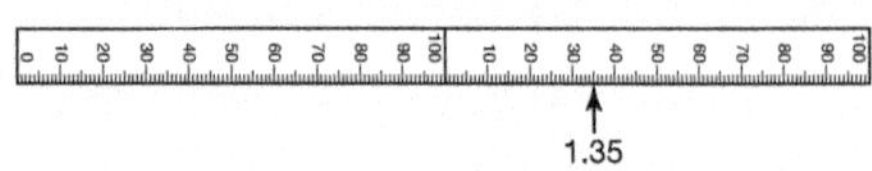

a) Use words to represent each distance.

____

____

____

____

b) Mark each distance on the metre stick number line.

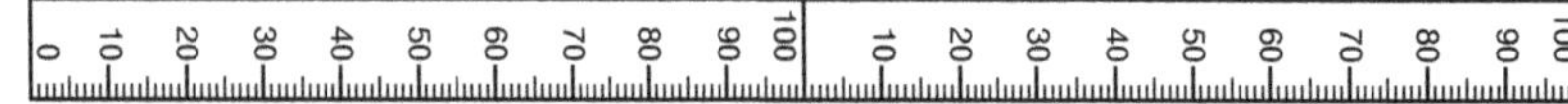

2. Write each decimal number in standard form.

a) six and seven hundredths ______________________________

b) five and ten hundredths ______________________________

c) fourteen and fifteen hundredths ______________________________

d) twenty-six hundredths ______________________________

3. Write a decimal number in standard form to fit each description.

a) 1 tenth greater than 4.16 ______________________________

b) 1 greater than 4.16 ______________________________

c) 1 hundredth greater than 4.16 ______________________________

4. Sally's best long jump distance is 1.63 m. Write in words how you would read her distance.

____

Exploring Equivalent Decimals

Rename a decimal tenth as a decimal hundredth.

1. Write a decimal tenth to describe the part of the grid that is shaded.

____

2. Write a decimal hundredth to describe the same part.

____

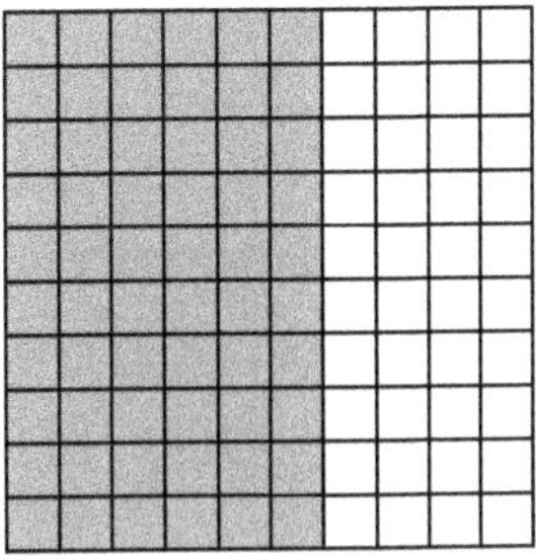

At-Home Help

Some decimal numbers can be read as tenths or hundredths.

For example, 0.30 can be read as
- "three tenths zero hundredths" or
- "thirty hundredths"

0.30 can be represented by the shaded part on this decimal grid.

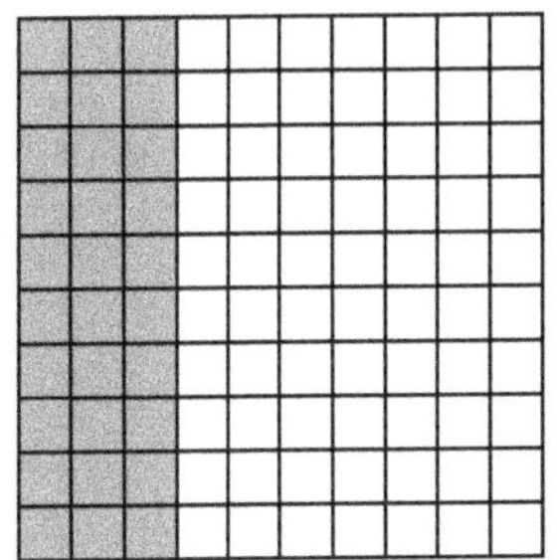

3. Shade in three more squares on the grid.

4. Write a decimal number for the total shaded part.

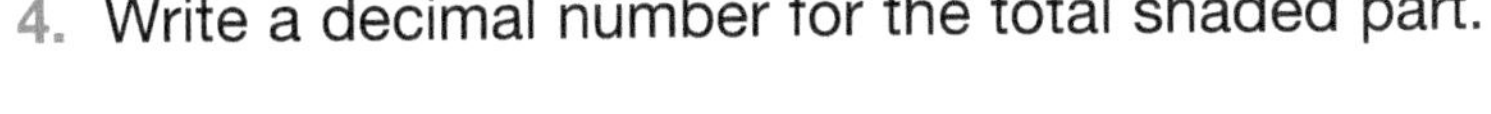

____

5. Write two ways to read this decimal number.

____

____

6. Show each decimal number on a grid by shading the appropriate squares.

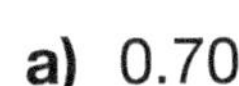

a) 0.70 **b)** 0.34 **c)** 0.07

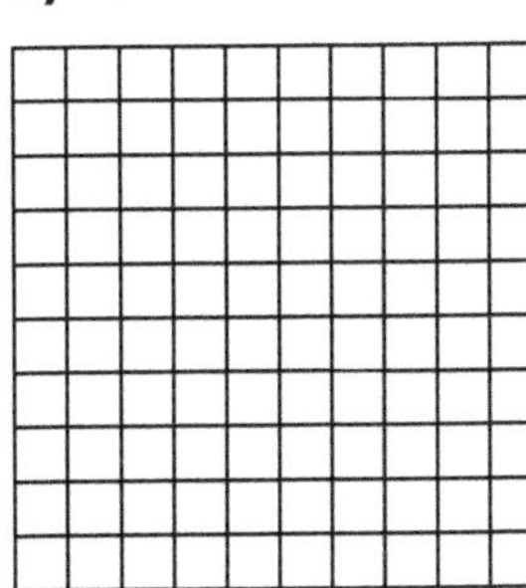

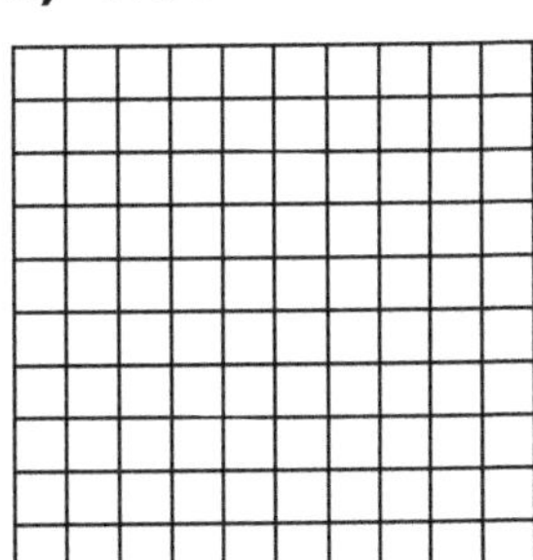

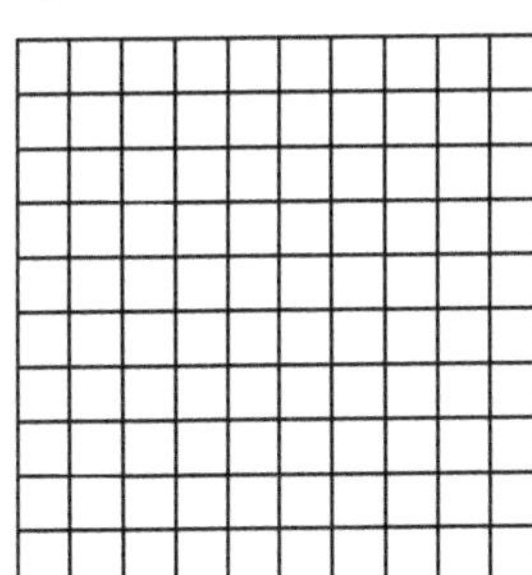

7. Which of these decimal hundredths can be expressed as decimal tenths? Give reasons for your choice.

0.70 0.07 0.77 0.17

____

____

Rounding Decimals

Goal **Interpret rounded decimals, and round decimals to the nearest whole and to the nearest tenth.**

1. Sarah rounded the length of her room to the nearest tenth of a metre. The length is 3.5 m.

3.4 3.5 3.6

   a) Write the numbers that round up from 3.4 to 3.5.

   ____

   ____

   b) Write the numbers that round down to 3.5.

   ____

   ____

At-Home Help

Decimal numbers can be rounded to the nearest whole number and the nearest tenth.

For example,
- 2.76 rounds up to 2.8
- 2.83 rounds down to 2.8

A number line helps with rounding.

2.76 2.83

2.7 2.8 2.9

Both 2.76 and 2.83 round up to 3.

2. Lori needs 4.47 m of ribbon for a school play.

   a) How much ribbon should she buy if ribbon is sold in lengths of whole metres?

   ____

   b) How much ribbon should she buy if ribbon is sold in lengths of tenths of a metre?

   ____

3. Round each number to the nearest whole number and the nearest tenth.

a) 3.65	b) 7.03	c) 0.79	d) 7.93
________	________	________	________
________	________	________	________

4. A gardener needs 8.74 m of hose to water a lawn.

   a) Round that length to the nearest tenth of a metre. ______________________

   b) Should he buy a hose of that length or a different length? Explain.

   ____

5. A number rounded to the nearest tenth is 7.9. What might the number be? List three possibilities.

   ____

Comparing and Ordering Decimals

Compare and order numbers to decimal hundredths.

1. Four members of the Sea Lions team competed in a relay race at a recent swim meet.

Swimmer	Stroke	Time
Zoe	Butterfly	2.54 s
Karilyn	Back	2.36 s
Andrea	Breast	2.75 s
Tanya	Freestyle	2.17 s

a) Who took the longest to swim her part of the race? What was her time?

____

b) Who swam the fastest? What was her time?

____

c) Order the times from shortest to longest.

____

2. Draw a representation of Zoe's time using base ten blocks. Draw a hundreds block to represent 1.

Ones	Tenths	Hundredths

3. Complete each number sentence using $<$ or $>$.

a) 3.94 ____ 3.99 **b)** 46.03 ____ 47.06 **c)** 20.80 ____ 20.08

4. Order each group of numbers from least to greatest using inequality signs.

a) 0.23, 4.75, 6.35, 0.79, 4.57 ______________________________

b) 5.15, 1.55, 0.51, 15.01 ______________________________

c) 0.31, 0.13, 0.03, 0.01 ______________________________

d) 6.1, 6.5, 6.06, 6.75, 6 ______________________________

Counting Money

Estimate, count, read, and write money amounts to $1000.

1.

a) Estimate the total. Explain your estimate.

____

____

b) Count the amount. Record it.

At-Home Help

When counting money, first count the bills. Then count the coins.

For example:
The amount shown is $420.80.

Different combinations of bills and coins can make the same amount.

2. Describe or draw another set of coins and bills that make the same amount as in Question 1.

3. Describe or draw each amount using the fewest bills and coins possible.

a) $16.50

b) $281.30

4. Describe or draw $281.30 using more bills and coins.

Test Yourself

Circle the correct answer.

1. Which container would you choose to hold 50 thousand nickels?

   A. 5 shoeboxes **B.** 5 lunchboxes **C.** 5 bathtubs **D.** 5 recycling boxes

2. Which representation is *not* the number 23 709?

   A. 20 000 + 3000 + 700 + 9

   B. 10 000 + 13 000 + 500 + 209

   C. 1 ten thousand + 13 thousand + 5 hundred + 20 tens + 9

   D. 10 000 less than 25 709

3. Which number sentence is incorrect?

   A. 20 899 < 28 100 **B.** 5697 > 5675

   C. 54 072 > 45 072 **D.** 34 521 < 34 125

4. Which number is rounded to the nearest hundred?

   A. 45 630 **B.** 75 000 **C.** 61 300 **D.** 10 001

5. What would 89 605 rounded to the nearest thousand be?

   A. 89 000 **B.** 89 600 **C.** 90 000 **D.** 90 600

6. Which number on the metre stick number line does the arrow point to?

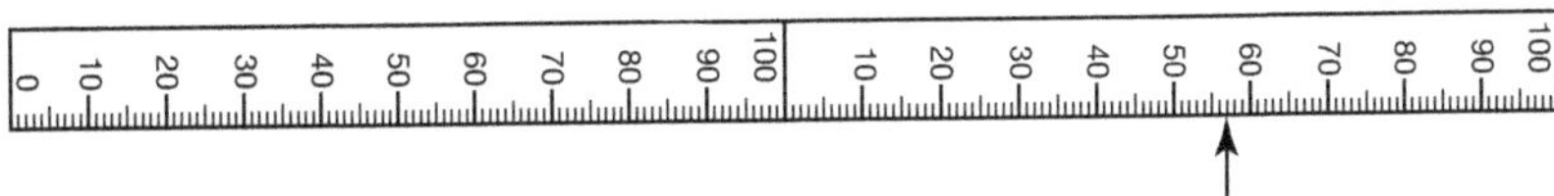

   A. 1.60 **B.** 1.50 **C.** 1.57 **D.** 1.55

7. Which description fits for the number 2.67?

   A. two and six tenths **B.** twenty-six and seven hundredths

   C. two hundred sixty-seven **D.** two and sixty-seven hundredths

8. Which number is 1 tenth greater than 2.67?

   A. 3.78 **B.** 2.78 **C.** 3.67 **D.** 2.77

9. What would 7.86 rounded to the nearest tenth be?

   A. 8.0 **B.** 7.8 **C.** 8.6 **D.** 7.9

Evaluating Survey Results

Decide whether the results of a survey would likely apply to other groups of people.

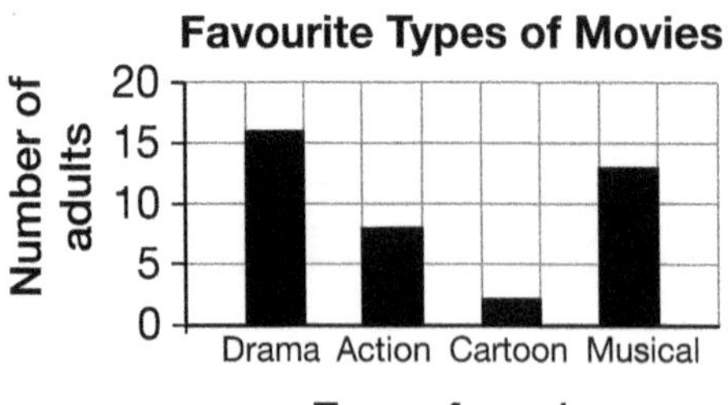

At-Home Help

Biased results are results of a survey that apply to one group but are not likely to apply to another group.

1. Which type of movie was the favourite for the adults surveyed? Explain why adults would prefer these movies.

____

____

2. Explain why you think the overall results are accurate for this group of people.

____

____

____

3. Would the results of this survey likely apply to students in a Grade 1 class? Explain.

____

____

4. Predict the results if your class were surveyed. Create a graph of your prediction.

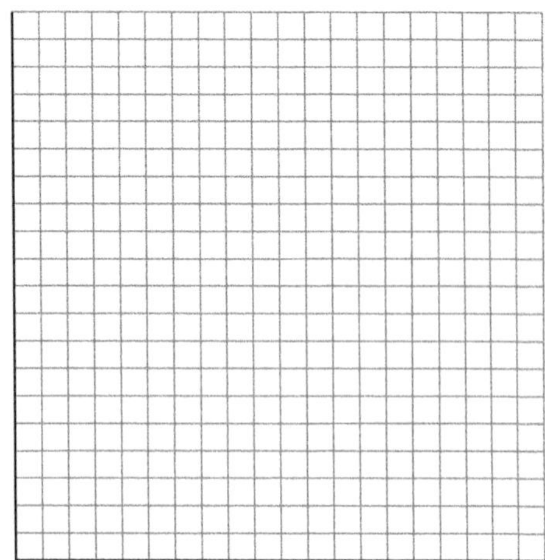

Broken-Line Graphs

Make and use a broken-line graph to identify trends.

1. 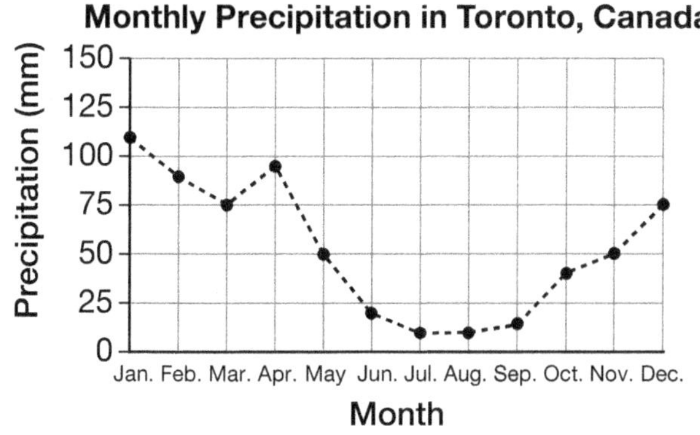

At-Home Help

A **trend** in a graph refers to the general direction of data. The data can increase, decrease, or stay the same.

A **broken-line graph** is a graph in which data points are connected point by point.

What trends do you see in this broken-line graph?

____

____

____

2. Make a broken-line graph of monthly precipitation in Sydney, Australia.

Monthly Precipitation in Sydney, Australia (mm)

Jan.	Feb.	Mar.	Apr.	May	Jun.	Jul.	Aug.	Sept.	Oct.	Nov.	Dec.
10	15	40	70	75	40	35	15	60	50	20	10

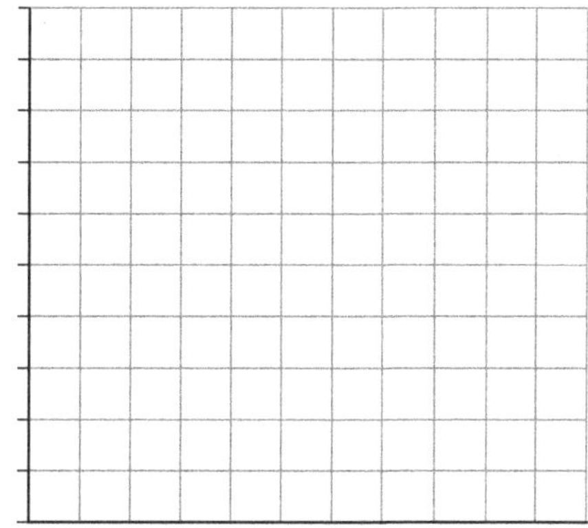

3. Compare your broken-line graph to the graph in Question 1. How are they similar?

Interpreting Circle Graphs

Calculate the number represented by each part of a circle graph.

Thirty-two Grade 5 students answered a survey question about their favourite subject and most difficult subject. These circle graphs show the results.

Favourite Subject

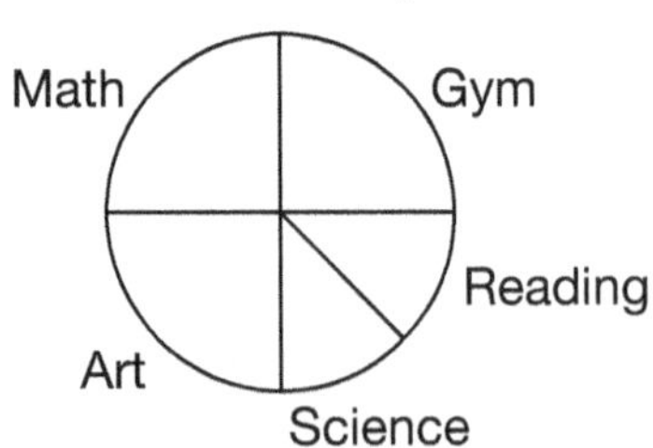

Most Difficult Subject

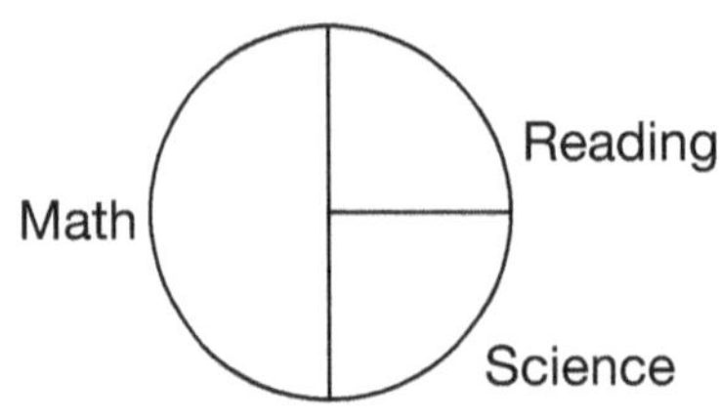

1. What fraction represents each part in the Favourite Subject graph?

   Math ________ Gym ________ Art ________

   Reading _____ Science _____

2. How many students are represented by each subject in the Favourite Subject graph?

   Math ________ Gym ________ Art ________

   Reading _____ Science _____

3. How many students are represented by each subject in the Most Difficult Subject graph?

   Math _______ Science _______ Reading _______

4. Suppose the survey applied to 40 students. How would your answers to Questions 2 and 3 change?

   ____

   ____

At-Home Help

A **circle graph** is a graph that displays data using a circle. Each section of the circle represents a data point. Circle graphs are used for data that represent parts of a whole.

For example, this circle graph shows the eye colour for a class of 24 students.

Eye Colour

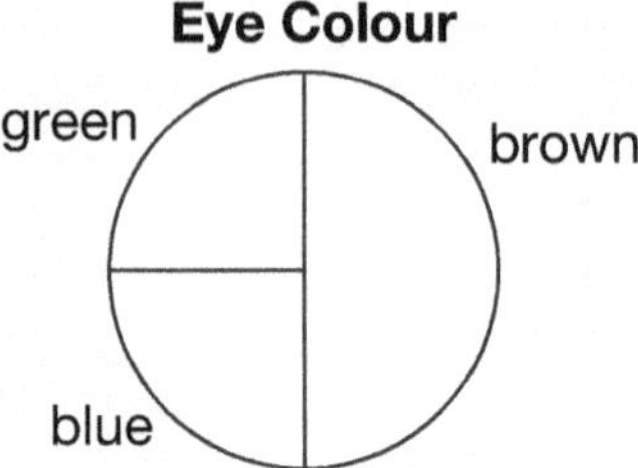

12 students have brown eyes. This number represents $\frac{1}{2}$ the class, so $\frac{1}{2}$ the circle represents brown.

6 students have green eyes. This number represents $\frac{1}{4}$ of the class, so $\frac{1}{4}$ of the circle represents green.

6 students have blue eyes. This number represents $\frac{1}{4}$ of the class, so $\frac{1}{4}$ of the circle represents blue.

Bar Graphs with Intervals

Use the range to estimate the size of intervals to construct a bar graph.

Akiko recorded the number of metres jumped during a triple jump. She collected data from 24 students in her class.

Metres jumped (triple jump)

15	18	4	12	10	6
10	20	15	7	17	10
9	13	5	8	16	12
14	19	3	15	11	13

1. What is the range of the data?

___

2. How many bars would you use if you made a bar graph of the data? Explain your choice based on the range. Include the intervals in your answer.

___

___

3. **a)** Make a tally chart for the data.

b) Draw a bar graph using your tally chart.

At-Home Help

Range is the spread of data. To find the range, look for the least and greatest data points.

For example, the range of the data is 53 to 80, which is 27 beats.

Heart Rates (beats in 1 min)

70	60	53
80	74	70
70	72	78

Before drawing some bar graphs, it is better to group data. **Intervals** refer to the size of the groups. All intervals should be the same size.

For example: Six students cycled between 0 and 4 km, and 3 students cycled between 5 and 9 km. The intervals on the graph are 0–4 and 5–9.

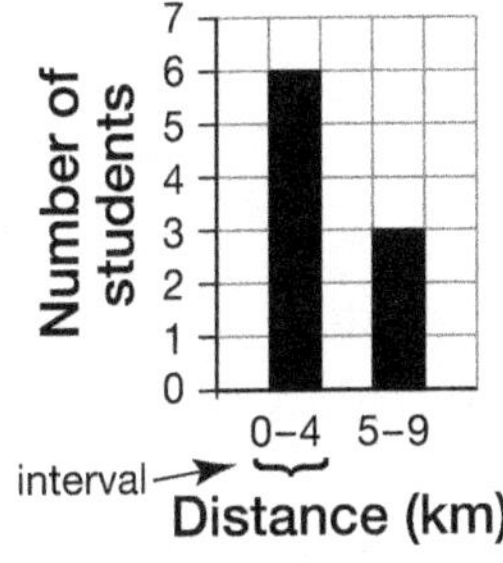

Pictographs

Use whole and partial symbols to display data on a pictograph.

Jose counted the number of birds on Memesagamesing Lake in Northern Ontario in July.

Type of bird	Number
Loon	75
Blue heron	40
Mallard duck	81
Cormorant	28

1. Draw a pictograph to show the data using whole and partial symbols. Make sure you show the scale.

2. Explain how you decided on the number of whole and partial symbols to show the number of birds.

3. Why are 81 and 28 difficult numbers to represent on the pictograph?

4. What other scale could you use for the pictograph?

At-Home Help

A **pictograph** is a graph that displays data using symbols. Each symbol represents a fixed number. Some data points can only be represented by using partial symbols.

For example, since 1 symbol represents 10 pies, 15 pies is represented with $1\frac{1}{2}$ symbols.

Types of Pies

Apple 

Blueberry 

Banana cream 

Lemon meringue 

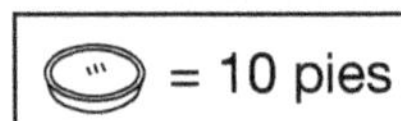

A **scale** on a pictograph shows the number represented by each symbol.

The scale for the pictograph above says that 1 symbol represents 10 pies.

Changing the Appearance of a Graph

Explain how changing the scale of a graph can affect its appearance.

Drake made a graph to show the results of a survey about favourite desserts.

Favourite Desserts

Dessert	Number of people
Pie	150
Cake	127
Ice cream	106
Fruit cup	95

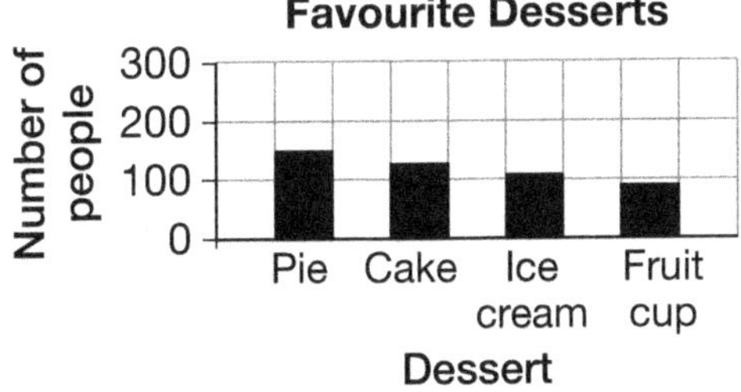

1. How does the scale affect the appearance of this graph?

____

____

2. Make another bar graph with a different scale to make the difference between the bars appear more dramatic.

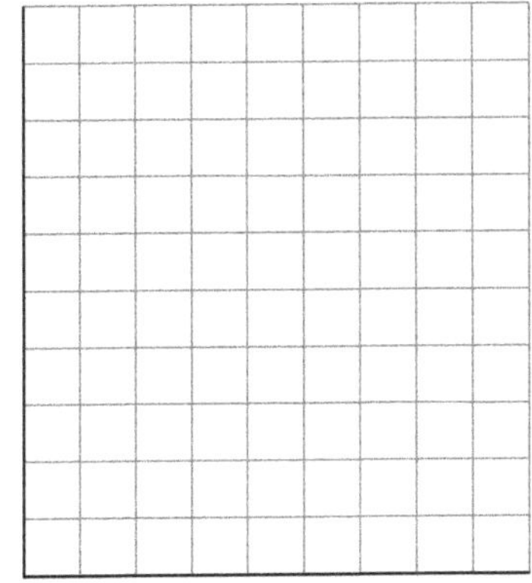

At-Home Help

The **scale** of a bar or line graph refers to the divisions on both the vertical and horizontal axes.

The scale of a graph can affect the appearance of data.

For example: The scale on the first graph goes from 0 to 200. This makes the difference between the bars not very clear.

The scale on the second graph goes from 0 to 20. The difference between the bars is very clear.

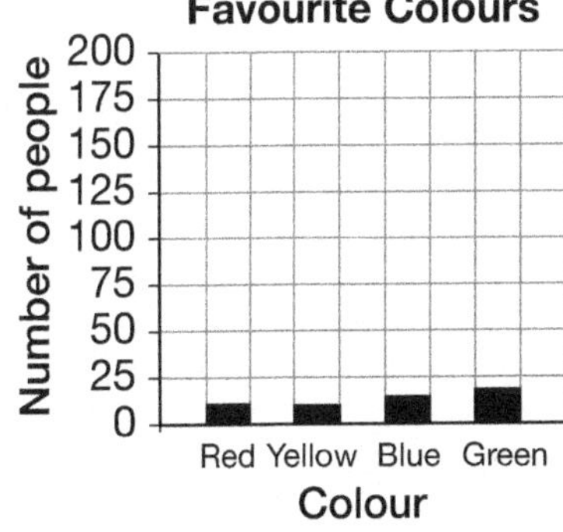

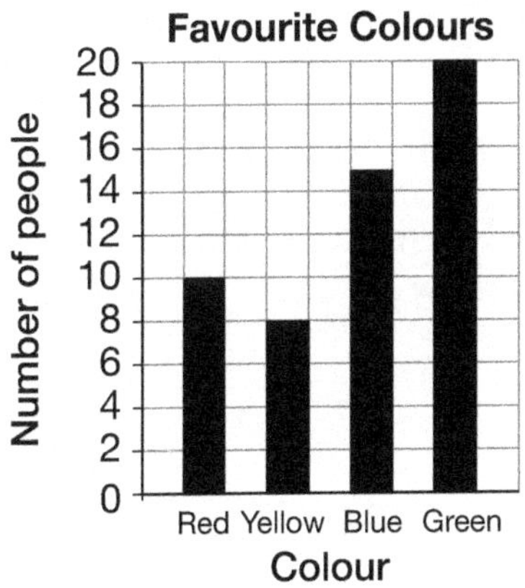

Graphing with Technology

Use graphing software to organize and display data.

Anton collected different types of materials for recycling. He was paid for each item he collected.

- 12 tins at 2¢ per tin
- 18 plastic containers at 5¢ per container
- 7 cardboard boxes at 10¢ per box
- 9 glass bottles at 15¢ per bottle

At-Home Help

A **spreadsheet** has columns and rows to organize data. Spreadsheets usually have columns of numbers that represent the result of math calculations.

1. Organize the data using a table or spreadsheet.

2. Construct a graph of your choice that would represent the data well. Use paper and pencil or a spreadsheet.

Mean and Mode

Calculate the mean and identify the mode of a set of data.

1. What is the mode of this group of numbers? Explain.

   6, 7, 4, 4, 9, 3, 2, 3, 7, 4, 9

   ____

2. **a)** What is the mean of 6, 7, and 8?

   ____

   b) What is the mean of 12, 14, and 16?

   ____

   c) What do you notice about the mean of each group of numbers in Parts **a)** and **b)**?

   ____

   ____

3. Calculate the mean and identify the mode of 32, 38, 33, and 33.

4. Create a group of four numbers that has a mode of 4 and a mean of 5.

   ____

At-Home Help

Mean is the rearrangement of numbers to make equal shares.

For example, the mean of 0, 5, 1, 1, 3 is 2.

0 5 1 1 3

2 2 2 2 2

Mode is the number that occurs most often in a group of numbers.

For example, the mode of 0, 5, 1, 1, 3 is 1.

Communicate About Graphs

Evaluate the accuracy of a graph and suggest ways to present data accurately.

Leo recorded the cross-country running times of each student in his class. He then drew a bar graph.

Time (min)

4	8	4	12	10	6
13	7	17	5	9	15
9	16	5	8	6	14
14	9	5	15	11	7

Leo's graph is not accurate.

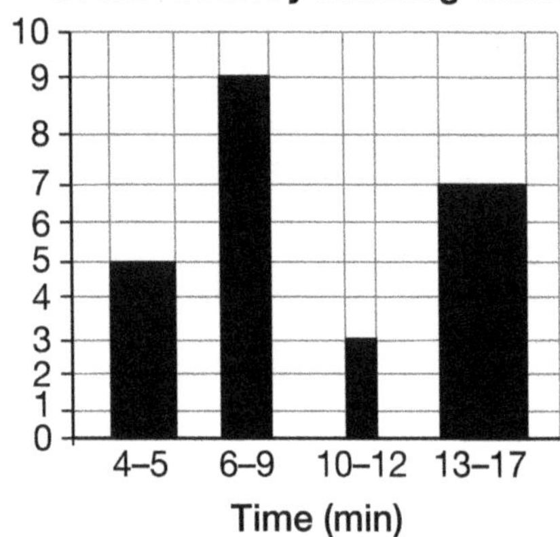

1. What is missing from the graph?

____

2. How is the graph not accurate? Use the Communication Checklist to help you.

____

____

3. Sketch a more accurate graph.

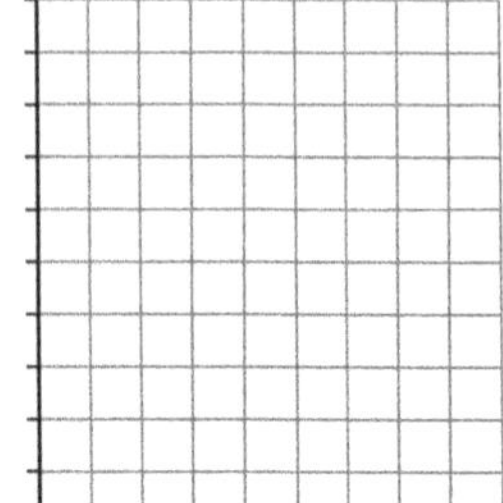

At-Home Help

Graphs show information accurately if these points are followed.

- All graphs should have a title.
- On a bar graph or a line graph, the horizontal and vertical axes should be labelled.
- The intervals along the horizontal axis should be equal. Similarly, the intervals along the vertical axis should be equal.
- All bars on a bar graph should be the same width.
- On a pictograph, all data points should be represented by the same symbol. The overall size of the symbol should also be the same.
- On any graph, the scale should be appropriate for the data points.

Communication Checklist

☑ Did you check the scale?
☑ Did you include all of the data?
☑ Did you draw and label the graph correctly?

Test Yourself

Circle the correct answer.

1. Paul surveyed 50 boys in his school. He asked them to list their favourite sport.

Sport	Number of boys
Bowling	5
Soccer	32
Curling	3
Cross country running	10

Which group would probably be close to the results of Paul's group?

A. senior citizens **B.** Grade 5 girls **C.** parents **D.** toddlers

2. What are the mode and mean of this group of numbers?

5, 4, 9, 7, 5, 6, 3, 1

A. 5 and 4 **B.** 4 and 5 **C.** 4 and 6 **D.** 5 and 5

3. What is the trend in this broken-line graph?

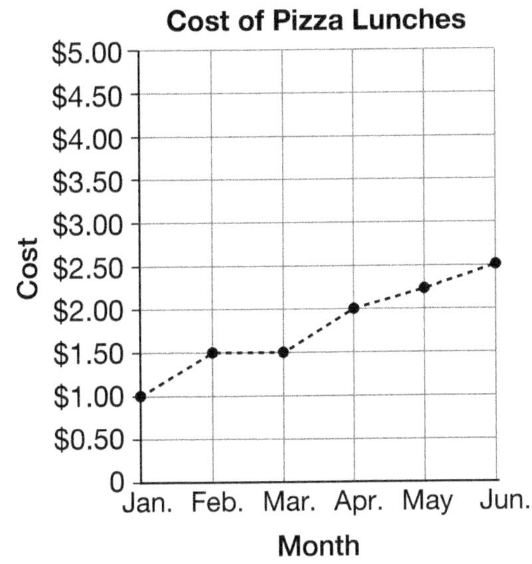

A. gradual decrease in cost **B.** no change in cost

C. gradual increase in cost **D.** steep increase in cost

Test Yourself Page 2

Use these data to answer Questions 4, 5, and 6.

Time (min)

20	36	5	49	21	57	36
16	67	16	60	23	44	51
10	21	44	9	46	68	32
63	37	8	68	47	55	19

4. What is the range of the data?

   A. 63 **B.** 61 **C.** 62 **D.** 64

5. What interval would be the best choice to make a bar graph?

   A. 2 **B.** 5 **C.** 8 **D.** 15

6. How many numbers would be in the interval 31–45?

   A. 4 **B.** 6 **C.** 5 **D.** 7

Use the pictograph to answer Questions 7 and 8.

100 students were surveyed about their favourite ride at the fair.

Favourite Rides

Ferris wheel	□ □ ▯
Bumper cars	▯
Roller coaster	□ □ □ □ ▫
Swing	□ ▫

□ = 12 students

7. What other scale could be used for this pictograph?

   A. □ = 10 students **B.** □ = 16 students

   C. □ = 15 students **D.** □ = 14 students

8. If the scale were changed to □ = 20 students, how would 65 students choosing the roller coaster be shown?

   A. □□ **B.** □□▫ **C.** □□□▫ **D.** □□▯

Adding and Subtracting Using Mental Math

Use mental math strategies to add and subtract.

1. Use mental math to calculate each answer. Explain your strategy.

   a) 54 + 29

   b) 88 + 32

   c) 100 − 48

   d) 70 − 14

2. The Boston Marathon is a 42 km run. Aaron ran the marathon in 100 min.

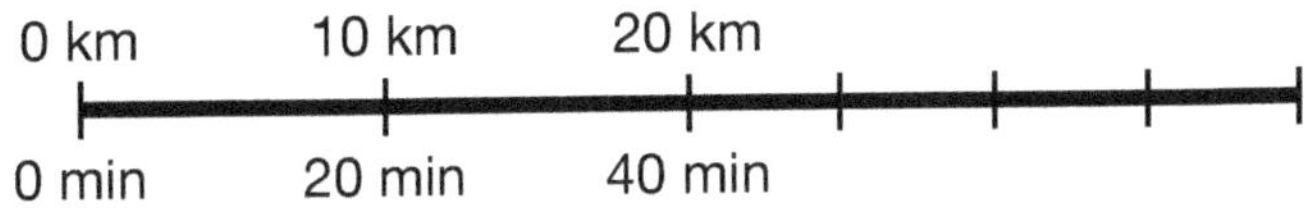

   Use mental math to calculate Aaron's distance and time at each point during the 42 km run. Describe your strategy.

At-Home Help

Rounding is a mental math strategy for adding and subtracting numbers. When you round, you will likely need to adjust your answer to get the exact answer.

For example:

23 + 58 can be rounded to 20 + 60 = 80. 23 is 3 more than 20 and 58 is 2 less than 60. So adjust answer by adding 1. Answer is 81.

76 − 40 can be rounded to 80 − 40 = 40. 76 is 4 less than 80. So adjust answer by subtracting 4. Answer is 36.

Regrouping is another mental math strategy for adding and subtracting numbers. Regroup numbers into 5s or 10s to make calculations easier.

For example:

43 + 92 can be regrouped as (43 + 2) + 90. Answer is 45 + 90 = 135.

80 − 19 can be regrouped as (80 − 10) − 9. Answer is 70 − 9 = 61.

Estimating Sums and Differences

Estimate sums and differences and justify your strategy.

1. Estimate which calculations are reasonable. Explain how you estimated.

   a) 2997 + 1158 = 4155

   ____

   ____

   b) 6053 − 4802 = 2251

   ____

   ____

   c) 8095 − 2559 = 5536

   ____

   ____

   d) 3273 + 897 + 4298 = 8238

   ____

At-Home Help

To check the reasonableness of a calculation, estimate the answer using one or more mental math strategies.

For example:

To check if
1198 +1510 + 1454 + 1354 = 8516
is reasonable, use rounding and regrouping. Then estimate the sum.

1200 +1500 + 1400 + (50 + 1350)
= 1200 + 1500 + 1400 + 1400
= 5500

So the sum 8516 is not reasonable.

2. The chart shows data for hockey players in a town.

Hockey players		Number of players
Boys	novice level	4854
	atom level	5013
Girls	novice level	3955
	atom level	2081

How many more hockey players are boys than girls? Estimate to check the reasonableness of your calculation. Show your work and justify your choice of estimation strategies.

Adding Whole Numbers

Add 3 four-digit whole numbers using paper and pencil.

1. Estimate and then add. Show your work.

a)
```
  2549
  3288
+ 7426
```

b)
```
  5283
  6094
+  846
```

c)
```
  7106
  5882
+ 4037
```

At-Home Help

When adding several whole numbers together, you can estimate the sum using rounding.

For example:

		Estimate
	1899	2000
	3045	3000
	+ 2357	+ 2000
Actual answer →	7301	7000

d) 1093 + 2764 + 898

e) 7549 + 3808 + 4261

2. Seven students wrote stories, each with a different number of words. What 3 stories have a total between 7000 and 8000 words? Show your work.

Student	Number of words
Raj	2419
Sima	3256
Ben	3780
Cathy	2934
Bill	4087
Dan	2593
Kew	1806

Solve Two-Step Problems

Select operations and solve two-step problems.

You will need a calculator.

1. Rachel shot baskets each day for a period of 2 weeks. She shot a total of 2260 baskets. Rachel shot 100 more baskets each day during the last 3 days. How many shots per day did she take during the first week?

At-Home Help

When solving word problems, follow these steps.

- First write down what you are asked to find out.
- Then look at the information you are given.
- Decide what information is important.
- Make a plan.
- Choose operations that use the given information to solve the problem.
- Check if your answer is reasonable.

Remember to show all your work.

2. Mr. James is 49 years of age. His sister is 45 years of age. What is the difference in age in each of these units of time? Show your work.

   a) months

   b) weeks

   c) days

3. A school has a total of 1258 students. There are 297 primary students and 364 junior students. How many senior students are there?

Communicate About a Choice of Calculation Method

Justify your choice of calculation method and explain each step in solving a problem.

1. Marcus was at Youth Camp. He had a total of 3025 points that he could spend at the camp store. About how many points does he have left?

Camp store item	Cost in points
Candy	875
Ice cream	436
Chips	297
Drinks	980

Alana wrote this rough copy to solve the problem.

> I only need to estimate, because the problem asks "about" how many points are left.
> Marcus spent about 2600 points.
> He had about 3000 points in total.
> He should have about 400 points left.

Write a good copy. Use the Communication Checklist to help you.

At-Home Help

When writing a solution to a word problem, first write a rough copy.

- If the problem does not ask for an exact answer, use estimation to find the answer.
- You can use rounding, regrouping, or any other mental math strategy.
- Check if your answer is reasonable.

Then write a good copy explaining all your steps.

Remember to show all your work.

Communication Checklist

☑ Did you explain your thinking?
☑ Did you show all the steps?
☑ Did you use math language?

2. Richard and his friends collected a total of 4548 old coins. The chart shows some of the coins.

Type of coin	Number of coins
Penny	789
Nickel	1516
Dime	934

a) Richard forgot to list quarters in the chart. About how many quarters were collected?

____

b) About how many more pennies would be needed to match the number of nickels?

____

Adding Decimals

Add decimal tenths and hundredths using base ten blocks and pencil and paper.

1. Estimate and then add. Show your work.

a)
$$\begin{array}{r} 8.3 \\ +\ 5.7 \\ \hline \end{array}$$

b)
$$\begin{array}{r} 6.89 \\ +\ 5.43 \\ \hline \end{array}$$

c) 5.16 + 3.87

d) 4.93 + 0.82 + 6.95

2. Estimate and then calculate the total distance. Show your work.

0.85 km and 5.28 km

3. Dmitri added 2.78 and 5.49. He also added 278 and 549. He compared his answers.

a) Explain how the answers are the same.

____

____

b) Explain how the answers are different.

____

____

At-Home Help

Decimal tenths and hundredths are added using the same rules as whole numbers.

- It is easier to add vertically if the decimal points are aligned.
- Add place values that are the same.
- If the sum of a place value is 10 or more, regroup using the next greater place value.
- Check your answer using estimation.

For example:

		Estimate
	1.76	2
	+ 0.45	+ 0
Actual answer →	2.21	2

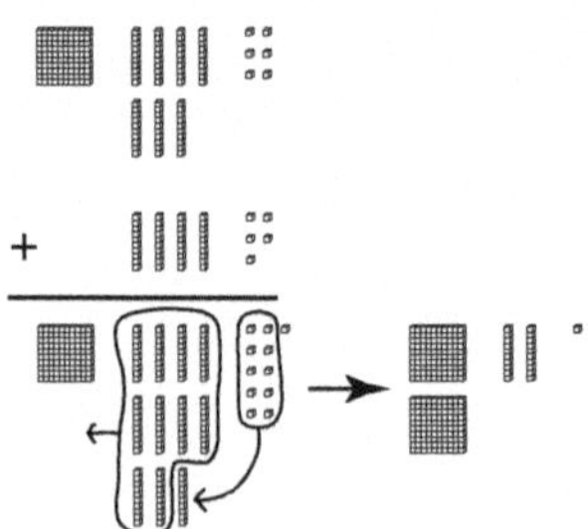

Adding Money

Use various methods to calculate the cost of purchases.

1. Estimate and then add. Show your work.

a) $23.65
19.88
+ 14.63

b) $18.63
+ 12.88

c) $52.64
0.86
+ 8.29

At-Home Help

Adding money amounts is the same as adding decimal hundredths.

Use estimation to check your sums.

For example:

		Estimate
	$29.95	$30
	+ 35.95	+ 36
Actual answer →	$65.90	$66

d) $2.65 + $1.74

e) $13.43 + $7.09

f) $48.91 + $0.72

2. **a)** Create a problem involving buying 2 or more video games. Solve your problem. Show your estimate and actual answer.

Name of video game	Cost
Hockey Super Stars	$26.50
World Cup Soccer	$23.78
Race Car Rally	$10.45
Wave Surfer	$9.99

b) Explain how you calculated your answer. Then check your answer.

Making Change

Calculate change from purchases.

1. Calculate the total cost and the amount of change.

a)

b)

c)

d)

At-Home Help

To calculate change from purchases, first find the total cost.

You can use estimation if you want to find the approximate cost.

Then subtract the total cost from the total amount of money you have.

2. You have been given $60 for your birthday.

Item	Cost
Shirt	$25.85
Binder	$15.99
Sunglasses	$9.43
Video game	$17.68
Book	$23.97

a) Choose 2 items you can buy. Calculate the total cost. Then choose 3 items and calculate the total cost. Show your work.

b) How much change will you receive? Show your work.

Subtracting Decimals

Use pencil and paper to subtract decimal tenths and hundredths.

1. Estimate and then subtract. Show your work.

a) 9.85 − 7.14 **b)** 6.03 − 1.57 **c)** 7.00 − 4.96 **d)** 8.67 − 5.82

e) 7.6 − 3.8 **f)** 9.00 − 5.16 **g)** 25.34 − 5.79

2. In long jump, Benjamin jumped 4.85 m while his friend Dan jumped 5.62 m. How much farther did Dan jump than Benjamin?

____

3. Sofia got an answer of 3.75 when she subtracted 5.25 from a whole number. What is the whole number? Explain how you got your answer.

____

____

At-Home Help

Decimal tenths and hundredths are subtracted using the same rules as whole numbers.

- It is easier to subtract vertically if the decimal points are aligned.
- Subtract place values that are the same starting from the smallest place value.
- If you can't find the difference for a particular place value, regroup using the next greater place value.
- Check your answer using estimation.

For example:

		Estimate
	3.00	3
	− 0.75	− 1
Actual answer →	2.25	2

Test Yourself

Circle the correct answer.

1. Which question would give an answer close to 2591?

   A. 3658 − 1149 **B.** 1468 + 1897 **C.** 1255 + 1349 **D.** 4513 − 2928

2. Using estimation, which question has an answer between 1350 and 1450?

   A. 1046 + 829 **B.** 6391 − 4869 **C.** 874 + 573 **D.** 2836 − 1264

3. Which calculation is correct?

   A. 1259 + 745 + 5567 = 7754 **B.** 1259 + 745 + 5567 = 6747

   C. 1259 + 745 + 5567 = 6574 **D.** 1259 + 745 + 5567 = 7571

4. Three transport trucks can move loads that total 4581 kg. Two of the trucks moved 2614 kg and 1088 kg. How much would you estimate the third truck moved?

   A. 780 kg **B.** 700 kg **C.** 900 kg **D.** 800 kg

5. What is the answer to 7246 − 3859?

   A. 4613 **B.** 3387 **C.** 4631 **D.** 3287

6. Sima is 3655 days old. Mario's cousin is 298 days older than Sima. Mario is 189 days younger than his cousin. How many days old is Mario?

   A. 3764 days **B.** 3953 days **C.** 3466 days **D.** 3769 days

7. What is the total cost shown?

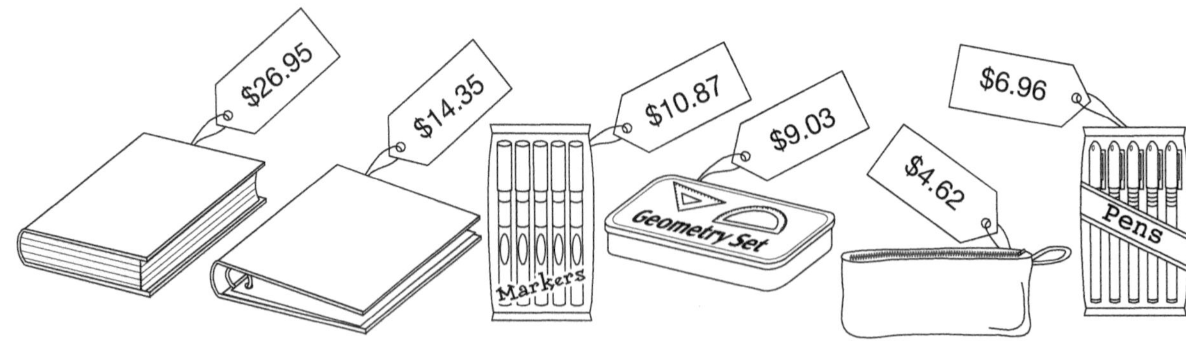

   A. $72.87 **B.** $67.78 **C.** $72.78 **D.** $67.87

8. Tina gave the store clerk a $100 bill for all the items in Question 7. How much change would she receive?

   A. $32.78 **B.** $27.78 **C.** $32.22 **D.** $27.22

Using Measurements to Describe Objects

Use logical reasoning to choose measurements.

You will need a ruler marked in millimetres.

Fill in the blanks with the correct measurements.

1. Anna's kitchen table seats _______ people.

   It is _______ cm wide, _______ m long,

   and _______ mm high.

   1.5 750 6 90

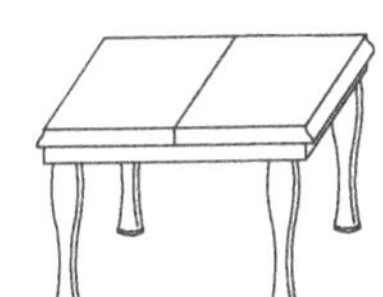

2. Tilo can cycle _______ km in one hour. The library is 5 km from his home. It will take Tilo about _______ min to cycle from home to the library. The speed limit for cars on city streets is _______ km/h.

   This is _______ times Tilo's speed.

   5 10 50 30

MAXIMUM
50
km/h

3. A box of crackers is _______ m high, _______ cm deep, and _______ mm wide. The box holds about _______ crackers.

   0.18 70 140 6

4. A new pencil is _______ m long and _______ mm wide.

   The eraser is _______ cm long.

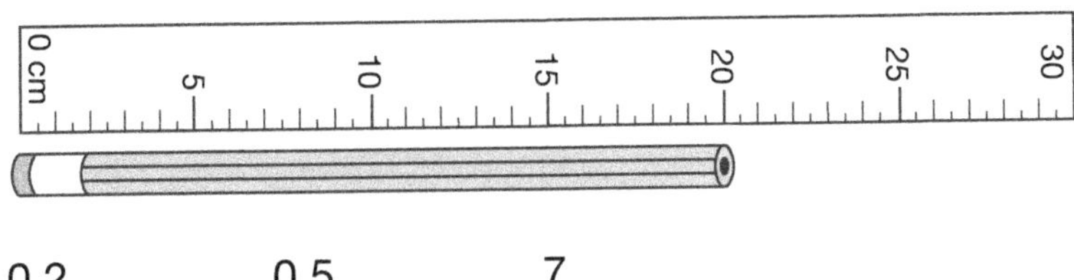

   0.2 0.5 7

At-Home Help

Measurements can be used to describe objects. To solve measurement problems, use the clues given and your own knowledge.

1 cm = 10 mm
100 cm = 1 m
1000 mm = 1 m

Measuring Lengths

Relate metric units of length to each other.

You will need a ruler marked in millimetres.

At-Home Help

When measuring objects, you may have to use tools that are available rather than ideal. You can use a 30 cm ruler to measure many lengths.

1 m = 100 cm
1 m = 1000 mm
1 cm = 10 mm

1. Describe how you can use a 30 cm ruler to measure ribbon for each length.

   a) 0.3 m ______________________________

   ____

   b) 105 cm ______________________________

   ____

   c) 750 mm ______________________________

   ____

2. Describe how to cut a piece of fabric 0.9 m long using a 30 cm ruler.

   ____

3. Draw each length.

   a) 112 mm

   b) a 0.3 m zigzag path

4. How can you calculate the thickness of one coin in millimetres? Use the information in the picture and a calculator.

   ____

   ____

   ____

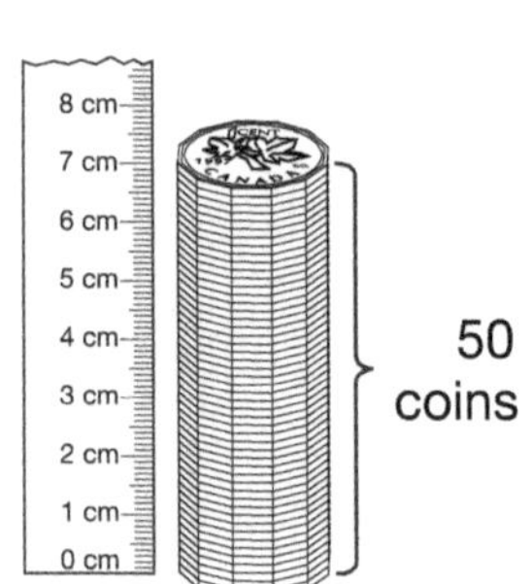

5. Two adjacent houses on a street are 1300 cm apart.

   a) Do you think the houses are in a rural or an urban area? Explain.

   ____

   b) What would be a better unit for describing the distance? Why?

   ____

Measuring Circumference

Measure around circular objects.

You will need a ruler marked in millimetres, and a tape measure.

1. Measure and record the width and circumference of each circle in centimetres. Complete the table.

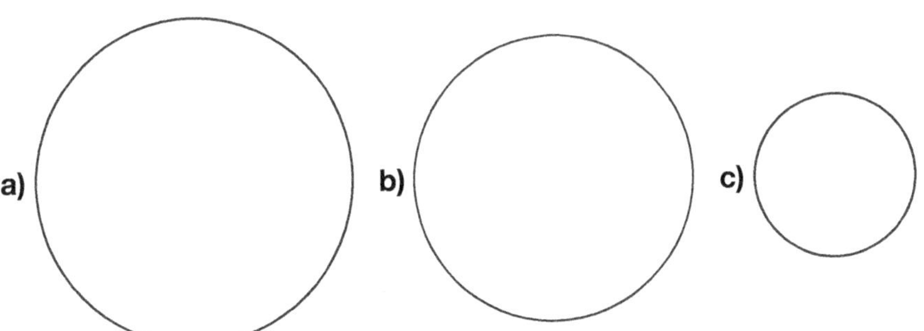

Circle	Width	Circumference
a)		
b)		
c)		

2. For each circle, is the circumference closer to two times, three times, or four times the width?

____

3. Liam is practicing for a 400 m race. If he runs around a circular track with a width of 100 m, will he run as far as the race distance? Explain.

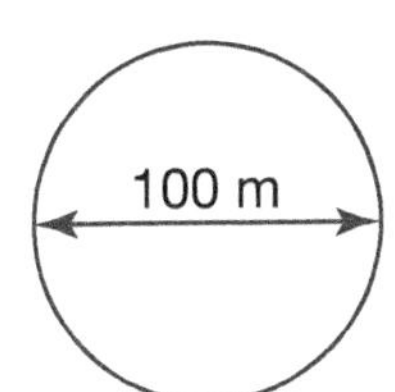

____

____

4. The hula hoops in the gym are 96 cm in width. What is the best estimate of their circumference?

3 m　　　270 cm　　　4000 mm

____

At-Home Help

Circumference is the distance around a circle or circular object.

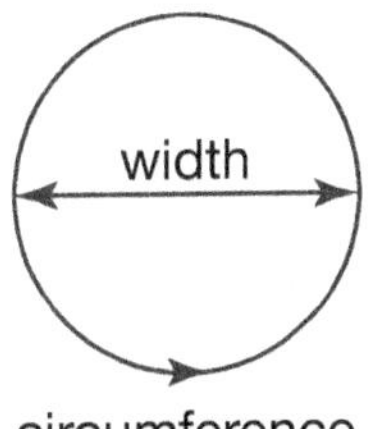

Circles have a particular relationship between width and circumference.

Measuring Perimeter

Measure perimeter on a grid.

You will need a metric ruler.

1. The initials for the Maple Leafs are shaded on the grid below. Estimate the perimeter. Check by measuring.

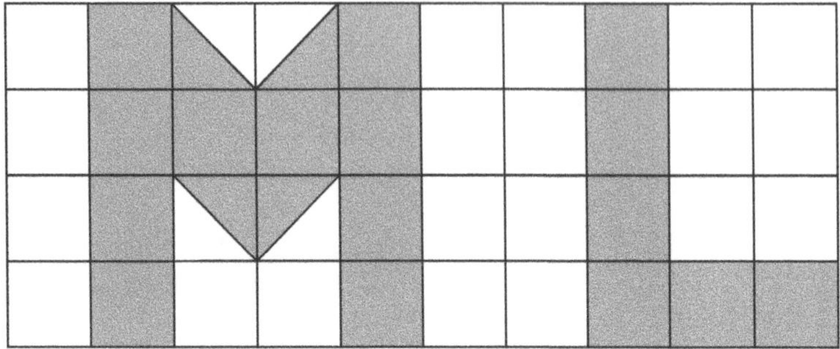

	Estimated perimeter	Actual perimeter
M		
L		
total		

2. Use the grid to draw two different shapes each with a perimeter of 16 cm. Each shape must have more than 4 sides.

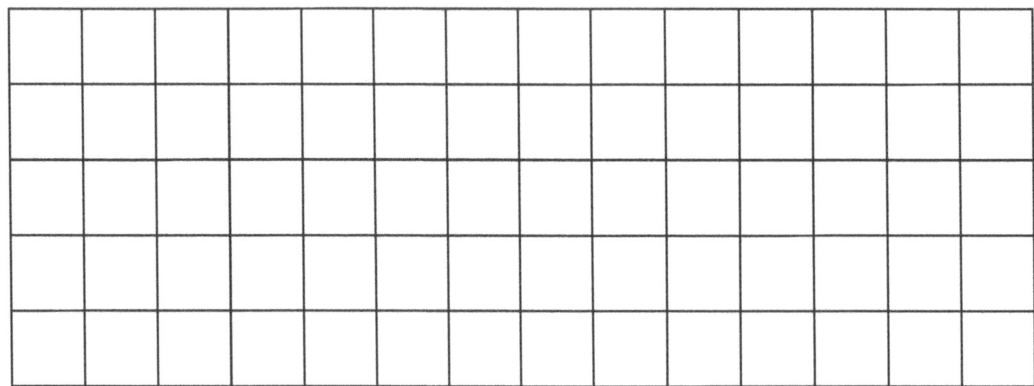

At-Home Help

Perimeter is the distance around an object. Using grid paper helps you measure the perimeter of irregular shapes. When the sides of shapes do not follow grid lines, use a ruler to measure the lengths accurately.

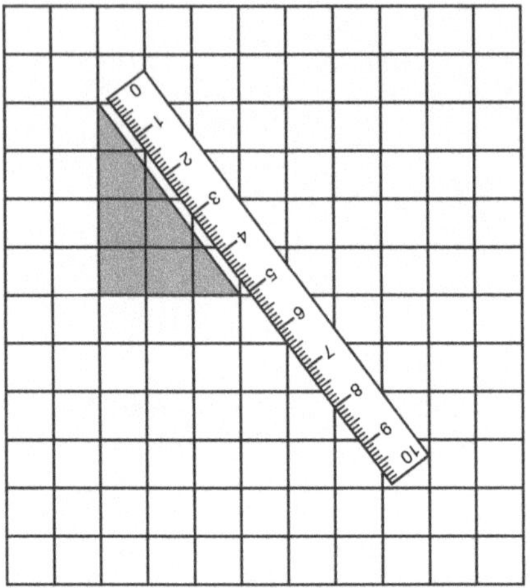

Perimeter is an outside measurement.

Measuring the Perimeter of a Rectangle

Develop and use a rule for calculating the perimeter of a rectangle.

1. Calculate the length of trim you would need to go around these blankets.

a)

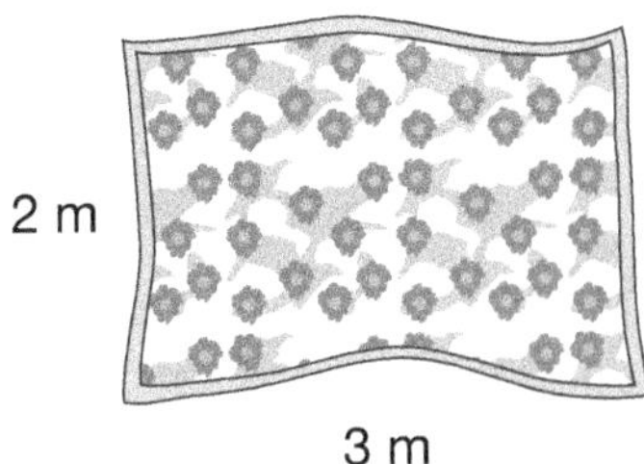

b)

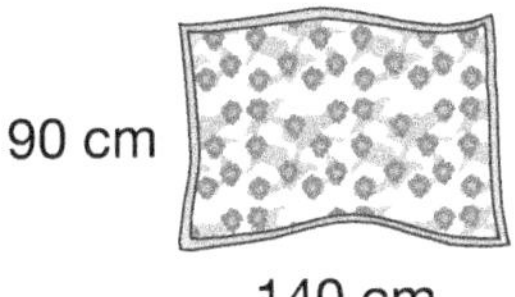

At-Home Help

In a rectangle, opposite sides are the same length. The perimeter of a rectangle can be calculated by adding the length and width, and then doubling the sum.

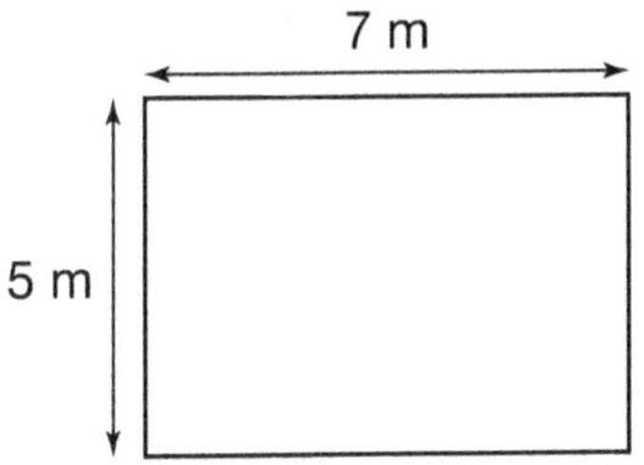

For example:

perimeter of this rectangle
= two times (5 m + 7 m)
= two times (12 m)
= 24 m

2. Which rectangle has the greater perimeter? How much greater is it?

a) 7.5 cm by 6 cm **b)** 7 cm by 7 cm

Rectangle ______ has the greater perimeter. It is ______ greater than ______.

3. **a)** How will the perimeter of this rectangle change if you add 4 m to the width?

The perimeter ________________________________.

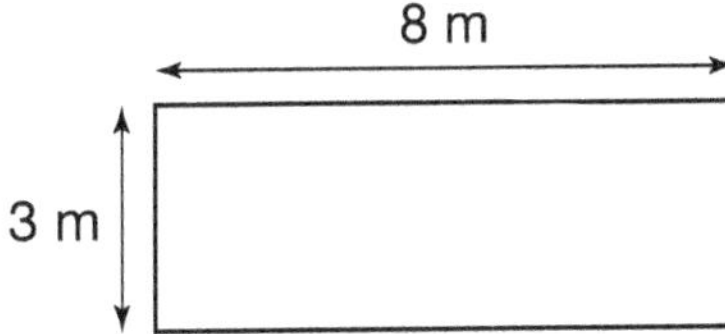

b) How will the perimeter change if you divide the length in half?

The perimeter ________________________________.

4. To calculate the perimeter of a square, Sue multiplies the width by 4. Is her rule correct? Explain.

____

____

Solve Problems Using Tables

Use tables to solve distance problems.

1. Tom cycles 150 m in one minute. He multiplies this by 10 then makes a table of his distances and times.

Distance (m)	Time (min)
1500	10
3000	20
4500	30

Complete the table to estimate how long it will take Tom to cycle 8 km.

It will take Tom about ____________ to cycle 8 km.

At-Home Help

Organizing data in tables helps you see patterns. Using tables is an effective problem-solving strategy.

For example, as the distance increases by 1000 m, the time increases by 10 minutes.

Distance (m)	Time (min)
1000	10
2000	20
3000	30

2. Rosa can paddle her kayak at the rate of 1 km every 5 minutes. At this rate how far will she paddle in 1 hour? Make a table to help you.

3. Tamara skates 120 m in one minute. Emma skates 1 km in 10 minutes. Create 2 tables to find out which girl can skate farther in 30 minutes. How much farther?

Measuring Time

Estimate and measure time to the nearest second.

1. Juanita is making popcorn. Estimate and then calculate the time it took to make the popcorn.

start

finish

I estimate the time to be ______________________.

I calculate the time to be ______________________.

2. Kevin wonders how long the songs on the radio are. He noted the start and end times of one song. Estimate and then calculate the time.

start

finish

I estimate the time to be ______________________.

I calculate the time to be ______________________.

3. A ride at the amusement park has a sign saying: "Five minutes of thrills and spills!"

Yoshi noted the start time of 11:55:26 and the finish time of 12:00:12. Was the sign accurate? Explain.

Five minutes
of thrills
and spills!

____

____

4. The school bell rings at 9:00:00. How much time is left before the bell?

____

At-Home Help

This clock shows when the traffic light turned red.

This clock shows when the traffic light turned green.

The traffic light was red for 1 min 43 s. From 8:47:29 to 8:48:00 is 31 s. From 8:48:00 to 8:49:00 is 1 min. From 8:49:00 to 8:49:12 is 12 s. So the total time was 1 min 43 s.

Recording Dates and Times

Goal **Write dates and times using numeric format.**

1. Colin's flight home landed on March 25, 2004, at 23 minutes 12 seconds after eight o'clock in the evening.

   Record the date and time in numeric format.

   ____

2. Colin departed three weeks before his return home at five minutes after noon.

   Record his departure time in numeric format.

   ____

3. Write each birth date and time in numeric format.

   a) July 18, 1999 at 3 minutes 15 seconds after midnight

   ____

   b) November 20, 2001 at 4 seconds after six thirty in the evening

   ____

4. The Internet Café charges $0.50 for each minute or part of a minute. How much should Sofie pay if she logs on at 16:48:33 and logs off at 17:00:26? Show your work.

At-Home Help

When dates are recorded in numeric format, the year is recorded first, then a hyphen, then the month (using two digits), then another hyphen, then the day (using two digits).

For example, March 10, 2004 would be written as 2004-03-10.

The times on flight, train, and ship schedules are recorded using a 24 hour clock. The hour is written first, followed by a colon, then the minute(s), also followed by a colon, then the seconds (all numbers must have two digits).

On a 24 hour clock, noon is written as 12:00:00. On digital clocks, midnight is displayed as 00:00:00. All hours are written according to the number of hours after midnight.

For example, 1 p.m. is written as 13:00:00.

Test Yourself

Circle the correct answer.

1. A student desk is about ______ m high. It measures about ______ mm across and about ______ cm from front to back. What are the measurements?

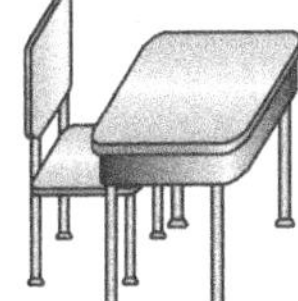

A. 0.8, 650, 410 **B.** 80, 650, 41

C. 0.8, 65, 41 **D.** 0.8, 650, 41

2. What is the thickness of 1 card in mm? Use the information in the picture to help you.

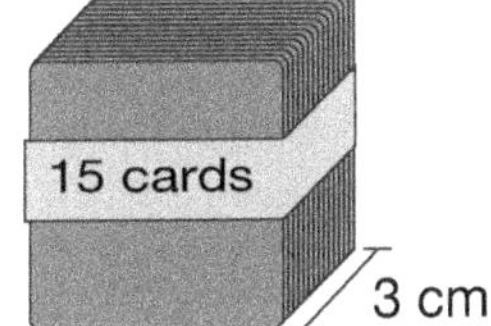

A. 2 **B.** 30

C. 3 **D.** 20

3. The width of Adam's bicycle wheel is 0.6 m. What is the best estimate of the circumference of the wheel?

A. 60 cm **B.** 1.2 m **C.** 2.5 m **D.** 190 cm

4. What is the perimeter of this shape?

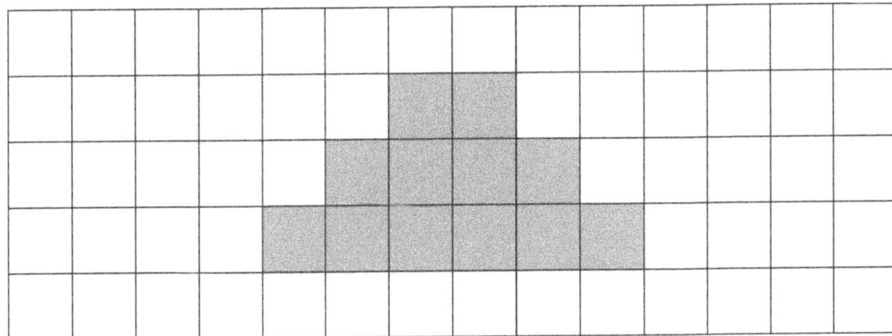

A. 14 cm **B.** 18 cm **C.** 12 cm **D.** 20 cm

5. A 7.5 cm by 6 cm photo is enlarged. The length and the width are doubled. What is the perimeter of the new photo?

A. 7.5 cm greater **B.** double the original perimeter

C. 12 cm greater **D.** 1.5 times the original perimeter

Test Yourself Page 2

6. Fiona rides her skateboard about 150 m in 1 minute. She made a table to track her distance and time. About how long will it take her to skateboard 4 km?

Distance (m)	Time (min)
1500	10
3000	20

A. 20 minutes

B. 23 minutes

C. 27 minutes

D. 30 minutes

7. Neil wants to synchronize the clocks in his home. When the radio announced it was exactly noon, three clocks in his home looked like this:

i

ii

iii

How must Neil correct the time on each clock?

A. (i) back 23 seconds, (ii) ahead 1 minute 44 seconds, (iii) back 2 minutes

B. (i) back 37 seconds, (ii) ahead 1 minute 44 seconds, (iii) back 2 minutes

C. (i) back 37 seconds, (ii) ahead 1 minute 16 seconds, (iii) back 2 minutes

D. (i) ahead 37 seconds, (ii) ahead 2 minutes 44 seconds, (iii) back 2 minutes

8. A hot air balloon will be launched at 40 minutes 30 seconds after 3 p.m. on Canada Day (July 1), 2017. How would the date and time of the launch be written in numeric format?

A. 2017-01-07 3:40:30

B. 2017-01-07 03:40:30

C. 2017-07-01 15:40:30

D. 2017-01-07 15:40:30

9. Which statement best describes circumference?

A. Circumference is the distance around a circle.

B. Circumference is the width of a circle.

C. Circumference is the distance around any object.

D. Circumference is the area of a circle.

Multiplying Tens

Use number facts to multiply by tens.

1. What number facts can you use to calculate these answers? Find the answers.

	Number fact	Answer
a) 40 × 30	______________	______________
b) 50 × 70	______________	______________
c) 60 × 20	______________	______________
d) 90 × 80	______________	______________

2. How can you use this array to calculate 30 × 60? Find the product.

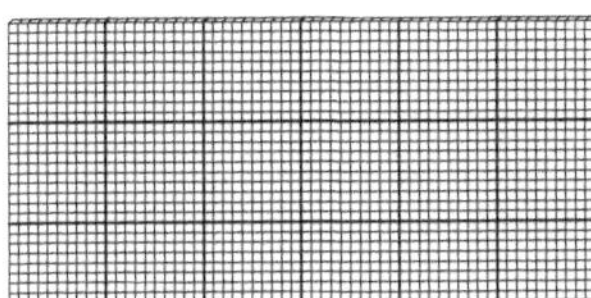

3. Use the array to multiply 40 × 20.

At-Home Help

A **product** is the answer to a multiplication question.

For example, 66 is the product of 11 × 6.

11 × 6 = 66

When you multiply tens, it is easier to use multiplication facts for the non-zero digits.

For example, to multiply 30 × 20 use the multiplication fact 3 × 2 = 6.

An array can help with multiplication.

30 × 20 = 600

4. Calculate the area of each rectangle.

a)

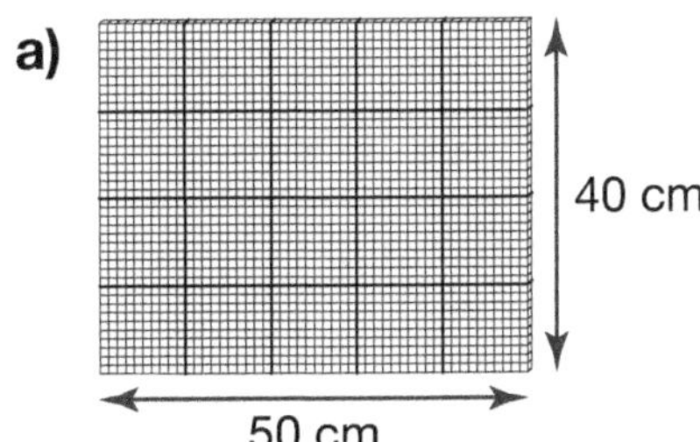

b)

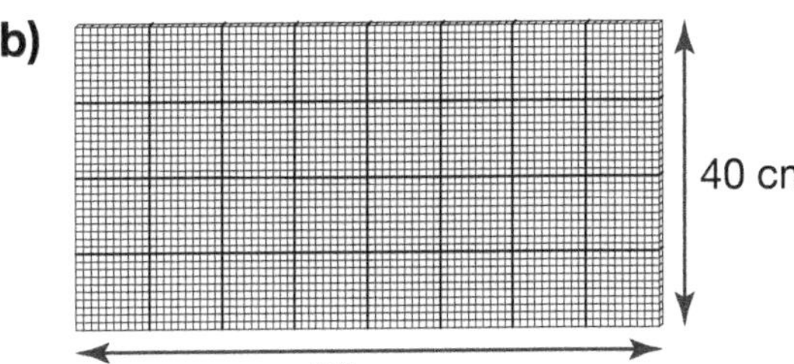

5. Calculate each product. Explain your thinking.

	Explanation
a) 30 × 60 = ______________	______________________________
b) 70 × 40 = ______________	______________________________

Estimating Products

Solve two-step problems and use estimation to check the reasonableness of a calculation.

1. Estimate which calculations are reasonable. Explain how you estimated.

   a) $224 \times 8 = 1792$

   b) $29 \times 58 = 1200$

   c) $1475 \times 99 = 213\,425$

   d) $49 \times 49 = 2401$

At-Home Help

To check the reasonableness of a multiplication, estimate the answer by rounding the numbers being multiplied to the nearest 10.

For example:

To check if $12 \times 39 = 468$ is reasonable, round 12 and 39 to the nearest ten. Then multiply.
$10 \times 40 = 400$

So the product 468 is reasonable.

2. Trevor has 60 nickels and 50 dimes. He wants to know if he can buy a book that costs $11.55. How much more money does he need to buy the book? Explain how you solved the problem.

3. A group of 25 hockey players are having a contest to see who can sell the most chocolate bars. Each group of 5 players gets a box of 30 chocolate bars.

   a) Calculate the greatest number of chocolate bars that can be sold. Show your work.

   b) Use estimation to show that your calculation in Part **a)** is reasonable. Explain your thinking.

Solve Problems Using Tree Diagrams

Use a tree diagram to solve combination problems.

Norman is designing hats for his baseball team. The designs include 3 colours, 2 logos, and 3 styles.

Colour	Logo	Style
Blue	Maple leaf	Button with stitching
Red	Baseball bat and ball	Button with no stitching
Black		Smooth top

1. How many different baseball hats can Norman design? Use a tree diagram.

At-Home Help

To find the number of combinations of items in a problem, use a tree diagram to list all possibilities.

Choose one item and list all the combinations for it. Repeat this process for all items.

For example, if you have 3 types of hats, 2 fabrics, and 4 colours, then the total number of different hats you can make is 24.

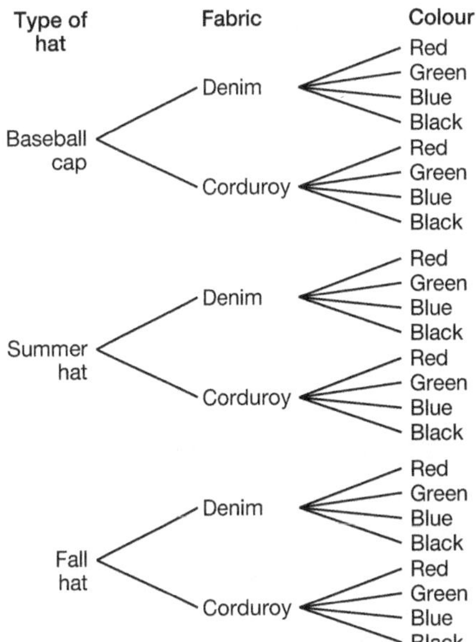

2. Create a tree diagram using 2 colours and 2 logos to get a total of 4 different hats.

Multiplying by Regrouping

Use mental math to multiply two two-digit numbers.

1. Use each number line to calculate.

   a) 12 × 14 = ______________

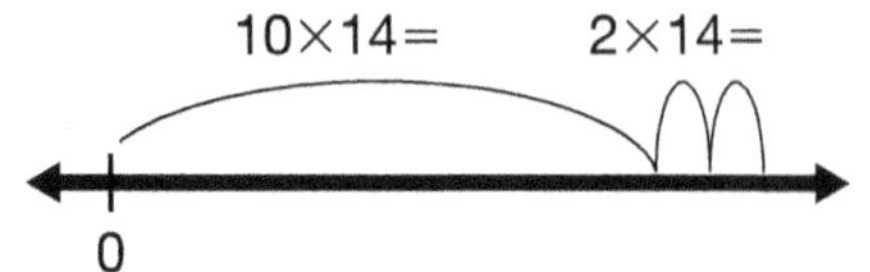

   b) 15 × 11 = ______________

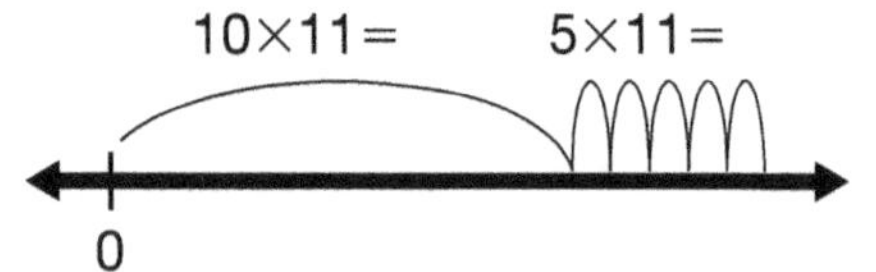

2. Use mental math to calculate.

   a) 12 × 16 = ______________

   b) 17 × 11 = ______________

3. Calculate.

   a) 11 × 12 = ______________

   b) 12 × 18 = ______________

   c) 15 × 13 = ______________

4. A roller coaster holds 15 people. How many people can go on the roller coaster in 22 rides?

5. How many cobs of corn are in 19 dozen?

At-Home Help

Regrouping is a mental math strategy for multiplying numbers. Regroup numbers into 10s to make calculations easier.

For example:

12 × 12 can be regrouped as (10 + 2) × 12. 10 × 12 = 120 and 2 × 12 = 24.

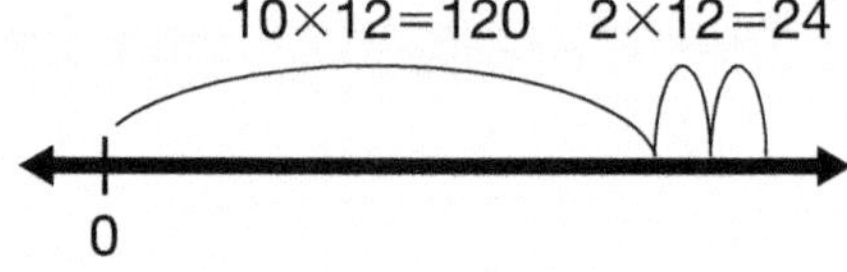

12 × 12 = 120 + 24
= 144

Multiplying with Arrays

Multiply two-digit numbers.

1. Calculate the number of cells in each table.

   a) 11 rows and 13 columns ____________________

   b) 17 rows and 21 columns ____________________

   c) 13 rows and 15 columns ____________________

2. What multiplication question is represented by these base ten blocks? Calculate the product.

   a) 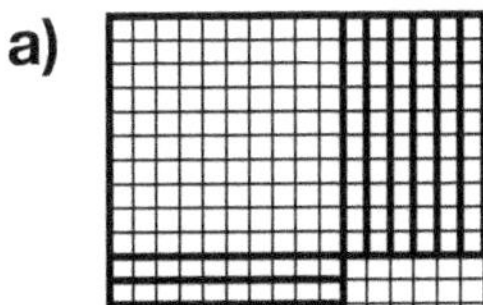

   b) 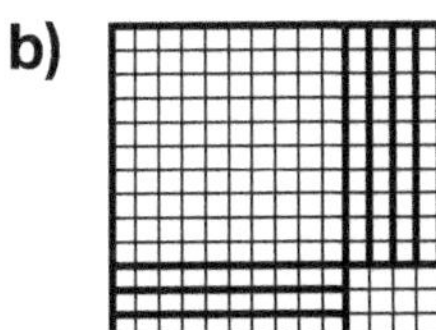

   c) 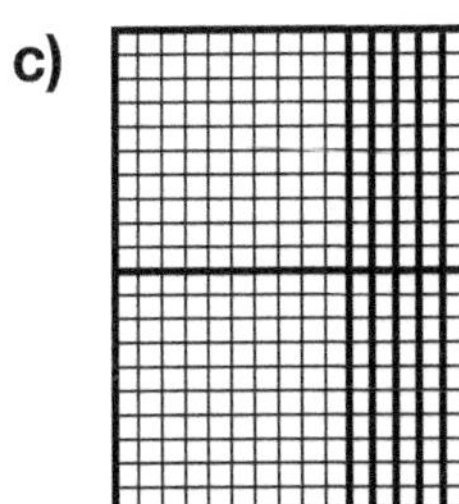

3. A quilt has 11 rows and 17 columns of squares. How many squares are on the quilt?

4. Two quilts are made of square patches each measuring 1 dm by 1 dm. What is the area of each quilt?

   a) 14 rows and 18 columns ______________________________

   b) 22 rows and 25 columns ______________________________

Dividing Hundreds by One-Digit Numbers

Use division facts to divide hundreds.

1. What division facts can you use to calculate these answers? Find the answers.

	Division fact	Answer
a) $800 \div 2$	____________	____________
b) $1500 \div 5$	____________	____________
c) $1200 \div 3$	____________	____________
d) $2800 \div 7$	____________	____________
e) $3600 \div 4$	____________	____________
f) $4200 \div 6$	____________	____________

2. Explain how using $16 \div 4$ can help you divide 1600 by 4.

____

____

At-Home Help

To divide hundreds by one digit, it is easier to use division facts for the non-zero digits.

For example, to divide $1200 \div 2$ use the division fact $12 \div 2 = 6$.

An array can help with division.

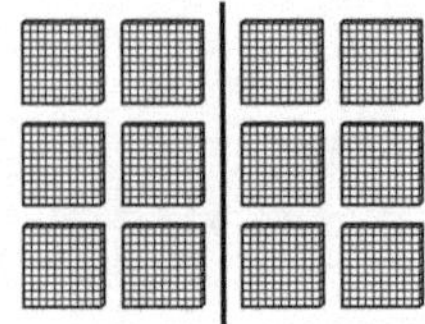

$1200 \div 2 = 600$

You can also check your answer using multiplication.

$600 \times 2 = 1200$

3. Explain how multiplication can help you check your answer to Question 2.

____

4. An 1800 m track is divided equally into 6 shorter runs. Use a division fact to predict the length of each short run.

Estimating Quotients

Goal **Overestimate and underestimate when dividing.**

1. Overestimate each division. Show the numbers you used to estimate.

Overestimate

a) $1427 \div 5$ ________________

b) $8\overline{)2394}$ ________________

c) $3\overline{)1713}$ ________________

d) $5406 \div 7$ ________________

2. Underestimate each division. Show the numbers you used to estimate.

Underestimate

a) $1135 \div 2$ ________________

b) $1303 \div 4$ ________________

c) $2645 \div 3$ ________________

d) $4495 \div 6$ ________________

3. For each question, is it more accurate to overestimate or underestimate? Explain.

a) $2914 \div 5$ ________________

____

b) $3759 \div 6$ ________________

4. Estimate to solve the problem. Explain your thinking.

The total attendance at 2 hockey games in March was 9498 people. Approximately what was the average attendance at each game?

____

At-Home Help

A **quotient** is the answer to a division question.

For example, 8 is the quotient of $48 \div 6$.

$48 \div 6 = 8$

To do some calculations, it is easier to overestimate and underestimate. The actual answer will be somewhere between both estimates.

With other calculations, either an overestimate or an underestimate gives a fairly accurate answer.

For example, $4753 \div 6$ would be $4800 \div 6 = 800$ as an overestimate. 800 is fairly accurate because 4753 is closer to 4800 than 4200.

$1095 \div 2$ would be $1000 \div 2 = 500$ as an underestimate. 500 is fairly accurate because 1095 is closer to 1000 than 1200.

$4539 \div 6$ would be $4200 \div 6 = 700$ as an underestimate and $4800 \div 6 = 800$ as an overestimate. The actual answer is about 750, or halfway between 700 and 800.

Dividing Greater Numbers

Divide a four-digit number by a one-digit number.

1. Estimate and then divide. Show your work.

	Estimate	Answer
a) 2641 ÷ 2	________	________
b) $3\overline{)2001}$	________	________
c) $6\overline{)3517}$	________	________
d) 2134 ÷ 9	________	________
e) $6\overline{)1604}$	________	________
f) 4395 ÷ 5	________	________

At-Home Help

To divide some numbers, you may need to regroup first.

2. Check two of the answers in Question 1 using multiplication and addition.

3. Eight dolphins in a pod each have about the same mass. Their total mass is about 1195 kg. What is the approximate mass of each dolphin?

4. Four trucks are ready to transport the 8 dolphins to a marine centre. Each truck can carry 225 kg. Can the trucks carry all the dolphins in one trip? Explain.

Choosing Multiplication and Division Methods

Choose and justify a calculation method.

Answer each question using the information given. Explain why you chose multiplication or division.

Did you know...

- the giant Canada goose has a mass of 7 kg
- it flies at a maximum altitude of 245 m from the ground
- it takes 30 days to hatch one nest of eggs
- it can fly about 40 km in 1 hour
- it can fly for about 16 hours each day

At-Home Help

To decide whether to multiply or divide in a problem, look to see if any totals are given.

For example, if the total cost of several items having the same value is given and the problem asks you to find the cost of each item, you need to divide.

If you are asked to find a total, you need to multiply.

For example, if you are given the volume of juice per bottle and the number of bottles, you can find the total volume by multiplying.

1. What would be the mass of a flock of 65 geese?

____

____

____

2. How many hours would the geese have flown in 12 days?

____

____

3. How many days would the geese fly if they flew for a total of 592 hours?

____

____

4. How many days would a goose sit on 15 nests of eggs?

____

____

5. Three geese fly at different altitudes from the ground. They are equal distances apart. Approximately what are the 3 different altitudes from the ground?

____

____

Test Yourself

Circle the correct answer.

1. What is the product of 50 × 40?

   A. 900 **B.** 200 **C.** 2000 **D.** 9000

2. What is the product of 90 × 30?

   A. 1200 **B.** 2700 **C.** 120 **D.** 270

3. What is the product of 600 × 60?

   A. 1200 **B.** 3600 **C.** 12 000 **D.** 36 000

4. Which estimate is most reasonable for 26 × 18?

   A. 550 **B.** 450 **C.** 750 **D.** 600

5. Which estimate is most reasonable for 38 × 35?

   A. 900 **B.** 1050 **C.** 1100 **D.** 1200

6. What is the product of 8 × 257?

   A. 2056 **B.** 1656 **C.** 2165 **D.** 2065

7. What is the product of 94 × 62?

   A. 5688 **B.** 5628 **C.** 5828 **D.** 5288

8. What is the area of this rectangle?

   A. 1611 square metres

   B. 1161 square metres

   C. 1616 square metres

   D. 1116 square metres

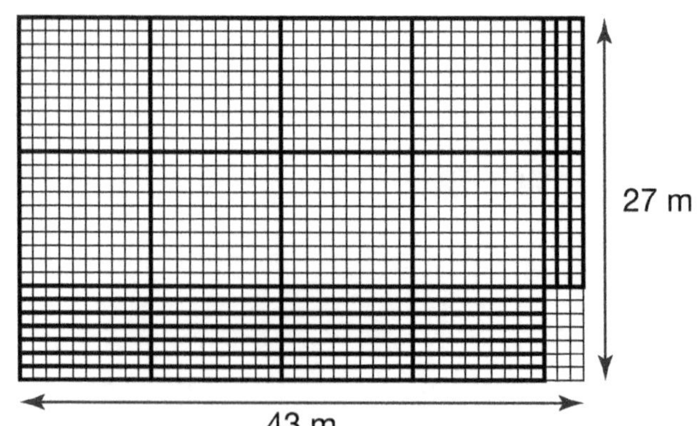

Test Yourself Page 2

9. What is the answer to 7396 ÷ 4?

   A. 1489 **B.** 1849 **C.** 1949 **D.** 1889

10. What is the answer to 4508 ÷ 8?

   A. 563 R1 **B.** 562 R3 **C.** 562 R4 **D.** 563 R4

11. What are the missing numbers from top to bottom?

```
   57
  ×4?
 ----
  3?2
 2???
 ----
 ????
```

   A. 4, 6, 280, 2822 **B.** 6, 4, 280, 2622 **C.** 6, 4, 260, 2822 **D.** 4, 6, 260, 2622

12. Tiles are to be placed on a kitchen wall. They are in 18 rows and 14 columns. How many tiles are needed?

   A. 254 tiles **B.** 245 tiles **C.** 252 tiles **D.** 225 tiles

13. The area of a rectangular room is 63 square metres. The longest side is 9 m long. What is the perimeter of the room?

   A. 32 m **B.** 30 m **C.** 31 m **D.** 33 m

14. A square room has a perimeter of 164 m. What is its area?

   A. 1861 square metres **B.** 1600 square metres

   C. 328 square metres **D.** 1681 square metres

Constructing Symmetrical Shapes

Construct 2-D shapes with one line of symmetry.

1.

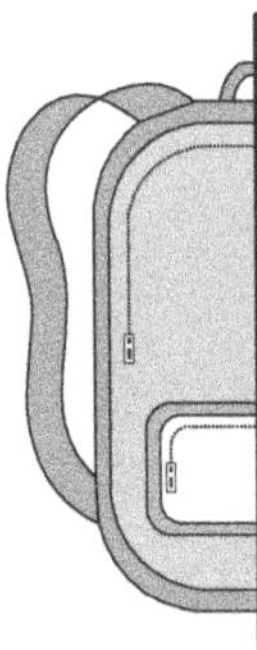

a) Use symmetry to complete the picture.

b) Describe the method you used. Check for symmetry.

____

____

____

2.

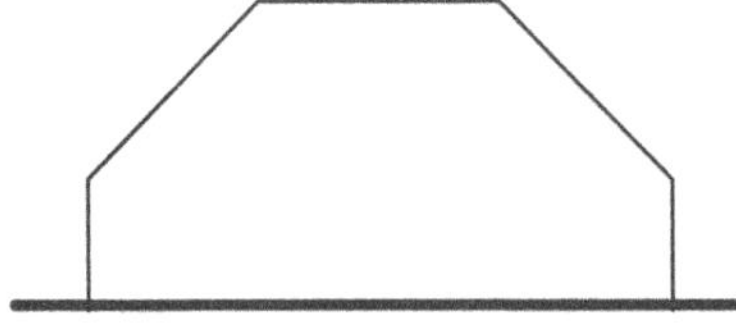

a) Use a different method from Question 1 to complete the picture.

b) Describe the method you used. Check for symmetry and describe your method.

____

____

____

____

____

At-Home Help

A line of symmetry may be horizontal or vertical.

To complete a picture that has a line of symmetry, use one of these two ways.

- Use a grid to draw a congruent half on the other side of the line of symmetry.
- Find matching points by measuring the distance from several points on the given half to the line of symmetry. Make sure distance is at right angles to line of symmetry. Then join all new points to make a congruent half.

Check for symmetry by using one of these two ways.

- Fold the completed picture along the line of symmetry to see if both halves match exactly.
- Use a transparent mirror to check for congruence of both halves.

Constructing Triangles

Draw triangles with given side lengths and angle measures.

You will need a ruler and a protractor.

1. Draw a triangle with side lengths of 3 cm and 6 cm. The angle between these two sides is 75°.

At-Home Help

You can draw a triangle if you know the measure of

- only one angle and one side
- two angles and one side without specifying where the side is
- two sides and one angle without specifying where the angle is

There is only one solution if two side lengths and one angle are given, and the angle location is known.

2. Draw two different triangles that each have one side length of 6 cm and angles of 125° and 25°.

3. Draw three different triangles that each have one side length of 5 cm and an angle of 60°.

Classifying Triangles by Angles

Investigate angle measures in triangles.

You will need a protractor.

1.

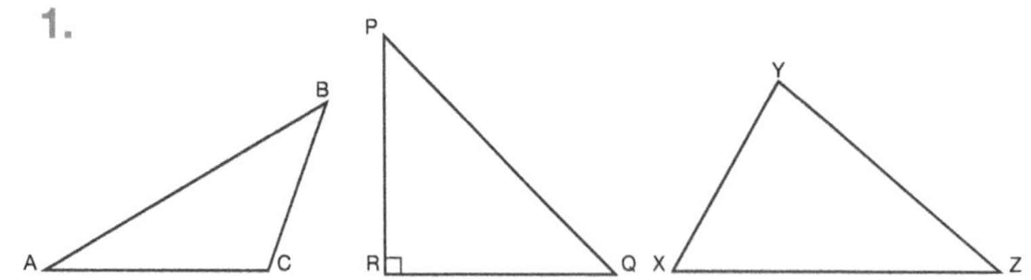

a) Measure and label all the angles in the triangles.

b) Classify the triangles. Give reasons for your answers.

Triangle ABC is ______________________.

Reason: ______________________

____

Triangle PQR is ______________________.

Reason: ______________________

____

Triangle XYZ is ______________________.

Reason: ______________________

____

At-Home Help

A **right-angled triangle** has one right angle.

A **right angle** measures 90°.

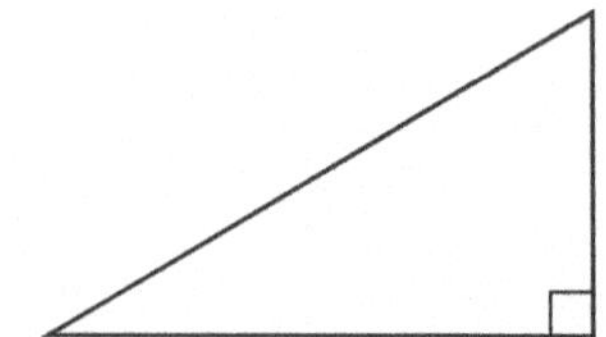

An **obtuse-angled triangle** has one obtuse angle.

An **obtuse angle** measures greater than 90°.

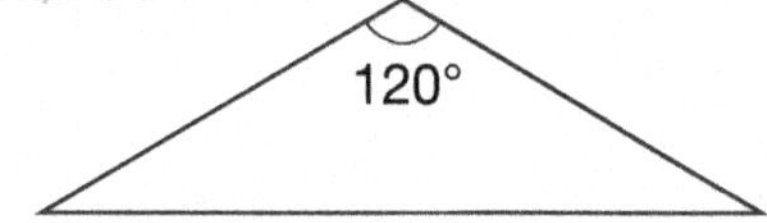

An **acute-angled triangle** has only acute angles.

An **acute angle** measures less than 90°.

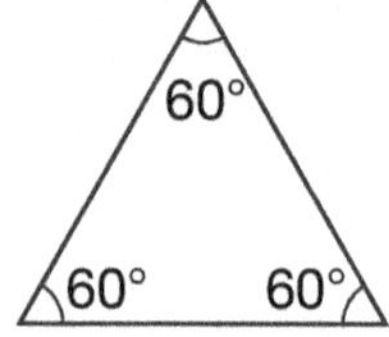

2. a) What type of triangle has an angle that measures 100° and an angle that measures 50°? Give your reasons.

____

____

b) What type of triangle has an angle that measures 60° and an angle that measures 90°? Give your reasons.

____

____

Classifying Triangles by Side Lengths

Investigate side lengths of triangles.

You will need a ruler.

1.

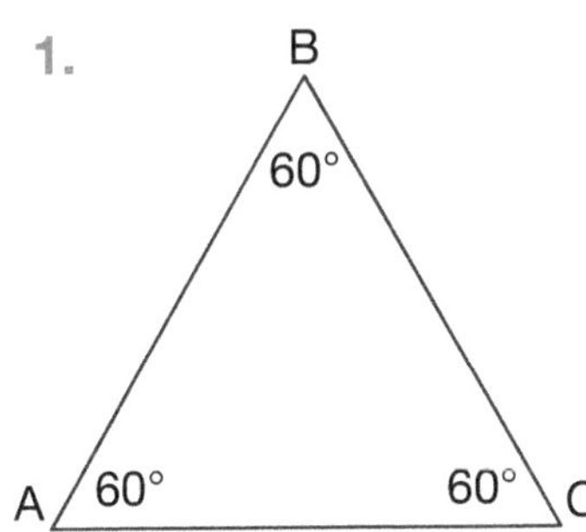

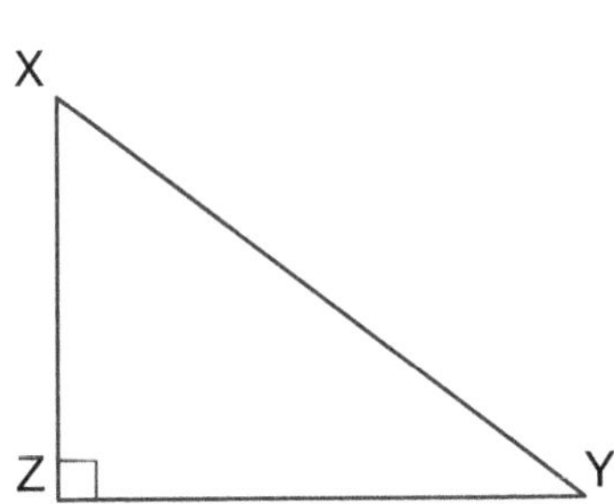

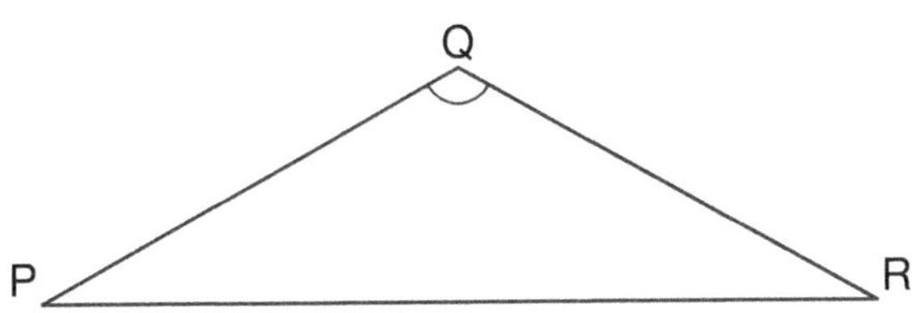

a) Measure and label all the side lengths of the triangles.

b) Classify the triangles according to their side lengths. Give your reasons.

Triangle ABC is ______________________________.

Reason: ______________________________

Triangle PQR is ______________________________.

Reason: ______________________________

Triangle XYZ is ______________________________.

Reason: ______________________________

At-Home Help

An **equilateral triangle** has all sides of equal length.

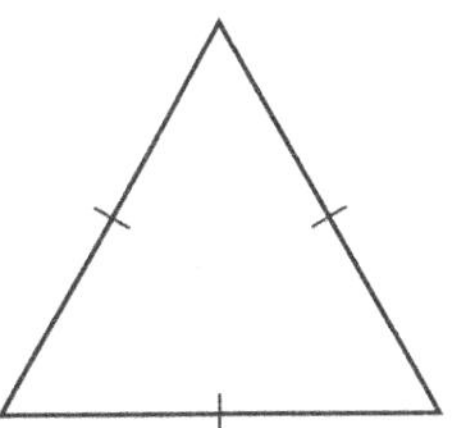

An **isosceles triangle** has two sides of equal length.

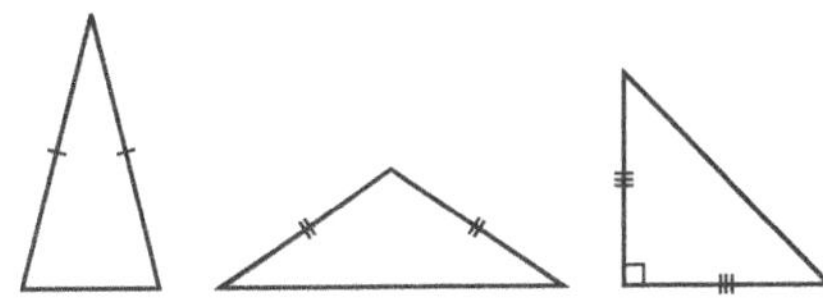

A **scalene triangle** has all sides of different length.

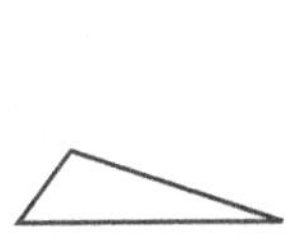

2. Classify the triangles according to their angle measures and side lengths.
Example: Triangle KLM is an obtuse-angled scalene triangle.

a) Triangle ABC is ______________________________.

b) Triangle PQR is ______________________________.

c) Triangle XYZ is ______________________________.

Measuring Angles in Polygons

Identify and classify regular polygons by their angle measures.

1. Match these shapes with the angle clues below. Name each shape.

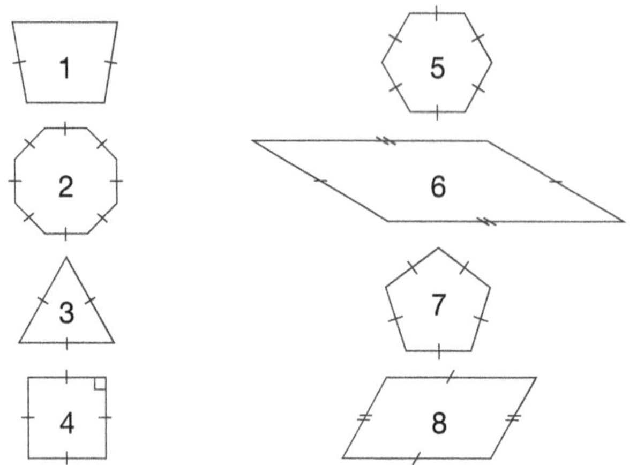

a) 100°, 100°, 80°, 80° ____________________

b) 120°, 120°, 60°, 60° ____________________

c) 60°, 60°, 60° ____________________

d) 90°, 90°, 90°, 90° ____________________

e) 30°, 30°, 150°, 150° ____________________

At-Home Help

A **regular polygon** is a polygon with equal angle measures and equal side lengths.

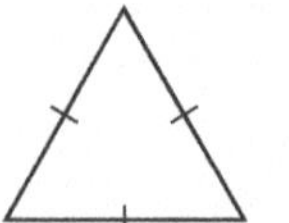

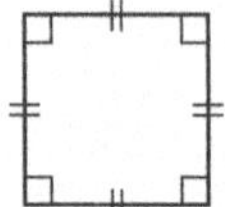

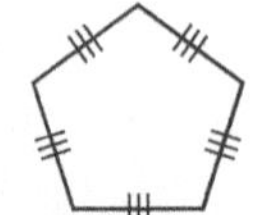

Regular polygons are identified by the number of sides.

The angle measure in a regular polygon increases as the number of sides increases.

For example: Each angle in a regular hexagon is greater than each angle in a square, because a hexagon has 6 sides while a square has only 4 sides.

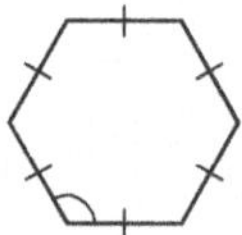

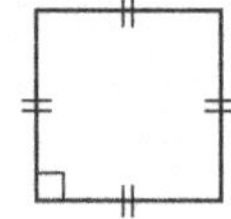

2. Write angle clues for the remaining polygons. Match the shapes with your angle clues. Name each shape.

Angle clue: ____________________ Shape: ____________________

Angle clue: ____________________ Shape: ____________________

Angle clue: ____________________ Shape: ____________________

3. Without measuring, predict the size of angle A. Use what you know about the relationship between the number of sides and angle measures in a regular polygon.

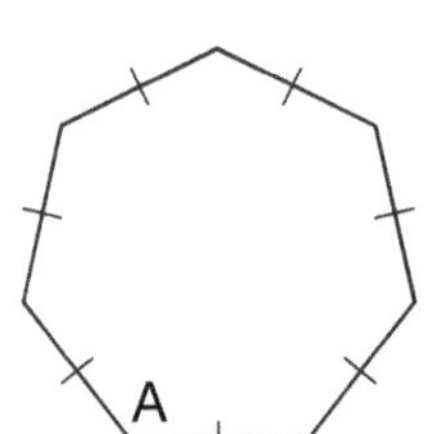

____

____

Properties of Polygons

Investigate properties of geometric shapes.

1. Match the polygons with the property riddles below.

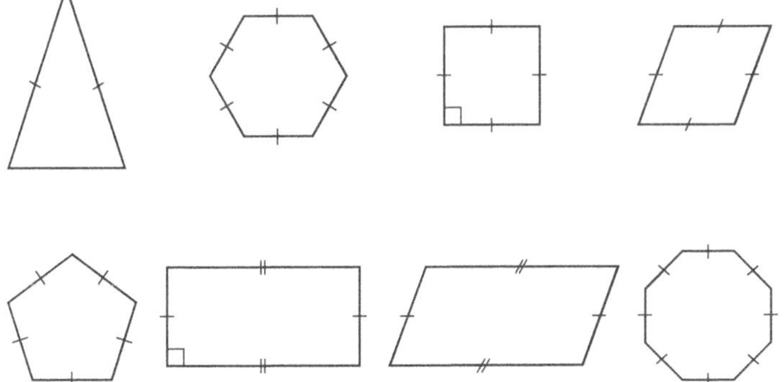

At-Home Help

The **properties** of a shape are the features that describe it.

For example:

The properties of a regular hexagon are 6 equal sides, 6 equal angles (all obtuse), 3 pairs of parallel sides, and 6 lines of symmetry.

Because no other shape shares all the same properties, a shape can be identified by its properties.

a) I have no parallel sides.
All my sides are equal in length.
All my angles are equal.
I have 5 lines of symmetry.
Who am I?

____

b) I have 3 pairs of parallel sides.
All my sides are equal in length.
All my angles are obtuse.
I have 6 lines of symmetry.
Who am I?

____

c) I have 2 pairs of parallel sides.
All my sides are equal in length.
I have 2 pairs of equal angles.
I have 2 lines of symmetry.
Who am I?

____

d) I have 2 pairs of parallel sides.
My opposite sides are equal in length.
All my angles are equal in size.
I have 2 lines of symmetry.
Who am I?

____

2. Write property riddles for two of the remaining polygons. Write about parallel sides, side lengths, angle measures, and lines of symmetry. Name each polygon.

a) _______________

____

____

____

____

____

b) _______________

____

____

____

____

____

Sorting Polygons

Sort and classify polygons by sides, angles, and vertices.

1. Use a Venn diagram to sort these shapes using two of the properties below.
   - number of sides
   - number of angles
   - number of vertices
   - number of lines of symmetry
   - parallel sides
   - equal side lengths
   - equal angles
   - kinds of angles

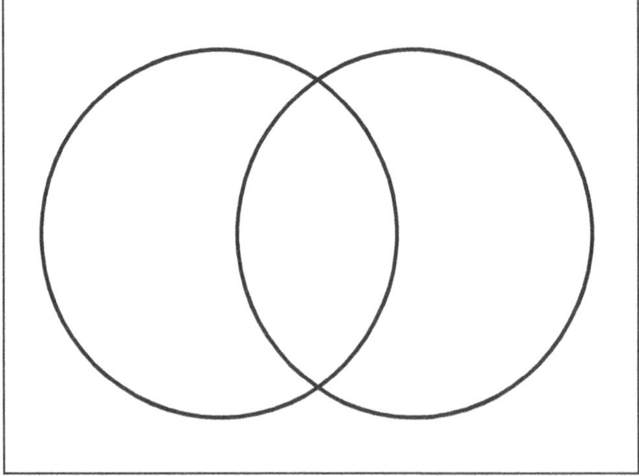

2. Are there any shapes inside both circles? If so, what properties do these shapes have in common?

____

____

3. Are there any shapes outside both circles? If so, why are they placed there?

____

____

At-Home Help

Polygons can be sorted based on
- number of sides
- number of angles
- number of vertices
- number of lines of symmetry
- parallel sides
- equal side lengths
- equal angles
- kinds of angles

In a polygon, the number of angles and the number of vertices are equal to the number of sides.

An **irregular polygon** is a polygon with different angle measures and different side lengths.

For example:

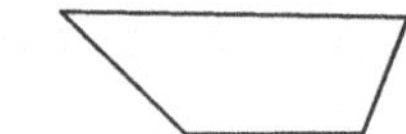

A **Venn diagram** is a drawing with overlapping circles inside a rectangle. This type of diagram is helpful when sorting shapes or numbers.

Communicate About Shapes

Use math language to describe geometric ideas.

1.

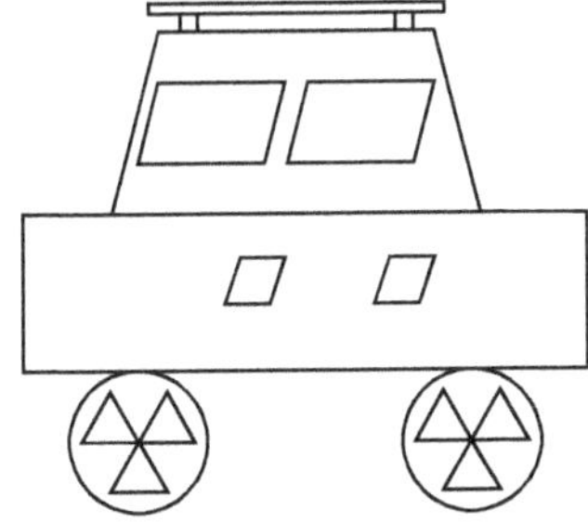

a) Write directions for a friend to draw the picture shown.

At-Home Help

To describe how to draw a picture made of polygons, remember to use the Communication Checklist.

The true test of whether or not your directions are clear is if someone else can reproduce the picture exactly.

Communication Checklist

☑ Did you show the right amount of detail?

☑ Did you use math language?

☑ Did you include only necessary information?

b) Use the Communication Checklist to identify the strengths of your directions. List them.

____

____

____

2. If possible, test your directions by having your parent use them to draw the picture.

Test Yourself

Circle the correct answer.

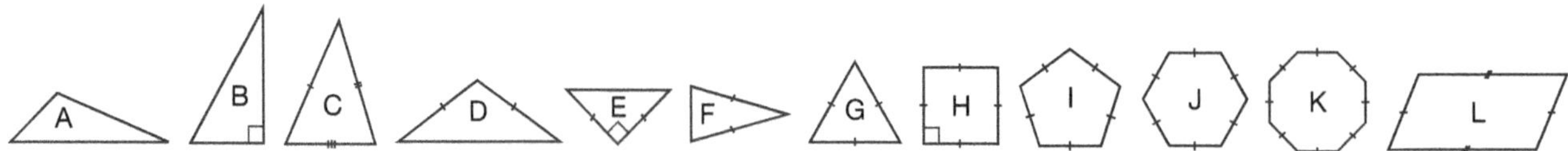

1. Which triangle has no lines of symmetry?

   A. shape A **B.** shape D **C.** shape F **D.** shape G

2. Which shape is a regular polygon?

   A. shape B **B.** shape C **C.** shape K **D.** shape E

3. Which shape has no parallel sides?

   A. shape J **B.** shape L **C.** shape H **D.** shape I

4. Which shape has 2 pairs of equal angles?

   A. shape L **B.** shape D **C.** shape H **D.** shape K

5. Which shape has no obtuse angles?

   A. shape A **B.** shape K **C.** shape L **D.** shape E

6. Which shape is a right-angled isosceles triangle?

   A. shape B **B.** shape F **C.** shape E **D.** shape D

7. Which shape has only acute angles?

   A. shape L **B.** shape H **C.** shape C **D.** shape K

8. Which shape is a scalene triangle?

   A. shape G **B.** shape A **C.** shape D **D.** shape F

9. Which shape is an irregular polygon?

   A. shape L **B.** shape H **C.** shape J **D.** shape I

10. Which shape is symmetrical?

    A. shape B **B.** shape L **C.** shape C **D.** shape D

Areas of Polygons

Estimate and measure the area of polygons.

1. A hockey team chose this logo for their uniforms.

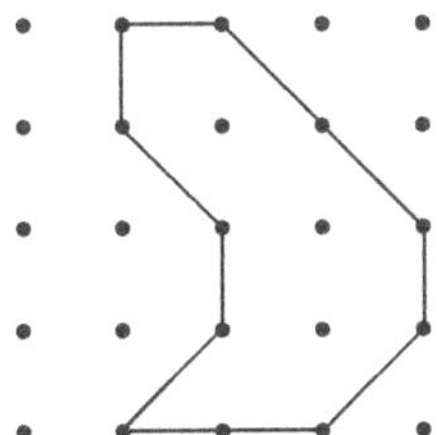

a) Estimate the area in square units.

____

b) Measure the area in square units.

____

2. For each polygon, estimate and then measure the area in square units.

At-Home Help

A grid is like an area ruler. Each full square on the grid has an area of 1 square unit. Many shapes drawn on grids can be divided into squares and right-angled triangles.

For example:

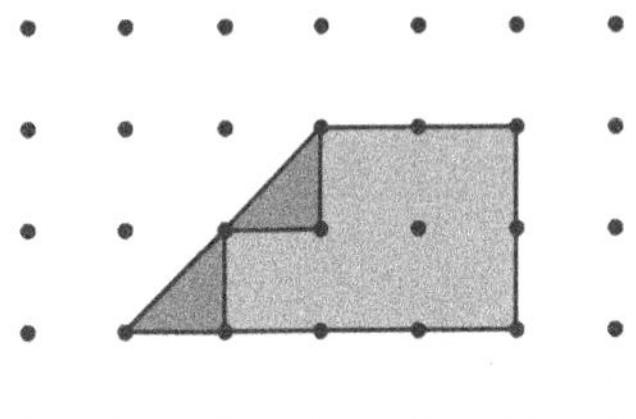

In this shape, there are 5 full squares (lightly shaded) and 2 half squares (darkly shaded). So the total area is 6 square units.

	Estimated area	Measured area
a) 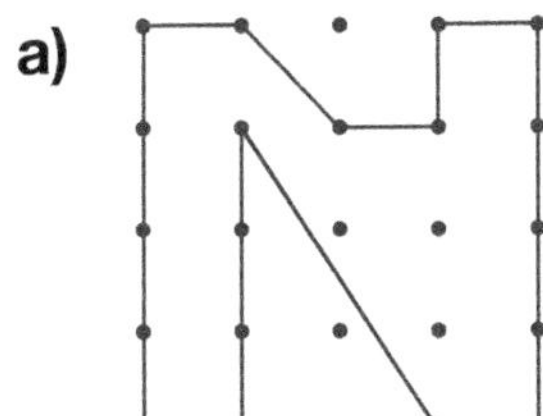	_______________	_______________
b)	_______________	_______________
c) 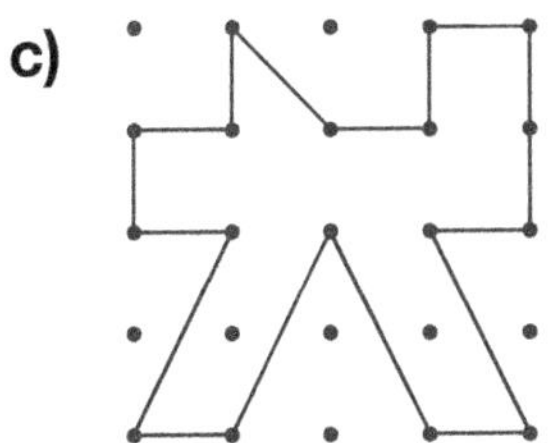	_______________	_______________

Areas of Irregular 2-D Shapes

Develop methods to measure the areas of irregular 2-D shapes.

Find the area of this tulip shape to the nearest square unit using each of the methods below.

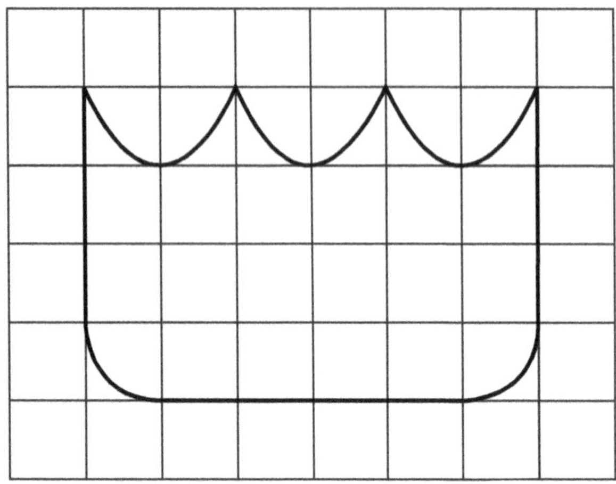

1. Count the full squares. For part squares, if less than half a square is covered, round down. If more than half a square is covered, round up.

Full squares	Part squares	Total area
______	______	______

2. Count the full squares. For part squares, count how many squares you could make by putting together the part squares.

Full squares	Part squares	Total area
______	______	______

3. Count the full squares. For part squares, count only those that are half or more.

Full squares	Part squares	Total area
______	______	______

At-Home Help

A grid is useful when measuring the area of an irregular 2-D shape to the nearest square unit.

On centimetre grid paper, each full square has an area of 1 square centimetre. Part squares that cover less than half a square can be rounded down. Part squares that cover more than half a square can be counted as 1 full square. Part squares can also be grouped to make up about 1 full square.

For example:

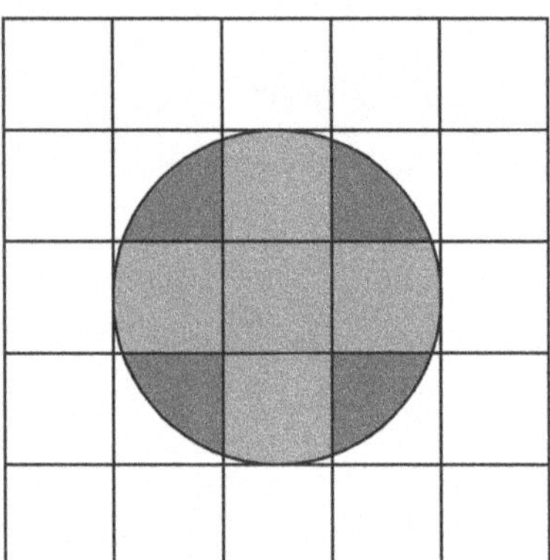

This circle covers 5 full or almost full squares (lightly shaded). There are 4 remaining part squares (darkly shaded), which can be grouped to give about 2 more full squares. So the total area of the circle is about 7 square units.

Relating Perimeter and Area of Rectangles

Explore relationships among side lengths, perimeter, and area of rectangles.

Camille has 20 cm of decorative tape to put around the perimeter of a bookmark.

1. Sketch all possible rectangles she can design with a perimeter of 20 cm.

2. Calculate the area of each rectangle in Question 1. Record your answers in the table.

Length of side 1 (cm)	Length of side 2 (cm)	Area (cm^2)

3. How are the areas and the shapes of the rectangles related?

At-Home Help

Perimeter is the distance around a shape. Rectangles with the same area may have different perimeters.

For example:

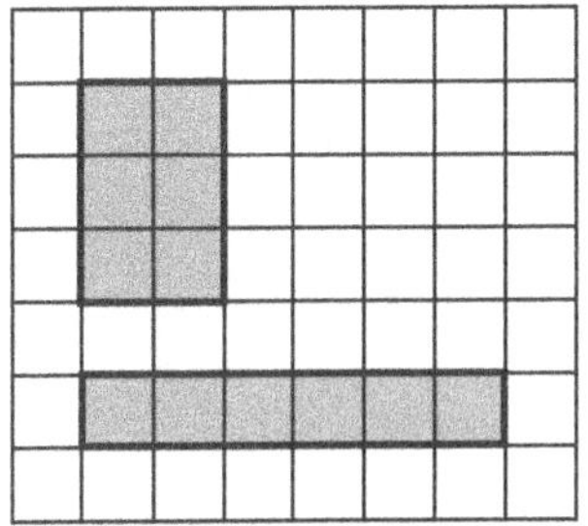

Both rectangles have an area of 6 cm^2, but the perimeter of both rectangles is not the same. The top rectangle has a perimeter of 10 cm while the bottom rectangle has a perimeter of 14 cm.

Rectangles with the same perimeter may have different areas.

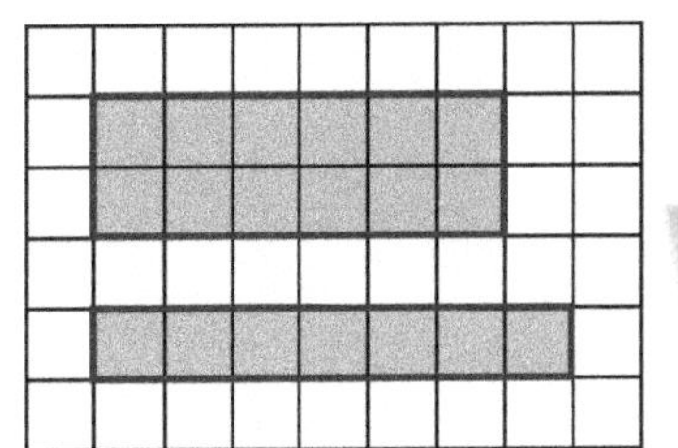

Both rectangles have a perimeter of 16 cm, but the area of both rectangles is not the same. The top rectangle has an area of 12 cm^2 while the bottom rectangle has an area of 7 cm^2.

Perimeter is an outside measurement while area is an inside measurement.

Area Rule for Rectangles

Develop and explain a rule for calculating the area of a rectangle.

1. Jasmine is choosing address labels. Calculate each area. Use the rule for area of a rectangle. Show your work.

a) 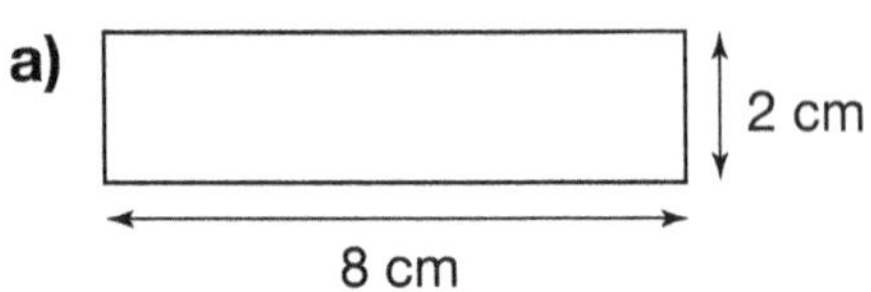

b) 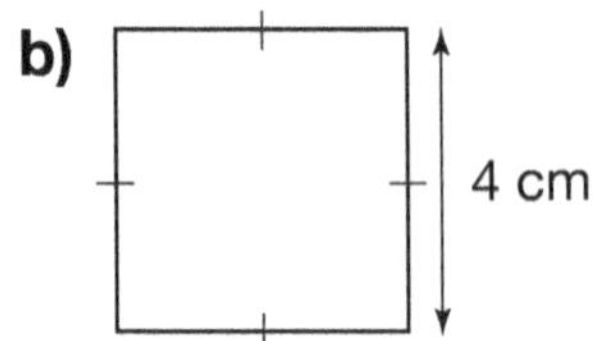

2. Calculate the area of each rectangle. Use the rule for area of a rectangle. Show your work.

a) 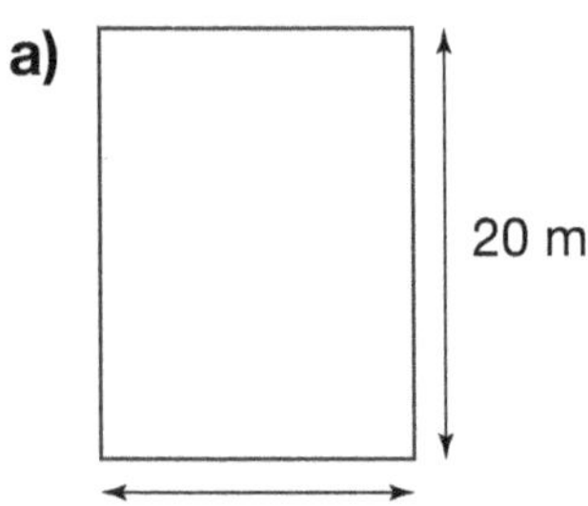

b) 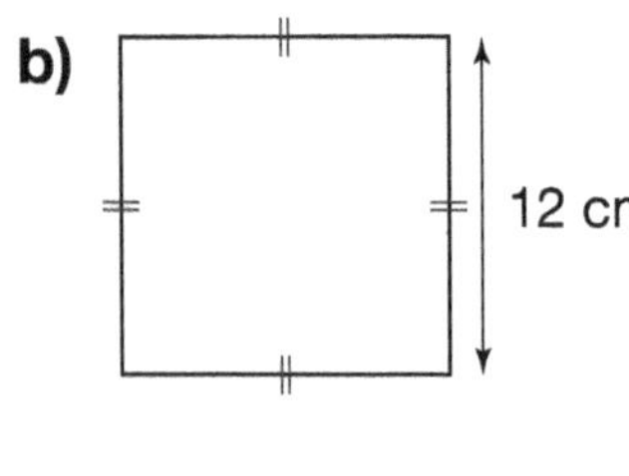

3. Nancy is using 1 cm^2 tiles to make rectangular coasters. Each tile costs $0.15. Which coaster will cost the most? Explain.

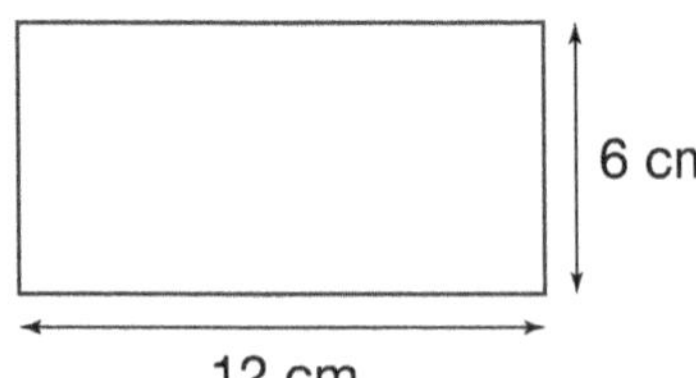

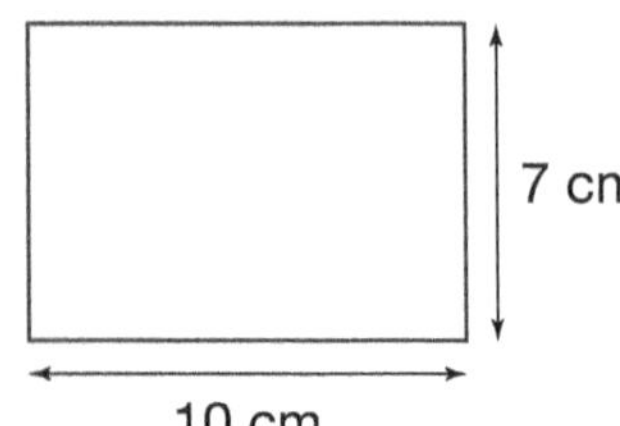

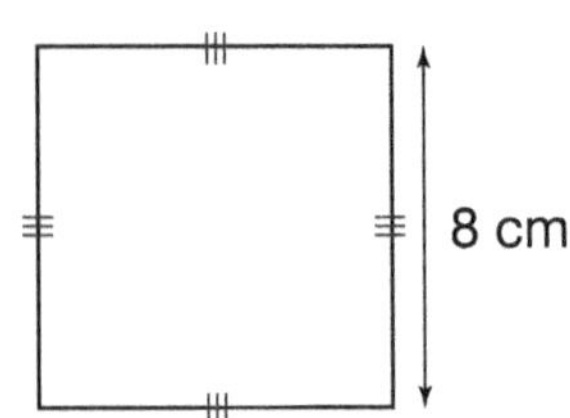

____

At-Home Help

The area of a rectangle, when viewed on a grid, is like a multiplication array.

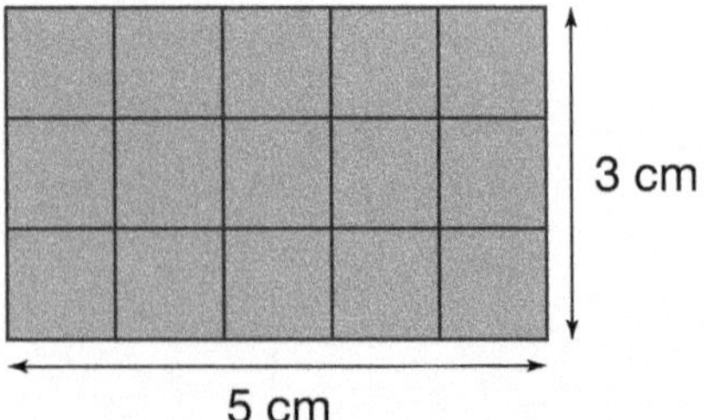

For example, this rectangle has a width of 3 cm and a length of 5 cm. The area of the rectangle can be found by multiplying the length by the width.

$5 \text{ cm} \times 3 \text{ cm} = 15 \text{ cm}^2$

The general rule for the area of a rectangle is

area = length × width

Solve Problems by Solving Simpler Problems

Solve problems by breaking them into smaller parts.

1. Alain's parents are purchasing new flooring for their living room. The flooring costs $20 for each square metre.

   How much will the flooring cost before taxes?

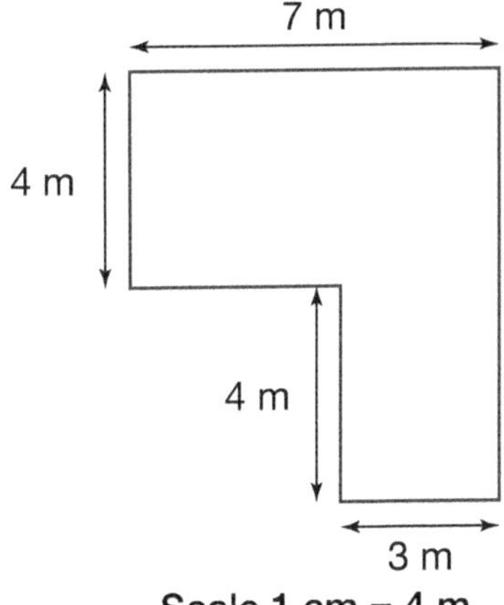

Scale 1 cm = 4 m

   a) Calculate the area by dividing the shape into two parts. Use 2 different sets of rectangles. Did you get the same answer? Explain why or why not.

   ___

   ___

   ___

   b) Calculate the cost of the flooring.

2. A photograph is 12 cm by 16 cm. It has a mount that is 3 cm wide all around it. What is the area of the mount? Show your work.

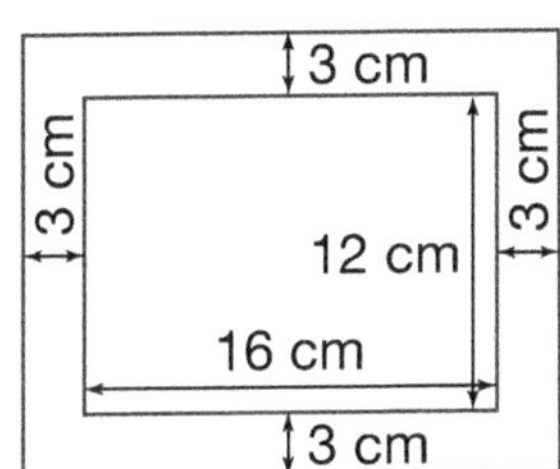

At-Home Help

The area of a complex shape can sometimes be found by dividing it into several smaller parts. The total area is then equal to the sum of the areas of the smaller parts.

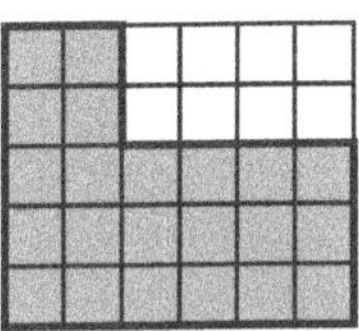

For example, the area of this shape can be calculated two ways.

area = area of 2 cm by 2 cm square + area of 6 cm by 3 cm rectangle

$= 2 \times 2 + 6 \times 3$
$= 4 + 18$
$= 22\ cm^2$

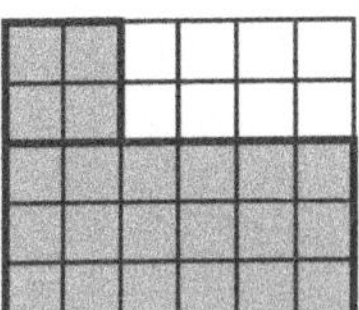

or area = area of 5 cm by 2 cm rectangle + area of 4 cm by 3 cm rectangle

$= 5 \times 2 + 4 \times 3$
$= 10 + 12$
$= 22\ cm^2$

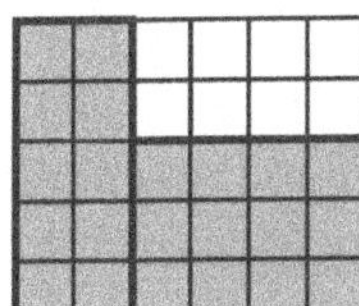

Modelling Area

Model area using an appropriate scale.

1. Jasleen's parents are planning a community garden. The dimensions are 20 m by 16 m. They want to make a scale model of the garden on centimetre grid paper.

   a) Choose an appropriate scale. Explain your choice.

   ____

   ____

   ____

   b) Model the garden. Include the scale.

   c) What is the area of the garden? Include the units.

   ____

   d) What is the area of the model? Include the units.

   ____

At-Home Help

Large objects, such as floor plans, towns, and buildings, can be modelled using a scale. A **scale model** may be larger or smaller than the real object but must be the same shape. A scale model is similar to the real object.

When choosing a scale, consider the size of the object and the space you have available for the model.

For example, to draw a model of a 20 m by 12 m patio on the grid below, an appropriate scale would be 1 cm = 4 m. The model will then be 5 cm (20 ÷ 4) by 3 cm (12 ÷ 4).

Scale 1 cm = 4 m

Remember to always include the scale on your model.

2. Would you measure each area in square kilometres, square metres, square centimetres, or square millimetres?

   a) a restaurant ______________________

   b) a function key on a calculator ______________________

   c) a country ______________________

   d) a postcard ______________________

Coordinate Grids

Use coordinate pairs to identify and describe locations on a grid.

1. Ari drew this logo on a coordinate grid.

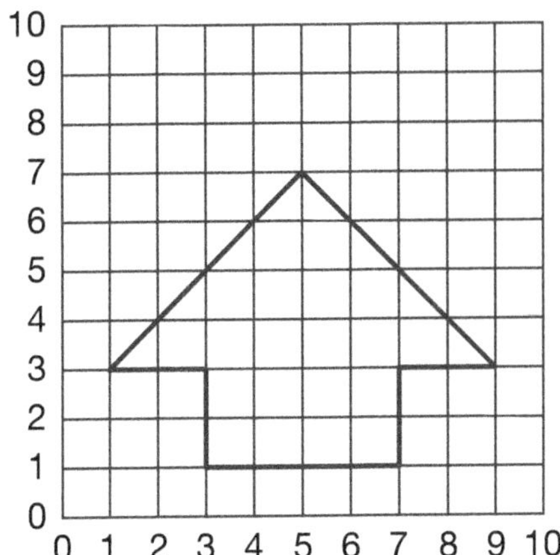

a) What points on the grid could you use to describe the logo? Write the coordinates for each point.

____

____

b) Write instructions for drawing the logo from these points.

____

____

At-Home Help

A **coordinate grid** is a grid with each horizontal and vertical line numbered in order. **Coordinates** identify locations on a coordinate grid, and are sets of numbers that describe where a vertical and a horizontal line meet. The coordinate from the horizontal axis is always written first.

For example, the vertices of the triangle below have coordinates (3, 1), (7, 8), and (10, 2).

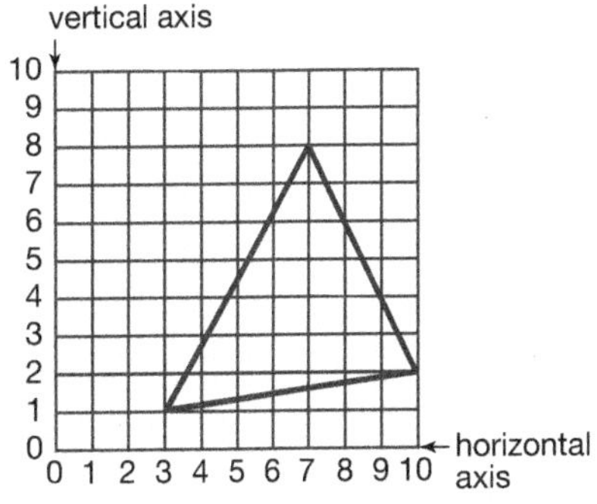

2. Ken started drawing the initial of his first name on a coordinate grid.

a) Name the coordinates he has used so far.

____

b) Write the coordinates he would need to finish the letter K. Mark these points on the grid and finish the initial.

____

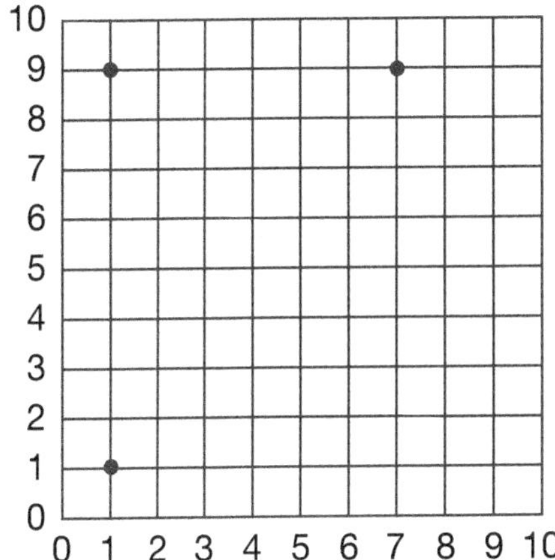

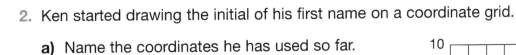

Test Yourself

Circle the correct answer.

1. What is the area of each shape in square units?

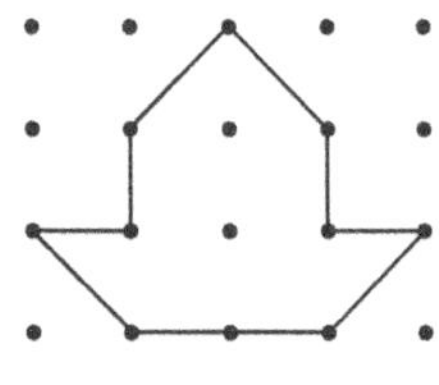
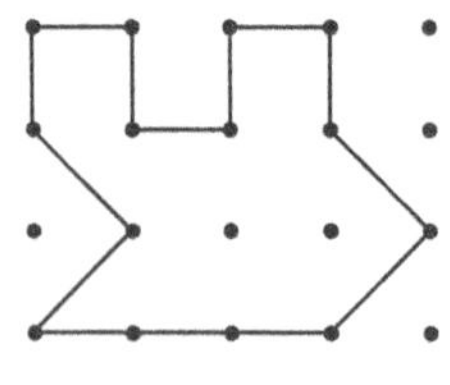

A. 6 square units, 8 square units | **B.** 7 square units, 7 square units

C. 8 square units, 6 square units | **D.** 9 square units, 8.5 square units

2. What is the area of each shape to the nearest square centimetre?

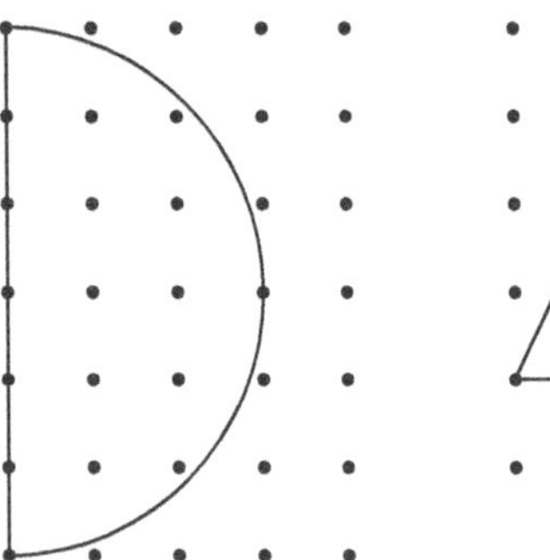
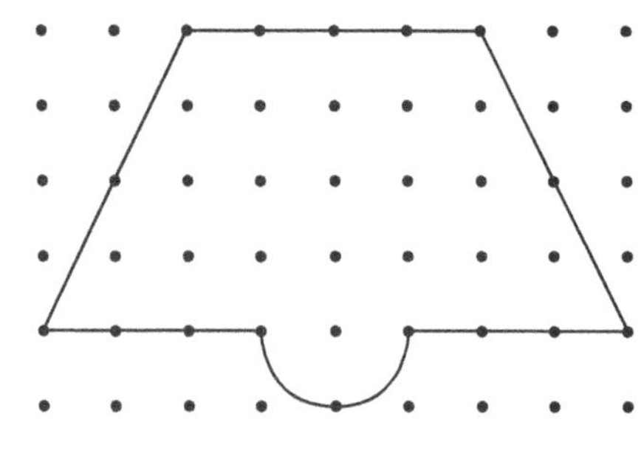

A. 11 cm^2, 24 cm^2 | **B.** 14 cm^2, 26 cm^2

C. 17 cm^2, 24 cm^2 | **D.** 18 cm^2, 28 cm^2

3. Pat made a rectangle using square stickers. The stickers are 1 cm^2. The perimeter of the rectangle is 22 cm. Of all the rectangles Pat could have made, what are the dimensions of the rectangle with the smallest area and the rectangle with the largest area?

A. 2 cm by 9 cm, 4 cm by 7 cm | **B.** 3 cm by 8 cm, 4 cm by 7 cm

C. 4 cm by 7 cm, 5 cm by 6 cm | **D.** 1 cm by 10 cm, 5 cm by 6 cm

4. A rectangle has an area of 48 cm^2. What dimensions would give the shortest perimeter?

A. 6 cm by 6 cm **B.** 6 cm by 8 cm **C.** 4 cm by 12 cm **D.** 2 cm by 24 cm

Test Yourself Page 2

5. What is the area of each rectangle?

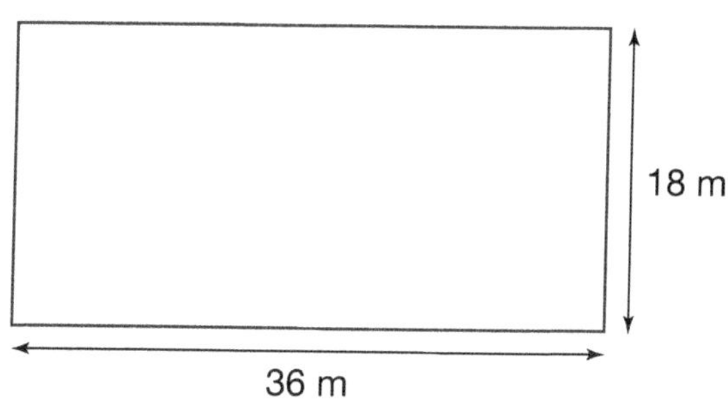

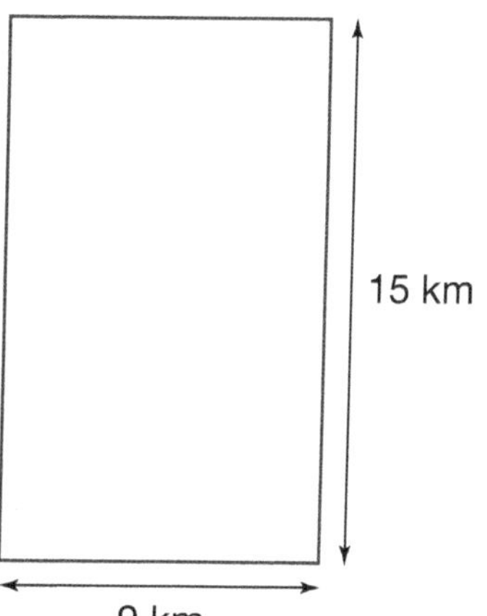

A. 648 cm^2, 24 cm^2

B. 648 m^2, 135 km^2

C. 108 cm^2, 135 cm^2

D. 108 m^2, 24 km^2

6. A zoo has the shape of an 18 km by 12 km rectangle. A scale model of the zoo is shown below. What are the areas of the zoo and the model?

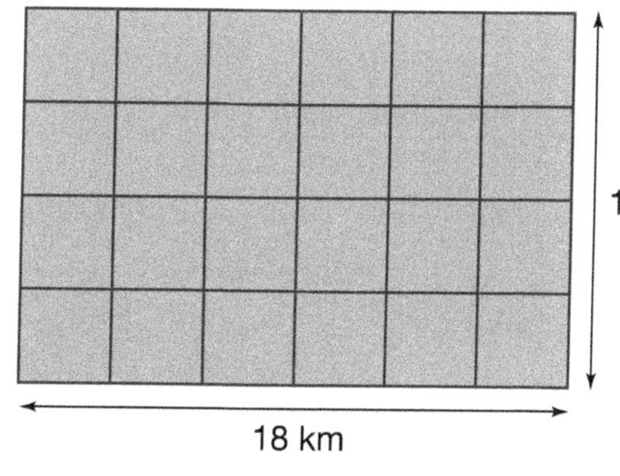

Scale 1 cm = 3 km

A. 60 km^2, 24 cm^2

B. 60 km^2, 20 cm^2

C. 216 km^2, 20 cm^2

D. 216 km^2, 24 cm^2

7. What coordinates would describe this shape?

A. (7, 5), (5, 8), (3, 8), (1, 5), (3, 2), and (5, 2)

B. (5, 7), (8, 5), (8, 3), (1, 5), (3, 2), and (5, 2)

C. (5, 7), (8, 5), (8, 3), (5, 1), (2, 3), and (2, 5)

D. (5, 7), (5, 8), (3, 8), (1, 5), (3, 2) and (5, 2)

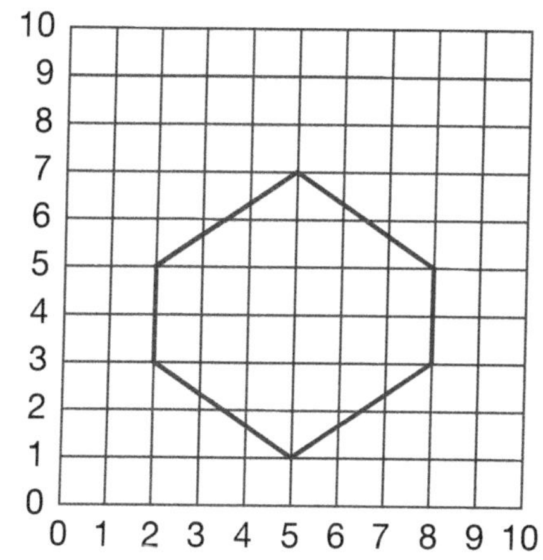

Estimating Products

Estimate products of decimal numbers using whole numbers.

1. Each team banner uses 1.9 m of fabric. The fabric costs $7.99 for each metre.

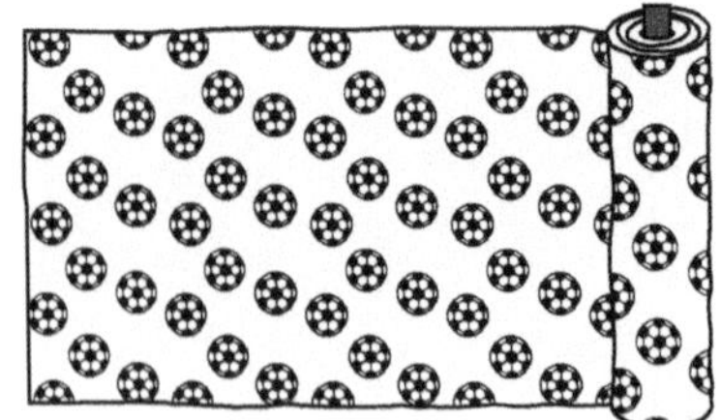

At-Home Help

To estimate decimal products, round each decimal to the nearest whole number. To get a closer estimate
- add a little if you rounded down
- subtract a little if you rounded up

For example:
To calculate 3.7 × 5.1, round 3.7 up to 4 and 5.1 down to 5.
Estimated answer is 4 × 5 = 20.

5.1 is closer to 5 than 3.7 is to 4. So to get a closer estimate, subtract a little from 20. Closer estimate is 20 − 2 = 18.

a) Estimate the number of metres needed for 30 banners.

____

b) Estimate the cost of fabric for 30 banners.

____

c) Calculate the cost of fabric for 30 banners using a calculator. Explain why your estimate was higher or lower than the exact amount.

____

____

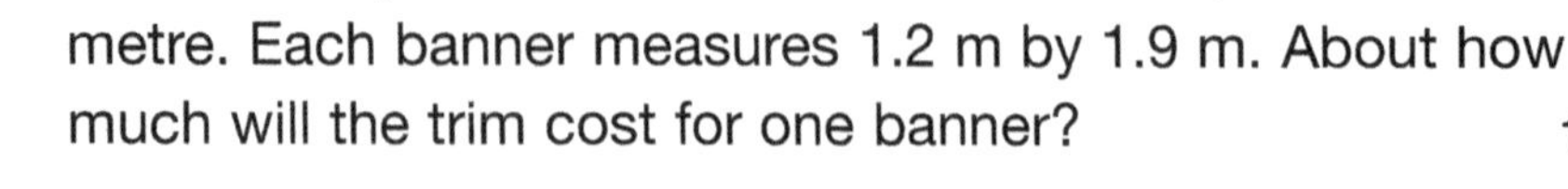

2. Trim for the perimeter of each banner costs $2.89 for each metre. Each banner measures 1.2 m by 1.9 m. About how much will the trim cost for one banner?

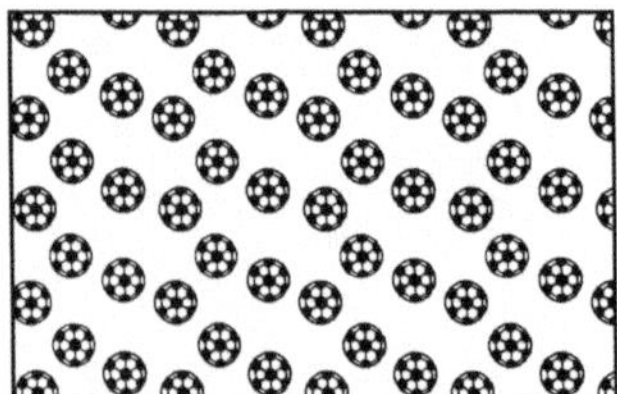

3. Estimate each product using whole numbers.

a) 8 × 2.6 ______________________________

b) 7.5 × 1.2 ______________________________

c) 5.1 × $4.49 ______________________________

Multiplying by 10 or 100

Multiply decimal tenths and hundredths by 10 and 100.

1. A math text is 2.5 cm thick. How high would a stack of 10 math texts be?

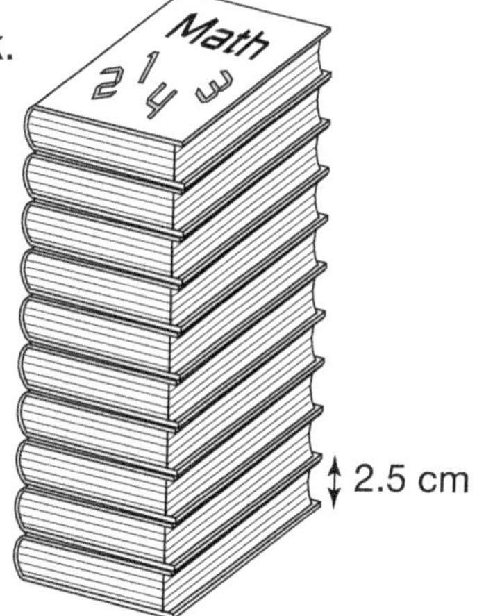

At-Home Help

When you multiply a decimal number by 10, the digit in the tenths place moves to the ones place.

For example:
$6.8 \times 10 = 68$

Similarly, when multiplying a decimal number by 100, the digits in the tenths and hundredths places increase in place value.

For example:
$4.57 \times 100 = 457$

2. A box of pencils is 19.5 cm long.

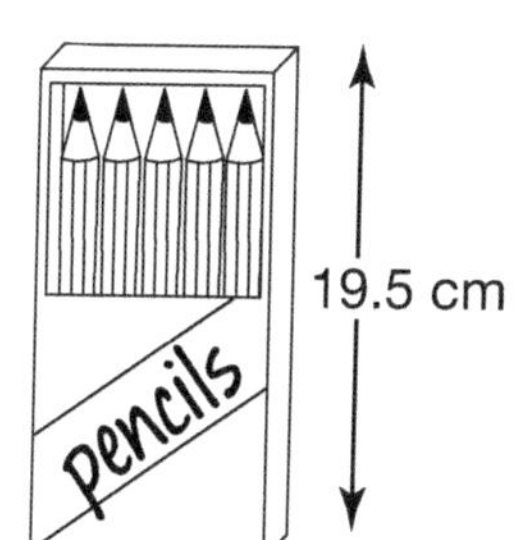

a) How long would 10 boxes placed end to end be?

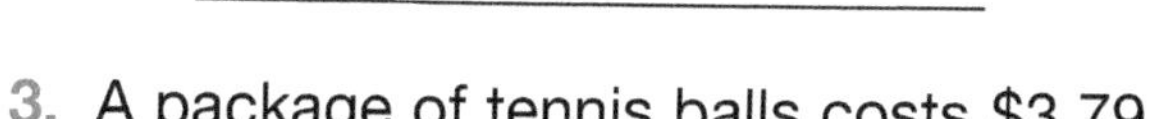

b) How long would 100 boxes placed end to end be?

3. A package of tennis balls costs $3.79.

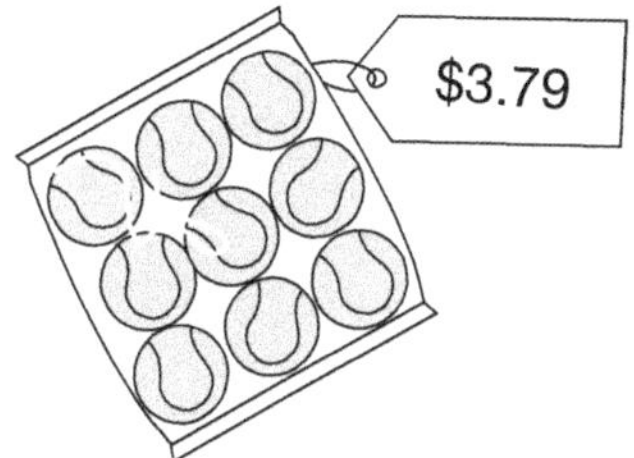

a) What is the cost of 100 packages? ___________

b) What is the cost of 10 packages? ___________

4. The mass of a package of tennis balls is 0.45 kg. What would the mass of 10 and 100 boxes be? Circle the correct answer.

45 kg, 450 kg　　4.5 kg, 45 kg　　4.5 g, 45 g　　0.45 kg, 4.5 kg

Multiplying Tenths by Whole Numbers

Multiply decimal tenths by whole numbers using drawings and symbols.

You will need a ruler or tape measure.

When you multiply a whole number by a decimal tenth, it is like multiplying two whole numbers except you have to put in the decimal point because it is tenths.

For example:
$57 \times 2 = 114$
$5.7 \times 2 = 11.4$

1. The mass of a stapler is 0.2 kg. What is the mass of 9 staplers?

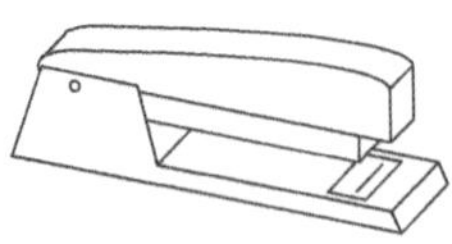

2. Mrs. Gulliver used four 1.7 m pieces of border for a bulletin board. How many metres did she use?

3. Rajiv lined up six loonies. Each loonie is 2.5 cm wide. How long is the line of loonies?

4. Bianca drinks 0.7 L of milk each day. How much milk does she drink in one week?

5. Measure the width of this workbook to the nearest tenth of a centimetre. How long would 6 workbooks be if they were put together side by side?

Multiplying Hundredths by Whole Numbers

Multiply decimal hundredths by whole numbers using models, drawings, and symbols.

1. Neela ordered 4 tickets. Each ticket cost $4.75.

   a) Calculate the total cost.

   b) How could you have predicted that the cost was less than $20.00? Explain.

   ____

   ____

   ____

At-Home Help

When you multiply a whole number by a decimal hundredth, it is like multiplying two whole numbers except you have to put in the decimal point because it is hundredths.

For example:
$675 \times 3 = 2025$
$6.75 \times 3 = 20.25$

2. Multiply.

   a) 3.43×5 **b)** 6.26×2

3. Evan cycled 6.68 km. Nadia rode twice as far on her bike. How do you know that Nadia rode more than 13 km?

   ____

   ____

Communicate About Estimation Strategies

Explain estimation strategies to determine if a solution is reasonable.

1. Each Canadian dollar is worth $0.76 US. Estimate the cost in US dollars of a software package priced at $30.00 Canadian. Explain your thinking.

____

____

____

2. Use the exchange rate in Question 1. Estimate the cost in US dollars of adult and child admission to the Toronto Zoo. Admission costs in Canadian dollars are $18.00 for adults and $12.00 for children. Explain how you estimated.

Adult admission is about $__________ US.

Child admission is about $__________ US.

____

____

____

____

____

____

At-Home Help

Use the Communication Checklist when explaining and justifying your estimation strategies. You may round or group numbers to make your explanations more clear. You may also want to use models to justify your answer.

For example, to estimate 1.79×8, you may say: "I round 1.79 to 2, then I multiply $2 \times 8 = 16$. I know my estimate is a bit high because I rounded up."

Communication Checklist

- ☑ Did you show all your steps?
- ☑ Did you use a model?
- ☑ Did you explain your thinking?

3. One euro is worth about $1.67 Canadian. Tim estimates that a book that costs 25 euros would cost about $30.00 Canadian. Explain how you would decide if this estimate makes sense.

____

____

____

4. A can of apple juice contains 1.36 L of juice. Serina bought 9 cans of juice. What is the best estimate of the amount of juice she bought? Circle the correct answer.

12 L 14 L 9 L 18 L

Choosing a Multiplication Method

Justify the choice of a multiplication method.

At-Home Help

If numbers are simple in a question, you can use mental math. Multiplying by 10 or 100, or multiplying one-digit numbers, can be done mentally.

For example, $7.00 × 8 = $56.00.

If you can multiply numbers without a lot of regrouping, use pencil and paper.

For example, $5.20 × 7 = $36.40.

If you have to use a lot of regrouping to multiply, use a calculator.

For example, $6.47 × 12 = $77.64.

1. If you know the cost of 10 tiles, how can you calculate the cost of 100 tiles?

____

2. If you know how much water to add to 1 can of juice concentrate, how can you calculate how much to add to 2 cans?

____

3. Calculate the cost of 5 kg of each fruit.

   a) Which calculation(s) would you do mentally? Explain your thinking.

   ____

   ____

   b) Which calculation(s) would you do with pencil and paper? Explain your thinking.

   ____

   ____

   c) Which calculation(s) would you do with a calculator? Explain your thinking.

   ____

   ____

Test Yourself

Circle the correct answer.

1. What whole numbers would be best to estimate the product of $5.7 \times \$3.35$?

   A. $5 \times \$3$ **B.** $5 \times \$4$ **C.** $6 \times \$3$ **D.** $6 \times \$4$

2. Fabric for a flag costs $7.69 for each metre. The flag is 6.3 m long. Vanessa estimated the cost by multiplying $6 \times \$8 = \$48$. How would you describe her estimate?

   A. very high **B.** very low **C.** close **D.** high

3. You multiply a decimal number by 10 and the product is 55. What is the decimal number?

   A. 5.5 **B.** 55 **C.** 55.5 **D.** 0.55

4. An insect's image is 1.4 cm in length. It is enlarged to 100 times that length. What is the enlarged length?

   A. 14 cm **B.** 140 cm **C.** 14 m **D.** 1.4 cm

5. A hundreds block represents 1. What multiplication question is modelled here?

   A. $1.7 \times 4 = 6.8$

   B. $1.7 \times 4 = 5.8$

   C. $4 \times 1.7 = 8.6$

   D. $4 \times 1.7 = 68$

6. A hundreds block represents 1. This arrangement models a multiplication question. It can also show a related multiplication question. What are the two questions?

   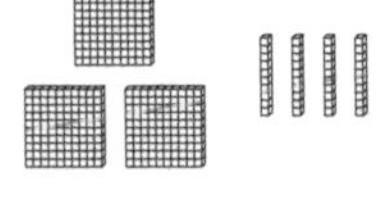

   A. 4×3.5 and 2×8

   B. 4×3.5 and 7×8

   C. 4×3.5 and 4×7

   D. 4×3.5 and 2×7

Test Yourself Page 2

7. A binder costs $3.69 and a package of paper costs $1.49. Megan buys 3 binders and 4 packages of paper. What is the total cost before taxes?

   A. $11.07 **B.** $19.23

   C. $17.03 **D.** $5.96

8. Serge cycles 0.15 km each minute. How far will he cycle in 12 minutes?

   A. 18 km **B.** 1.8 km **C.** 180 km **D.** 1.5 km

9. Serge has to cycle 5 km. He cycles at a rate of 0.15 km/min. About how long will it take him to cycle 5 km?

   A. about 15 min **B.** about 60 min **C.** about 30 min **D.** about 1.5 h

10. Ed has to calculate these products. He wants to do the calculations efficiently.

    (i) 6.17×11 (ii) 4.10×5 (iii) $5.32 × 2 (iv) $8.00 × 8

    What methods should Ed use?

    A. (i) a calculator, (ii) pencil and paper, (iii) pencil and paper, (iv) mentally

    B. (i) mentally, (ii) a calculator, (iii) pencil and paper, (iv) a calculator

    C. (i) pencil and paper, (ii) a calculator, (iii) mentally, (iv) mentally

    D. (i) pencil and paper, (ii) mentally, (iii) mentally, (iv) a calculator

11. A package of stickers costs $3.69. How can you calculate how much 5 packages cost?

    A. Multiply $3.69 by 10.

    B. Divide $3.69 by 10.

    C. Multiply $3.69 by 5.

    D. Divide $3.69 by 5.

Estimating Quotients

Estimate quotients when dividing decimal numbers.

Heather is wrapping gifts. She has 5.25 m of ribbon.

At-Home Help

A **quotient** is the answer to a division question.

For example, 2 is the quotient of 14 ÷ 7.

14 ÷ 7 = 2

When you divide a decimal number by a whole number, it is easier to estimate the answer if you round the decimal to the nearest whole number.

For example, to estimate the answer to 8.8 ÷ 4, you may round 8.8 to 9.

9 ÷ 4 is about 2.

1. Heather wants to use this ribbon for 2 gifts. Estimate the length she will use for each gift.

   ____

2. She wants to use this ribbon for 3 gifts. Estimate the length she will use for each gift.

   ____

3. How could you use your answer to Question 1 to estimate the length needed for 4 gifts?

   ____

4. The shortest length of ribbon Heather can use to decorate a gift is about 0.5 m. Does she have enough ribbon to decorate 10 gifts?

   ____

Dividing by 10

Use regrouping to divide decimal numbers by 10.

1. Craig wants to calculate the length of his running stride. He ran 14.6 m in 10 strides.

   a) Calculate the length of Craig's stride.

   Craig's stride is ______________ long.

   b) Use multiplication to check your answer to Part **a)**.

At-Home Help

When you divide any number by 10, the quotient has the same digits as the dividend but each digit moves to the next lower place value.

For example, using whole numbers, 350 ÷ 10 = 35. The 3 hundreds in 350 become 3 tens, the 5 tens become 5 ones, and the 0 ones become 0 tenths.

Using decimal numbers, 67.8 ÷ 10 = 6.78. The 6 tens become 6 ones, the 7 ones become 7 tenths, and the 8 tenths become 8 hundredths.

2. A patio is 4.4 m long. It is divided into 10 equal sections for placing flower pots. How wide is each section?

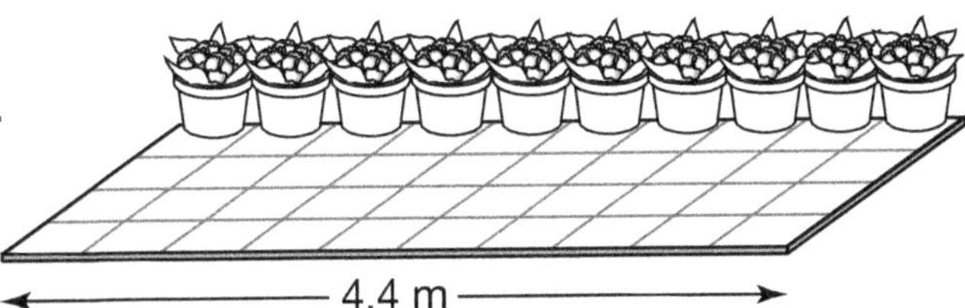

3. A bike rack has sections to park 10 bikes. What is the width of each section if the bike rack is 6.5 m long?

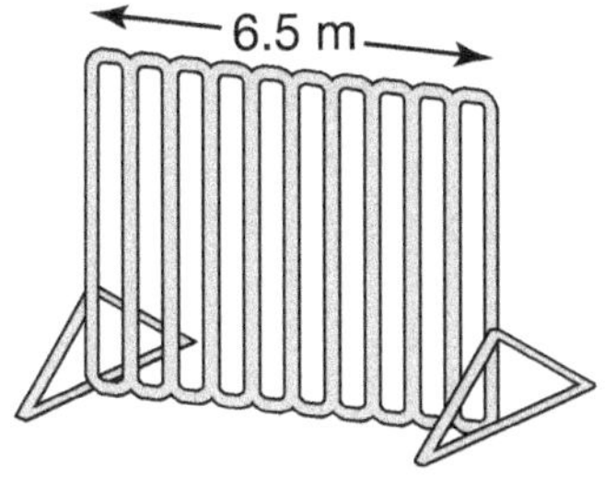

4. Calculate.

   a) 23 ÷ 10   **b)** 16.9 ÷ 10   **c)** 66.2 ÷ 10

   d) $10\overline{)44.4}$ **e)** $10\overline{)239.7}$ **f)** $10\overline{)263.1}$

Calculating a Decimal Quotient

Goal **Express quotients as decimal numbers to tenths or hundredths.**

1. Graciela has 6 kg of strawberries to divide equally into 8 bags. Calculate the mass of each bag to 2 decimal places. Show your work.

At-Home Help

When you divide numbers, it is sometimes possible to find a quotient to the nearest tenth or hundredth. This is done by regrouping the remaining ones to tenths and any remaining tenths to hundredths.

For example:

$$\begin{array}{r} 2.75 \\ 4\overline{)11.00} \\ \underline{8} \\ \mathbf{3}.0 \\ \underline{2.8} \\ 0.\mathbf{2}0 \\ \underline{0.20} \\ 0.00 \end{array}$$

When 3 ones remain, regroup as 30 tenths.

When 2 tenths remain, regroup as 20 hundredths.

11 ÷ 4 to the nearest hundredth is 2.75.

2. What will be the mass of each bag if the scale measures mass to tenths of a kilogram?

   a) 7 kg divided into 2 bags ____________________

   b) 4 kg divided into 8 bags ____________________

3. Calculate to 2 decimal places.

   a) 14 ÷ 8 **b)** 12 ÷ 5 **c)** 4 ÷ 5 **d)** 2 ÷ 8

4. Jacob wants to cut a 22 m length of string into 8 equal pieces. Calculate the length of each piece to 2 decimal places.

Dividing Decimals by Whole Numbers

Divide a decimal by a one-digit whole number using models and symbols.

1. Sam's garden is 1.5 m by 6 m. He divided it into 4 equal sections.

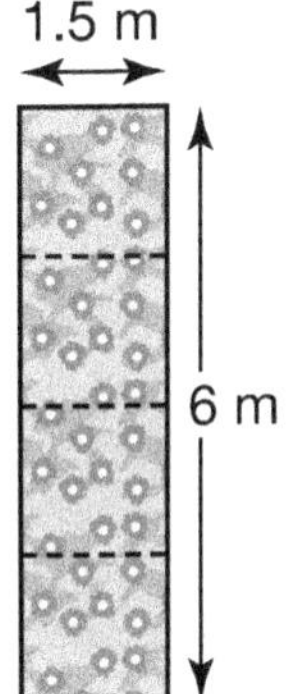

   a) Estimate the area of each section. Show your work.

   b) Calculate the area to two decimal places. Show your work.

2. Calculate to two decimal places.

   a) 1.98 ÷ 2   b) 7.26 ÷ 3

   c) 13.64 ÷ 4   d) 5.85 ÷ 5

At-Home Help

When you divide a decimal number by a whole number, apply the same rules for division as when you divide two whole numbers. Any whole number remainder is regrouped to tenths and combined with any tenths. Then any remaining tenths are regrouped to hundredths and combined with any hundredths.

For example:

```
   5.63
4)22.52
  20
   2.5
   2.4
   0.12
   0.12
   0.00
```

When 2 ones remain, regroup as 20 tenths and combine with 5 tenths.

When 1 tenth remains, regroup as 10 hundredths and combine with 2 hundredths.

22.52 ÷ 4 to the nearest hundredth is 5.63.

3. A bulletin board measures 2.35 m by 6 m. It is divided into 3 equal sections. Calculate the area of each section to two decimal places.

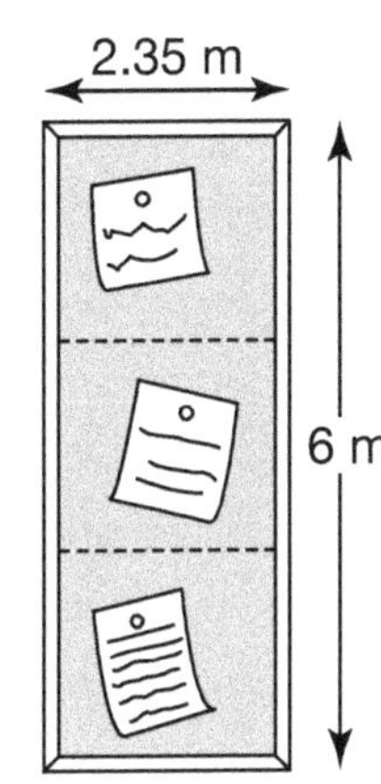

4. A hula hoop travels 17.04 m after 6 complete turns.

   a) Estimate the circumference of the hula hoop.

   b) Calculate the circumference of the hoop to the nearest hundredth of a metre.

   c) How far will the hula hoop travel after 4 complete turns?

Choosing a Calculation Method

Justify your choice of calculation method.

Ms Shishido is making origami swans from a sheet of coloured paper. The paper measures 10.5 cm by 46.5 cm. She divides the area into 6 equal parts. Each part has a length of 10.5 cm.

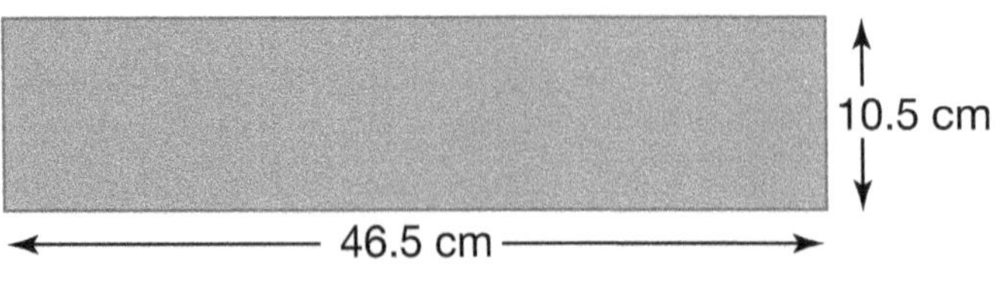

At-Home Help

To solve problems, it is important to choose an appropriate calculation method.

- If the numbers are easy to work with, use mental math.
- If the problem asks "About how many ..." use estimation.
- If the problem asks for an accurate answer and you cannot easily calculate the numbers in your head, then use paper and pencil or a calculator.

1. About how wide is each part? ______________

   To get my answer I used ______________

   because ______________________________.

2. How wide is each part to the nearest hundredth of a centimetre? ______________

   To get my answer I used ______________ because ______________

   ______________________________.

3. If the coloured paper were divided into 3 equal parts, how wide would each part be? ______________

   To get my answer I used ______________ because ______________

   ______________________________.

4. If 10 swans were made from the coloured paper, what would be the width of each part? ______________

   To get my answer I used ______________ because ______________

   ______________________________.

Dividing to Compare

Use division and other operations to solve problems about money.

You will need a calculator.

1. Vasco, his father, and his grandfather, who is a senior citizen, tour the zoo regularly by bus. Vasco is in Grade 5.

	Single-fare ticket	Book of 5 tickets
Adult	$3.50	$14.00
Senior and student	$2.50	$9.50
Child (12 and under)	$1.25	$4.50

a) What is the cost difference per ticket between a single-fare ticket and a book of tickets? Show your work.

b) How much would each person save by using a book of tickets instead of single-fare tickets? Show your work.

2. A package of 3 energy-efficient light bulbs costs $9.87. A package of 5 bulbs costs $14.95.

a) What is the cost difference per light bulb between the two packages? Show your work.

b) If 15 high-efficiency bulbs are purchased, what will be the cost difference between buying them in packages of 3 and packages of 5?

At-Home Help

There are two ways to compare costs if you know the cost of a package of items and the cost of an individual item.

- Find the cost per item in the package by dividing the cost by the number of items.
- Multiply the cost of an individual item by the number of items in the package.

For example:

The cost of a package of 5 tennis balls is $3.95 and the cost of one tennis ball is $1.19.

cost of one tennis ball in package
= $3.95 ÷ 5
= $0.79
difference = $1.19 − $0.79
= $0.40 per tennis ball

OR

cost of 5 tennis balls
= 5 × $1.19
= $5.95
difference = $5.95 − $3.95
= $2.00 per 5 tennis balls

It is more expensive to buy the tennis balls individually.

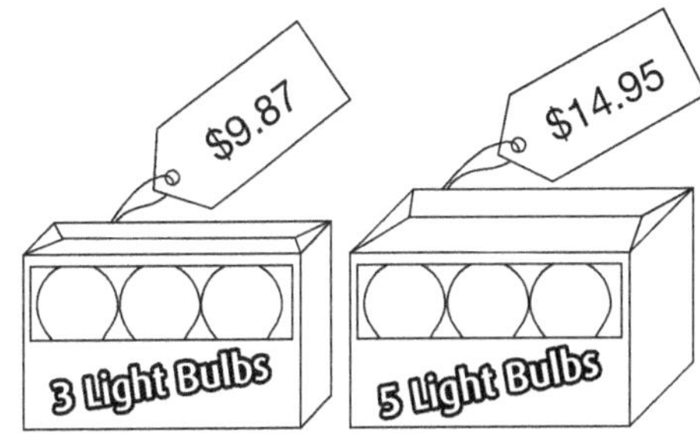

Calculating the Mean

Use division to calculate the mean.

1. Karen and Fariq play basketball on different teams. Their team scores for last month are shown below.

Karen's team scores	Fariq's team scores
26	37
33	13
17	22
24	

Calculate the mean score for each team.

At-Home Help

The **mean** of a set of numbers is equal to the sum of all the numbers divided by the number of numbers in the set.

For example:

7, 8, 9, 11, 11, 14

sum = 7 + 8 + 9 + 11 + 11 + 14
= 60
mean = 60 ÷ 6
= 10

2. Calculate the mean of each set of numbers.

a) 5, 8, 8, 9, 10

b) 2, 3, 4, 5, 6

c) 120, 130, 342, 376

d) 12.4, 11.2, 9.1, 7.7

3. **a)** Create a set of 5 different numbers where the mean is one of the original numbers.

b) Create a set of 3 different numbers where the mean is not one of the original numbers.

Solve Problems by Working Backward

Goal

Use a working backward strategy to solve problems.

1. Keisha delivers advertising flyers. He delivered 16 flyers in his own apartment building. Then he divided the remainder into 3 groups of 27 to deliver in nearby buildings.

   a) How many flyers did Keisha have originally?

   b) Draw a diagram as in At-Home Help to show how you solved the problem by working backward.

At-Home Help

To solve some problems, it is easier to find the answer by working backward.

Start by drawing a diagram to help figure out each operation you need to use.

Remember that multiplication is the opposite operation to division, and subtraction is the opposite operation to addition.

For example:

A number is multiplied by 5. Then 5 is added to it and the result is 40. What is the original number?

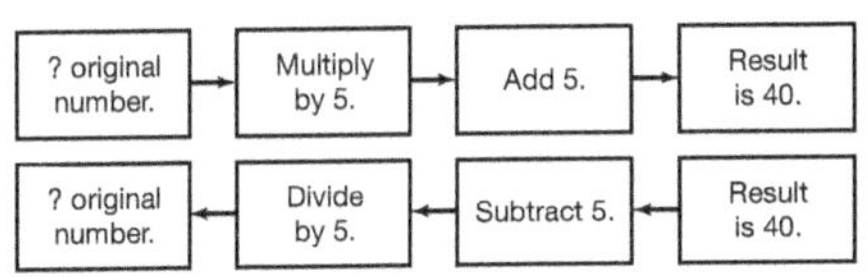
? original number.
Multiply by 5.
Add 5.
Result is 40.
? original number.
Divide by 5.
Subtract 5.
Result is 40.

The original number is 7.

2. Frank collects comic books. He tripled his collection last month. Then his friend gave him 20 more comics. Now he has 68 comics.

   How many comics did Frank have one month ago? Use a working backward strategy. Show your work.

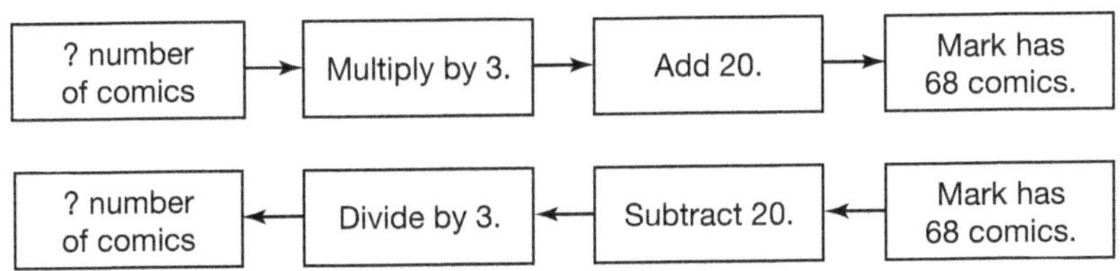
? number of comics
Multiply by 3.
Add 20.
Mark has 68 comics.
? number of comics
Divide by 3.
Subtract 20.
Mark has 68 comics.

3. A number is multiplied by 8. Then 6.4 is added to the product. The result is 80. What is the original number?

4. Tickets for a concert were sold during the week. 23 were sold on Monday. 30 were sold on Tuesday. On Wednesday 39 were left. How many tickets were there originally?

Test Yourself

Circle the correct answer.

1. A 1.89 L carton of lemonade is shared equally by 6 people. What is the best estimate of each person's share?

   A. 0.3 L **B.** 0.4 L

   C. 0.5 L **D.** 0.6 L

2. Jason's mother drove to work and back, and nowhere else, each day for 5 days. The odometer showed she had driven 95.3 km. What is the distance from her home to her workplace?

   A. 953 m **B.** 95.30 km **C.** 9.53 km **D.** 0.953 km

3. A 45.7 m wide parking lot is divided into 10 parking spaces. What is the width of one parking space?

   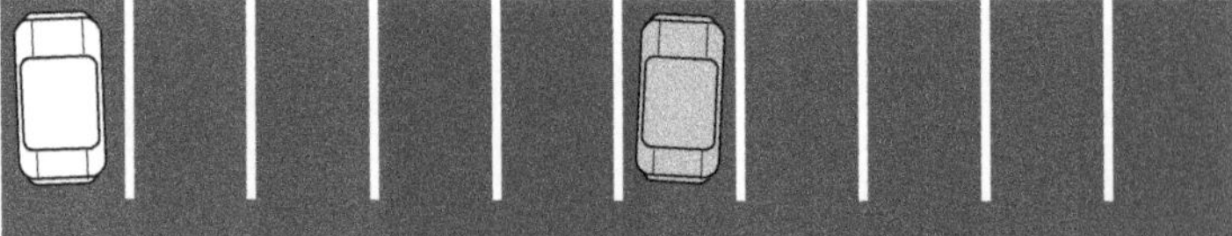

   A. 457 m **B.** 45.70 m

   C. 4.57 m **D.** 0.457 m

4. A 1.2 kg package of trail mix is shared equally by 8 people. What is the mass of each person's share?

   A. 120 g **B.** 0.15 kg **C.** 1.5 kg **D.** 1.2 kg

5. An open office space measures 24 m by 3.5 m. It is divided into 8 equal-sized cubicles. What is the area of each cubicle?

   A. 84 m^2 **B.** 84 cm^2 **C.** 105 m^2 **D.** 10.5 m^2

6. What methods would you use to do these calculations?

   (i) What is the cost of 10 L of gas?

   (ii) About how much would 25 L of gas cost?

   (iii) How much change would Mr. Kwan receive if he paid $40.00 for 25 L of gas?

   A. (i) mental math, (ii) a calculator, (iii) estimation

   B. (i) mental math, (ii) estimation, (iii) a calculator

   C. (i) estimation, (ii) mental math, (iii) a calculator

   D. (i) a calculator, (ii) estimation, (iii) mental math

Test Yourself Page 2

7. A package of 6 containers of yogurt costs $2.94. Individually these containers cost $0.65. What is the cost difference between purchasing the package and purchasing 6 individually?

   A. $0.96 **B.** $0.16 **C.** $1.96 **D.** $0.80

8. High temperatures for a five-day period were recorded.

Temperature (°C)	17.3°C	18.7°C	14.4°C	19.2°C	11.9°C

   What is the mean high temperature for this period?

   A. 14.4°C **B.** 16.3°C **C.** 16°C **D.** 17.3°C

9. How would you label these statements?

   (i) The mean of a set of numbers must be one of the original numbers.

   (ii) The mean of a set of numbers can be one of the original numbers.

   (iii) The mean of a set of numbers must lie within the range of the numbers in the set.

   A. (i) true, (ii) false, (iii) true **B.** (i) false, (ii) true, (iii) false

   C. (i) true, (ii) false, (iii) false **D.** (i) false, (ii) true, (iii) true

10. A scout group is divided into 6 equal squads. At the last meeting, Squad A had 2 members absent and 7 members present. How many members are in the group altogether?

    A. 42 **B.** 30 **C.** 50 **D.** 54

11. A case of 4 1 L cartons of juice costs $8.96. Individual cartons cost $2.49. What is the cost difference per carton between a case and 4 individual cartons?

    A. $0.25 **B.** $0.30

    C. $0.20 **D.** $0.26

Making 3-D Shapes

Draw and build 3-D shapes.

1. **a)** Sketch all the faces of the tent. The base has been drawn for you.

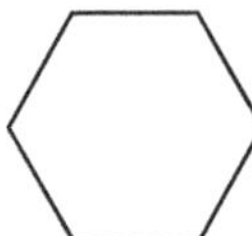

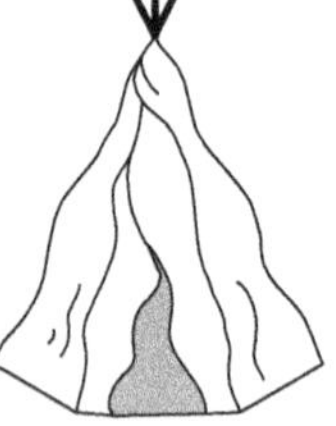

b) What shape is the base? ____________________

c) What shape are the other faces? ____________________

d) Use modelling clay to make the 3-D object. Make the base first and then the faces that join at the top vertex.

e) Draw the model starting with the base. Locate the top vertex and join the vertices.

f) What is the shape of the tent?

____

At-Home Help

Steps to draw and build 3-D objects

- Find a model.

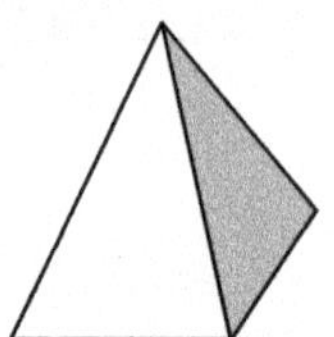

- Sketch all the faces.

A pyramid has a base and 3 or more triangular faces.

A prism has a base and top that are congruent, and 3 or more rectangular faces.

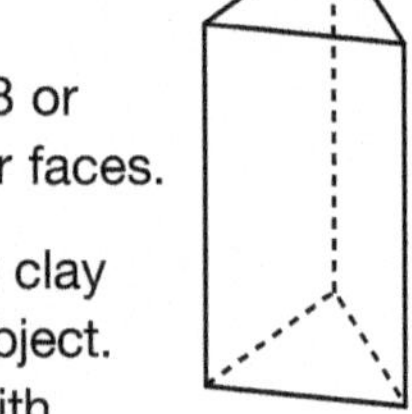

- Use modelling clay to make the object. Always start with the base.
- Draw the model. Always start with the base.

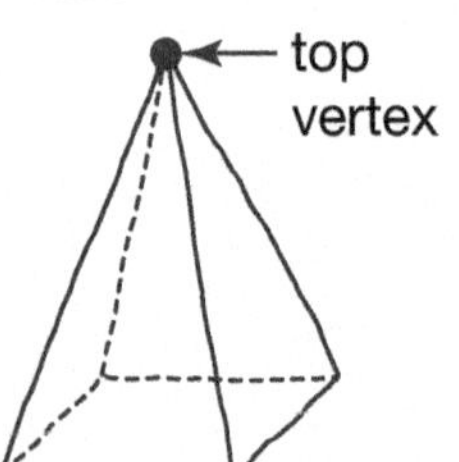

2. **a)** Draw the faces of a hexagon-based prism.

b) Draw the model of the prism.

Making Nets

Make nets for 3-D shapes.

1. 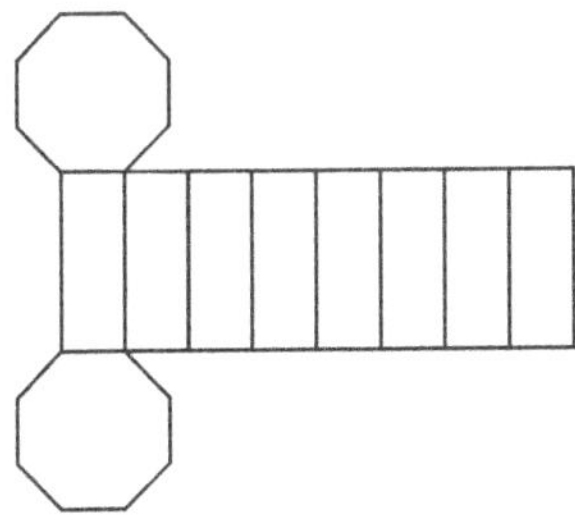

   a) Is this the net of a pyramid or a prism? Explain.

   ____

   ____

   ____

   ____

   b) Name the 3-D object.

   ____

   c) Draw another net for this object.

   d) Trace it on another piece of paper. Cut it out and fold to check.

2. **a)** Name the 3-D object.

   ____

   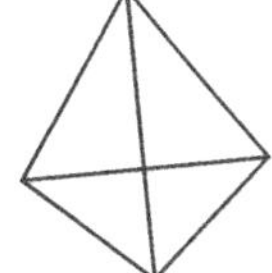

   b) Draw a net for this object.

At-Home Help

When you make nets from 3-D objects

- make sure all the faces are traced only once
- make sure the faces are connected in the drawing
- check that the appropriate faces are the same size and shape
- cut out the net and fold to check

This net of a pyramid has triangles attached to the base.

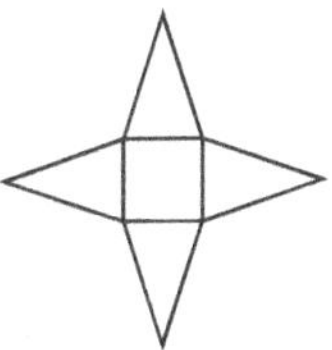

This net of a prism has rectangles all connected. The base and top are congruent, and are attached to opposite sides of the rectangles.

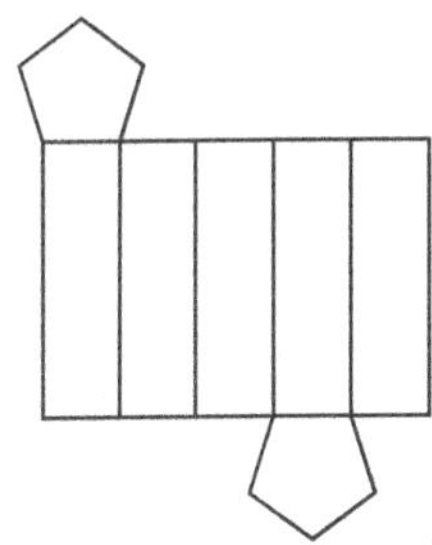

Identifying Nets

Match 3-D shapes with their nets.

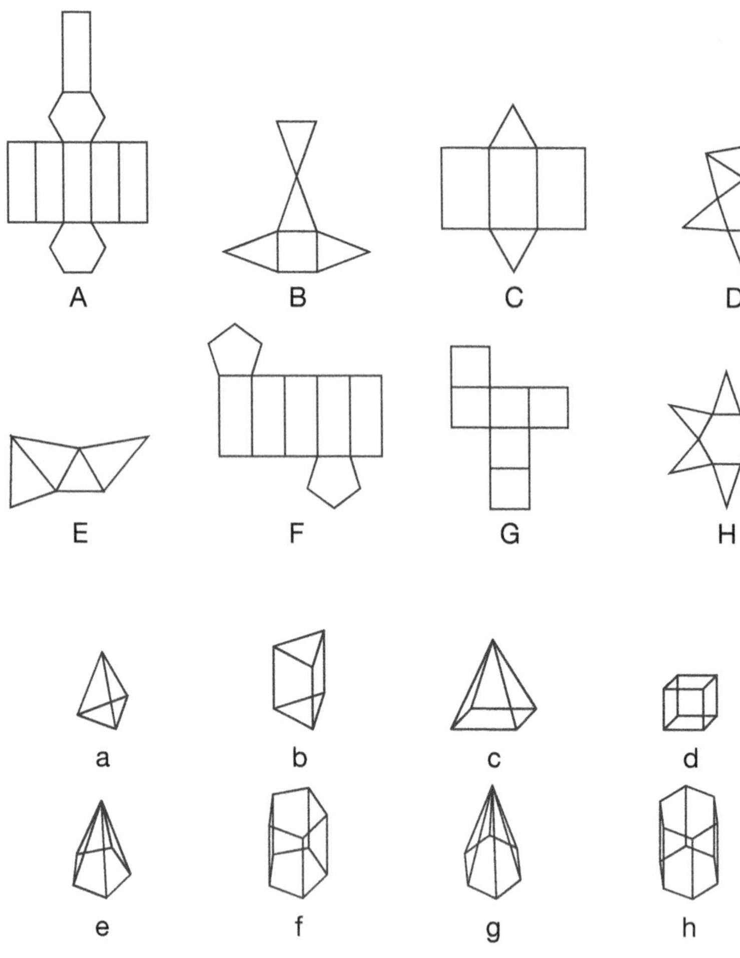

At-Home Help

To identify the nets of pyramids and prisms and match them with their 3-D models, ask yourself:

- Does the net have a top and a base that are congruent?
- What shape are the other faces on the net?
- Does the 3-D model have a top and a base that are congruent?
- What shape are the other faces on the 3-D model?

If the net has a base but no top and the other faces are triangles, then it is a pyramid.

If the net has a top and a base that are congruent and the other faces are rectangles, then it is a prism.

1. **a)** Identify the nets of the pyramids. ______

   b) Explain how you know they are nets of pyramids.

   ______

2. **a)** Identify the nets of the prisms. ______

   b) Explain how you know they are nets of prisms.

   ______

   ______

3. Match each pyramid with its net. ______

4. Match each prism with its net. ______

Communicate About Building a Model

Write clear instructions for building a model from a picture.

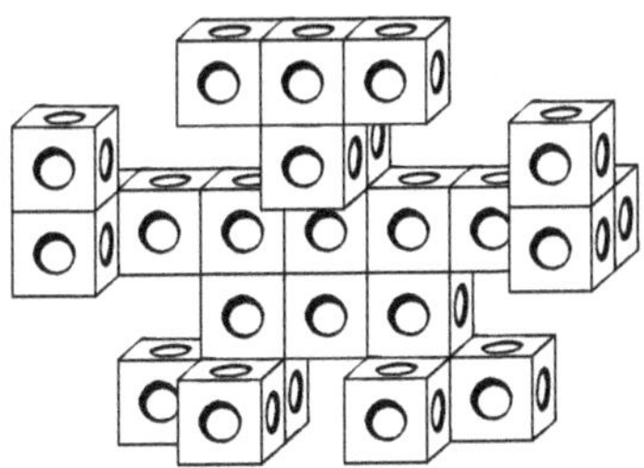

At-Home Help

When you communicate about building a model
- give clear instructions using math language
- show all the steps needed to build the model
- give directions in the correct order
- give the right amount of detail for each step
- do not give information that is not useful, such as the colour of the cubes

Communication Checklist

☑ Did you show all the steps?
☑ Did you use the right amount of detail?
☑ Did you use math language?

Wendy wrote instructions to make this cube creature.

You will need a whole bunch of cubes.
The head is like a T-shape.
The arms are sticking out, and each arm is 3 cubes.
Each hand is 1 cube, attached to the end of each arm.
The body is flat in the middle.
The legs are short, with 3 cubes each.

1. Go over Wendy's instructions. Revise and improve each line if necessary.

2. Check your instructions using the Communication Checklist.

3. How can you improve your instructions?

Measuring and Comparing Capacity

Estimate, measure, and compare capacities, and determine relationships among units.

1. **a)** Choose two cups of different sizes in your home. Label them A and B.

   b) Would you use millilitres or litres to measure the capacity of each cup? Write your choices in the chart and explain your thinking.

	Capacity unit
Cup A	
Cup B	

2. Use a big spoon or a soup ladle to compare the capacity of the two cups in Question 1.

   a) Estimate the number of spoonfuls that will fill each cup. Then measure and record the number in the table.

	My estimate: capacity in spoonfuls	**Actual capacity in spoonfuls**
Cup A		
Cup B		

   b) Which cup has a larger capacity? Explain how you know.

   ____

   ____

   c) Describe another method you could use to compare the capacity of the two cups.

   ____

   ____

   ____

At-Home Help

The **capacity** of a container refers to how much the container can hold. Capacity can be measured using millilitres or litres.

Compare the capacities of two containers using one of these ways.

- Fill each container with water. Then pour the water into a graduated pitcher to measure the capacity. The container with the larger capacity can hold the most liquid.

- Use a spoon or small cup. Record the number of spoonfuls needed to fill each container. The container with the larger capacity can hold the most spoonfuls.
- Fill one container with water. Then pour the water into the other container. If the water overflows, then the first container has a larger capacity. If the water does not fill the container, then the first container has a smaller capacity.

Measuring and Comparing Volume

Estimate, measure, and compare volumes using cubic centimetres.

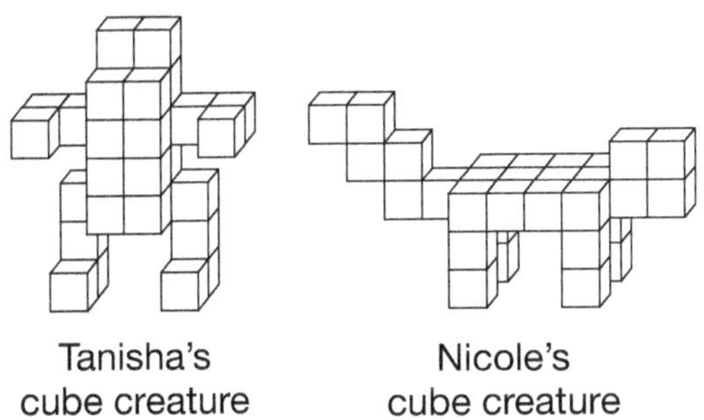

Tanisha's cube creature | Nicole's cube creature

At-Home Help

Volume is the space taken up by an object.

To measure the volume of a 3-D object made from centimetre cubes, count the total number of cubes using one of these two ways.

- Count the number of cubes in each section. Then find the total number of cubes for all sections.
- Look at the object from above. Count the number of cubes in each column. Then find the total number of cubes for all columns.

The unit for volume is cubic centimetres (cm^3).

Both creatures were made using centimetre linking cubes.

1. **a)** For Tanisha's creature, count and record the number of cubes in each body part.

Body part	Number of cubes
head	
body	
2 arms	
2 hands	
2 legs	
2 feet	

b) What is the volume of Tanisha's creature in cubic centimetres? Show your work.

2. **a)** For Nicole's creature, imagine you are looking at the creature from above. Count and record the number of cubes in each column.

0				3					0
1					1				2
0									0

b) What is the volume of Nicole's creature in cubic centimetres? Show your work.

Relating Capacity Units to Volume

Identify the relationship between capacity units and volume units.

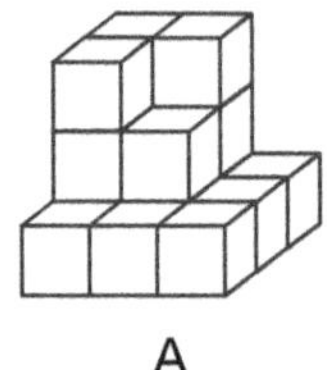

A

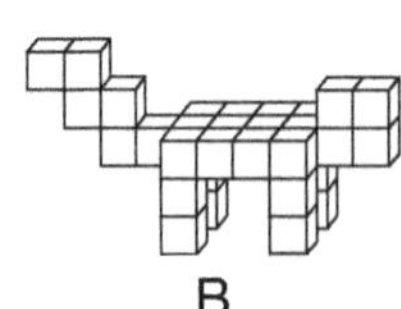

B

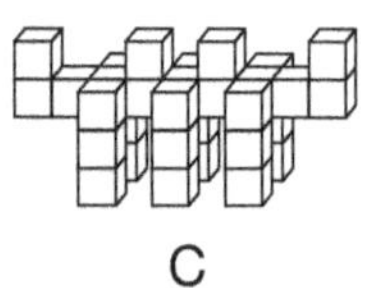

C

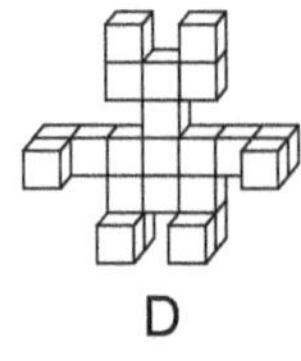

D

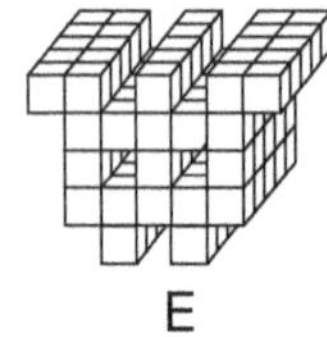

E

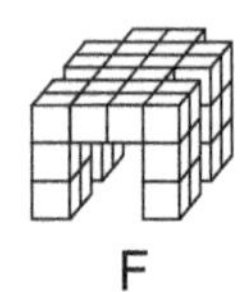

F

At-Home Help

The units of volume and capacity are related.

1 cm^3 = 1 mL

The volume of a 3-D object can be measured using water displacement.

- Record the volume of water in the measuring cup at the start.
- Then put the object under water.
- Record the volume of water with the object in the measuring cup.
- The difference between the 2 volumes is equal to the volume of the object.

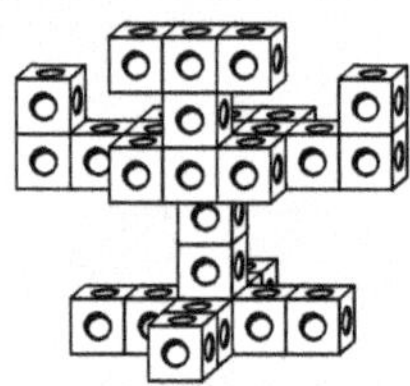

For example, the water level went from 400 mL to 430 mL when this object was put under water. So the volume of the object is 30 mL or 30 cm^3.

Models A to F were made using centimetre linking cubes.

1. Find the volume of each model in cubic centimetres. Write your answer below each model.
2. Each of the models A to F was put under water in a measuring cup to measure its volume.

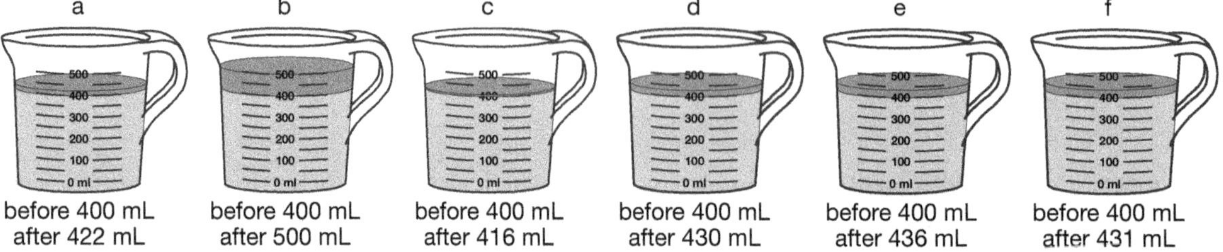

Find the capacity of displaced water in millilitres. Write your answer below each measuring cup.

3. Match each model with the correct measuring cup.

Model	Measuring cup
A	
B	
C	
D	
E	
F	

Measuring and Comparing Mass

Estimate, measure, and compare the masses of objects using appropriate units.

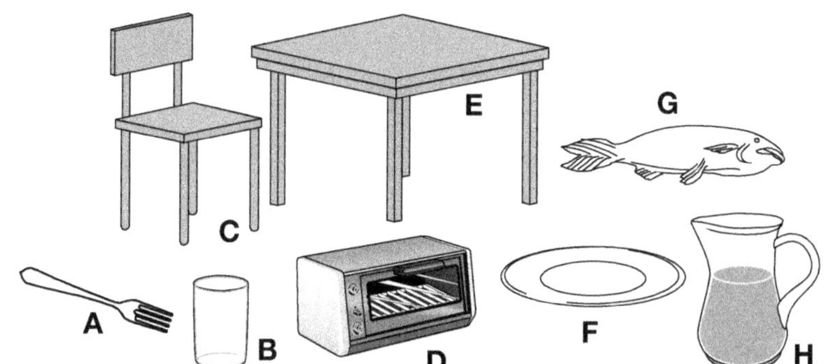

At-Home Help

The mass of most objects we can carry can be measured in grams or kilograms.

1 kg = 1000 g

1. Circle the unit you would use to measure the mass of the objects in the picture.

A g, kg	**B** g, kg	**C** g, kg	**D** g, kg
E g, kg	**F** g, kg	**G** g, kg	**H** g, kg

2. Match the masses below with the objects in the picture. There may be more than one possible answer for some masses.

a) 7 kg ____________	**b)** 30 g ____________
c) 10 kg ____________	**d)** 150 g ____________
e) 4 kg ____________	**f)** 35 kg ____________
g) 250 g ____________	**h)** 3 kg ____________

3. List three objects you can find in your home that would be best measured in grams.

____

____

4. List three objects you can find in your home that would be best measured in kilograms.

____

____

Using Tonnes

Relate tonnes to kilograms.

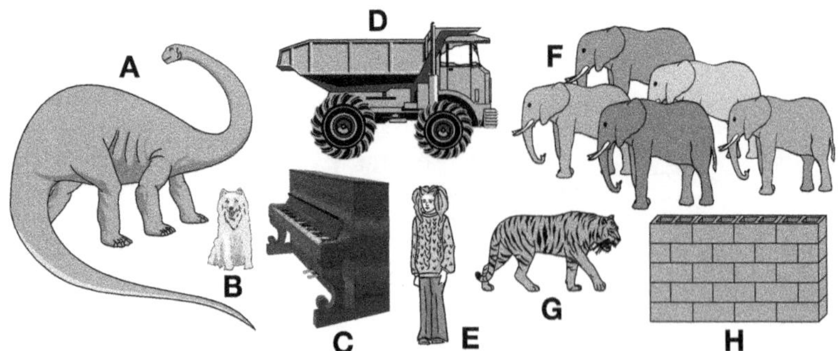

At-Home Help

Objects that are big and heavy, such as trucks, cars, or herds of elephants, are measured in metric tonnes.

A **tonne** is a unit used for measuring mass.

1 t = 1000 kg
1 kg = 1000 g

1. Circle the unit you would use to measure the mass of the animals or objects in the picture.

A kg, t	**B** kg, t	**C** kg, t	**D** kg, t
E kg, t	**F** kg, t	**G** kg, t	**H** kg, t

2. Match the masses below with the animals or objects in the picture. There may be more than one possible answer for some masses.

a) 6 t ____________________ **b)** 70 t ____________________

c) 65 kg ____________________ **d)** 10 t ____________________

e) 45 kg ____________________ **f)** 150 kg ____________________

g) 30 t ____________________ **h)** 40 kg ____________________

3. List three other objects that would be best measured in tonnes.

____

____

Test Yourself

Circle the correct answer.

Models

A

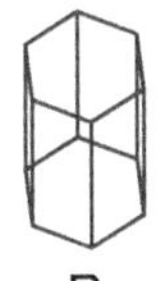

B

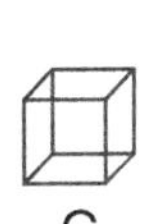

C

D

E

F

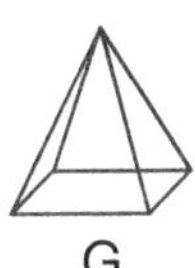

G

Nets

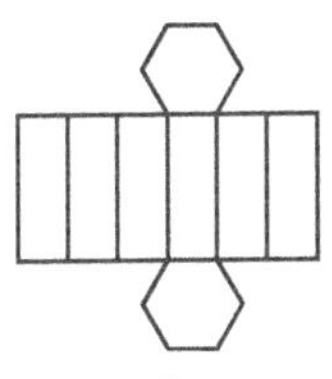

a

b

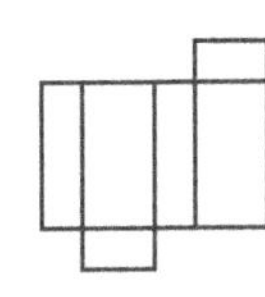

c

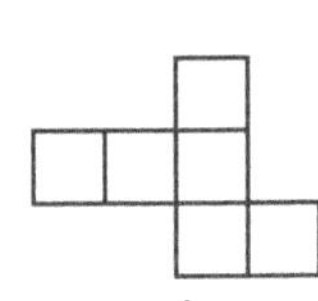

d

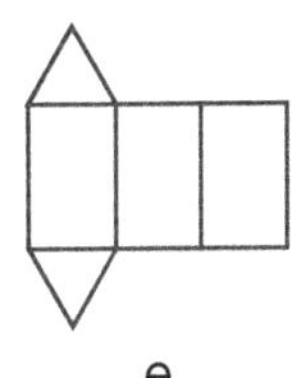

e

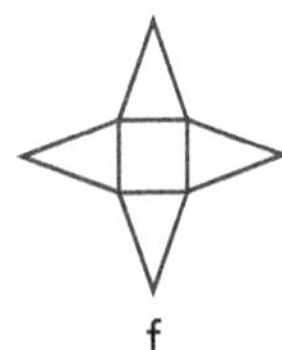

f

g

Use the pictures to answer Questions 1 to 5.

1. Which picture is the net of a pyramid?

   A. net e **B.** net a **C.** net c **D.** net f

2. Which net matches with model D?

   A. net b **B.** net g **C.** net d **D.** net c

3. Which model has no parallel edges?

   A. model B **B.** model G **C.** model E **D.** model C

4. Which model has 4 faces?

   A. model F **B.** model D **C.** model G **D.** model A

5. Which model matches with net e?

   A. model A **B.** model F **C.** model C **D.** model E

6. What is the most likely mass for a school backpack?

   A. 2 g **B.** 2 t **C.** 50 kg **D.** 2 kg

7. What is the most likely mass for a piano?

   A. 150 t **B.** 150 g **C.** 150 kg **D.** 15 kg

8. What is the most likely volume for an apple?

   A. 450 cm^3 **B.** 45 cm^3 **C.** 4500 cm^3 **D.** 4 cm^3

9. How much water would likely be displaced if a pencil were put under water?

   A. 150 mL **B.** 150 L **C.** 15 L **D.** 15 mL

Fraction Puzzles

Use patterns to represent the same fraction in different ways.

1. Name the fraction that is shaded and unshaded.

   a)   Shaded ____________

   Unshaded ____________

   b) Shaded ____________

   Unshaded ____________

2. Represent each fraction on a square.

   a) $\frac{1}{2}$ shaded

   b) $\frac{1}{4}$ shaded

   c) $\frac{2}{5}$ shaded

3. Which square in Question 2 was the most difficult to create? Explain.

   ____

   ____

4. Make 3 different rectangles where $\frac{3}{4}$ is shaded. Record your results in the chart below.

Number of shaded squares	Total number of squares in rectangle	Picture of shaded rectangle

At-Home Help

Fractions can be represented in different ways.

For example, both pictures show the fraction $\frac{1}{2}$.

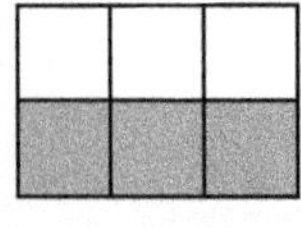

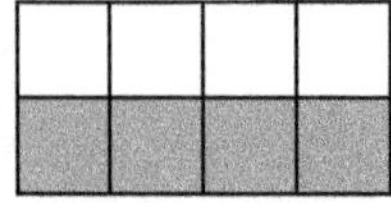

Equivalent Fractions

Make models of fractions and name equivalent fractions.

1. Colour each model to show each fraction.

   a) $\frac{1}{2}$

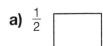

   b) $\frac{2}{3}$

   c) $\frac{4}{8}$

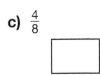

   d) $\frac{8}{12}$

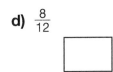

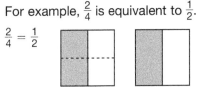

At-Home Help

Equivalent fractions are fractions that represent the same part of a whole or the same part of a set.

For example, $\frac{2}{4}$ is equivalent to $\frac{1}{2}$.

$\frac{2}{4} = \frac{1}{2}$

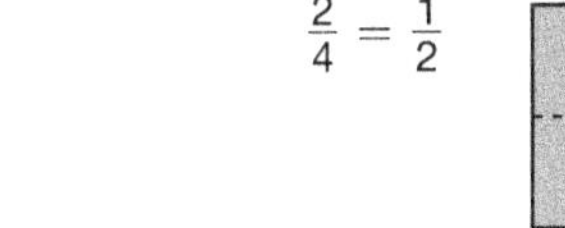

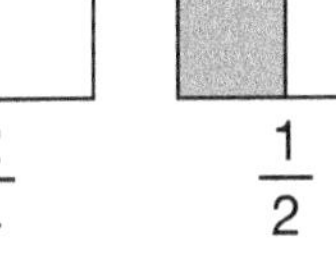

$\frac{2}{4}$ $\frac{1}{2}$

2. Which fractions in Question 1 are equivalent? Explain how you know.

____

____

3. Write the fraction to represent the shaded part in each model.

   a)

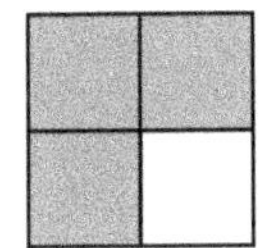

   b)

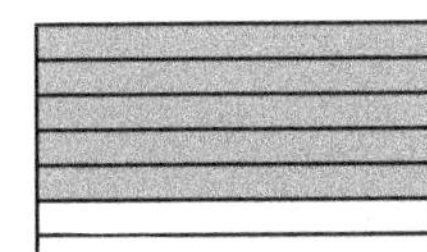

   c)

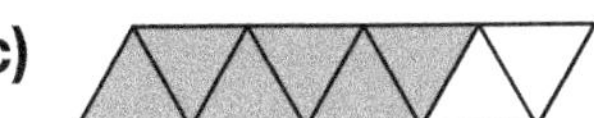

   d)

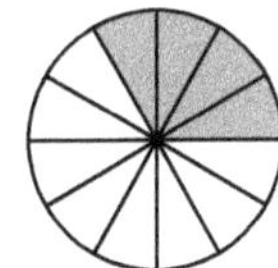

4. Sketch a fraction model that shows an equivalent fraction for Parts **c)** and **d)** in Question 3. Write the equivalent fraction.

   c)

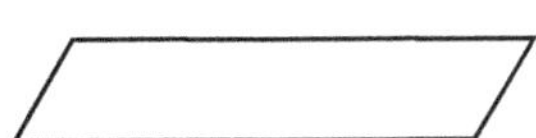

   d)

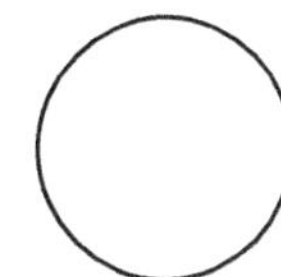

Comparing Fractions

Compare the size of fractions.

1. Compare. Write > or <. Explain your strategy.

   a) $\frac{3}{8}$ ______ $\frac{5}{8}$

   b) $\frac{4}{5}$ ______ $\frac{19}{20}$

   c) $\frac{4}{6}$ ______ $\frac{5}{9}$

2. **a)** Draw a tablecloth that is $\frac{1}{3}$ red and $\frac{1}{2}$ yellow. Which area is greater? Explain.

   b) What fraction of the tablecloth is not shaded? Explain.

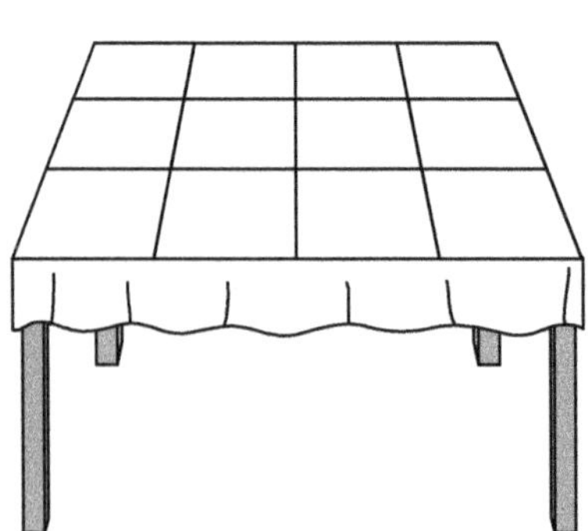

At-Home Help

Fractions can be compared when the denominators are the same, because the total number of sections and the size of the sections are the same.

For example, to compare $\frac{3}{5}$ and $\frac{4}{5}$, look at the numerators.

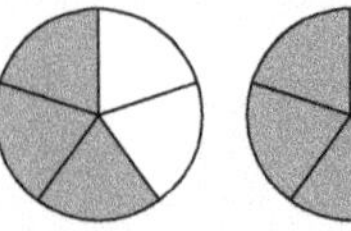

$\frac{4}{5}$ is greater than $\frac{3}{5}$.

If the denominators are not the same, model the fractions using a picture. Then compare the pictures.

For example, to compare $\frac{3}{8}$ and $\frac{2}{6}$ use a model.

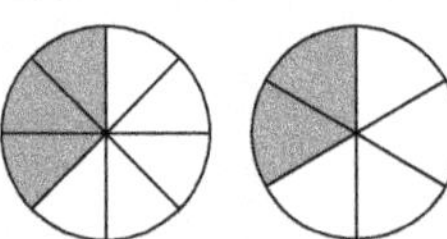

$\frac{3}{8}$ is greater than $\frac{2}{6}$.

Improper Fractions and Mixed Numbers

Represent and rename improper fractions as mixed numbers.

1. Draw a picture to represent each improper fraction.

   a) $\frac{14}{4}$

   b) $\frac{15}{10}$

   c) $\frac{12}{8}$

   d) $\frac{7}{2}$

At-Home Help

A **mixed number** is a number made up of a whole number and a fraction.

For example, $1\frac{1}{4}$ is a mixed number.

An **improper fraction** is a fraction with a numerator that is greater than or equal to the denominator.

For example, $\frac{5}{4}$ is an improper fraction.

Mixed numbers can be renamed as improper fractions.

For example, $1\frac{1}{4} = \frac{5}{4}$.

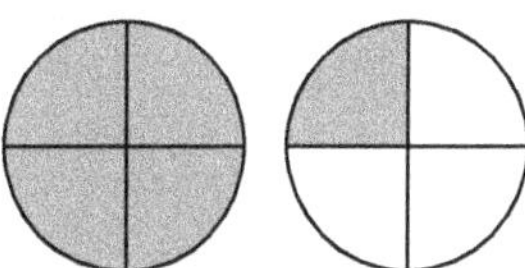

2. Rename each improper fraction in Question 1 as a mixed number.

   a) $\frac{14}{4}$ = ________ **b)** $\frac{15}{10}$ = ________ **c)** $\frac{12}{8}$ = ________ **d)** $\frac{7}{2}$ = ________

3. Change each mixed number to an improper fraction.

   a) $4\frac{1}{2}$ = ________ **b)** $3\frac{2}{8}$ = ________ **c)** $1\frac{3}{5}$ = ________

   d) $2\frac{5}{6}$ = ________ **e)** $5\frac{5}{10}$ = ________ **f)** $3\frac{4}{12}$ = ________

4. A hockey tournament for younger children is a total of 4 games. Each game is $\frac{2}{3}$ of an hour long. Use improper fractions and mixed numbers to represent each time. Explain your thinking.

   a) length of 1 tournament

   ____

   ____

   b) length of 2 tournaments

   ____

   ____

Relating Fractions to Decimals

Use the relationship between decimals and fractions to make comparisons.

You will need a calculator.

1. Calculate.

   a) $6 \div 8 =$

   b) $3 \div 20 =$

   c) $8 \div 25 =$

2. Order these fractions from least to greatest. Use inequality signs.

   $\frac{4}{5}, \frac{9}{50}, 3\frac{3}{25}$ ____________________

3. Write decimal equivalents for each fraction in Question 2.

   a) $\frac{4}{5} =$ **b)** $\frac{9}{50} =$ **c)** $3\frac{3}{25} =$

4. Order these decimals from greatest to least. Use inequality signs.

   0.20, 1.25, 0.55 ____________________

5. Write each decimal in Question 4 as a fraction.

   a) 0.20 = **b)** 1.25 = **c)** 0.55 =

6. Martin won $100 in a bingo game. He shared his prize equally with 8 people in his family.

   a) How much did each person get? Show your work.

   b) How would you write this decimal number as a mixed number?

At-Home Help

A **decimal equivalent** is a decimal that represents the same part of a whole or part of a set as a fraction. For example:

$\frac{1}{4} = \frac{25}{100}$
$= 0.25$

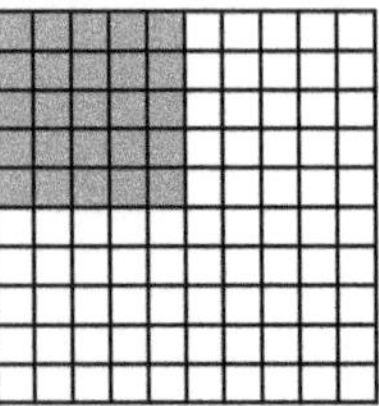

$\frac{5}{100} = 0.05$

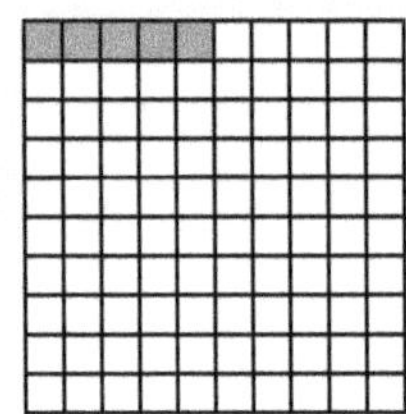

Solve Problems by Making Models

Solve fraction problems by making models of the information.

1. Math and reading classes begin at 10:15 a.m. They run for $2\frac{3}{4}$ hours. What time will math and reading finish? Show your work.

At-Home Help

To solve problems with fractions, start by making a model. You may use counters, shapes, or sketches.

You may need to arrange the counters or shapes into groups that match the fractions in the problem.

Use the arrangement to find the answer.

2. Danielle shares her snack with her friends. She has 16 carrots and 12 strawberries. She gives $\frac{1}{2}$ of her carrots and $\frac{2}{3}$ of her strawberries to her friends.

   a) How many carrots and strawberries does she give away? Show your work.

   b) How many carrots and strawberries does she have left for herself? Show your work.

3. Jin fills a container $1\frac{2}{3}$ full while Brad fills a container $\frac{7}{4}$ full. Who has more? How do you know? Show your work.

Ordering Fractions on a Number Line

Use number lines to compare and order fractions.

1. Use a number line to find the greatest fraction.

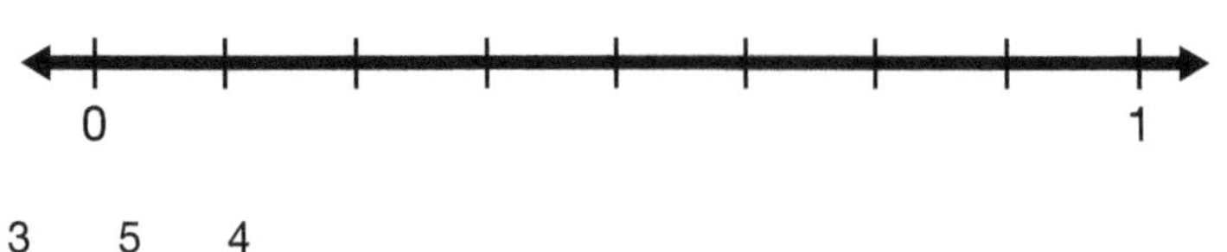

$\frac{3}{4}$ $\frac{5}{8}$ $\frac{4}{6}$ ______________________

2. Order these fractions from least to greatest. Use inequality signs.

$\frac{3}{4}$ $\frac{3}{8}$ $\frac{5}{6}$ $\frac{1}{3}$ $\frac{8}{9}$ $\frac{1}{2}$

____

3. Order these fractions from greatest to least. Use inequality signs.

$\frac{2}{4}$ $\frac{1}{4}$ $\frac{2}{3}$ $\frac{7}{8}$ $\frac{1}{3}$ $\frac{3}{5}$

____

4. Lise bought different lengths of material to make curtains. She bought $\frac{2}{3}$ of a length of silk, $\frac{5}{7}$ of cotton, and $\frac{4}{5}$ of corduroy. Which material is the greatest length? Show your work.

At-Home Help

To compare fractions, use a number line to mark the positions of the fractions.

The order of the fractions can be read from the number line.

For example, to order $\frac{3}{4}$, $\frac{2}{3}$, and $\frac{3}{8}$ from least to greatest, use a number line.

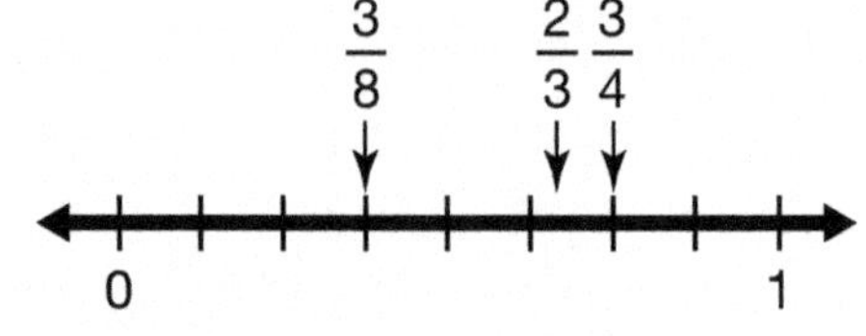

The correct order is $\frac{3}{8}$, $\frac{2}{3}$, and $\frac{3}{4}$.

Test Yourself

Circle the correct answer.

1. What fraction does *not* represent the shaded part of the picture?

A. $\frac{8}{12}$

B. $\frac{4}{6}$

C. $\frac{6}{12}$

D. $\frac{2}{3}$

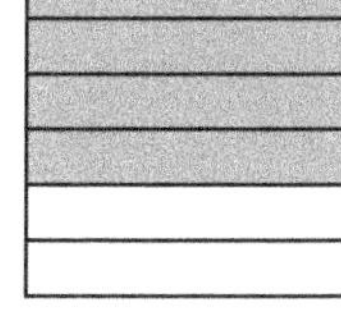

2. What fraction is equivalent to $\frac{4}{5}$?

A. $\frac{2}{3}$ **B.** $\frac{8}{12}$ **C.** $\frac{5}{4}$ **D.** $\frac{8}{10}$

3. Which shaded rectangle is the same as $\frac{6}{9}$?

A.

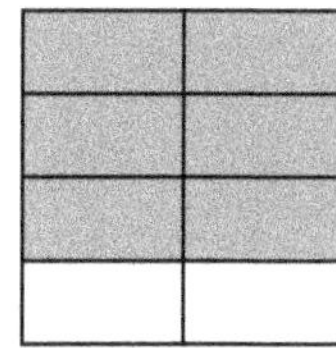

B.

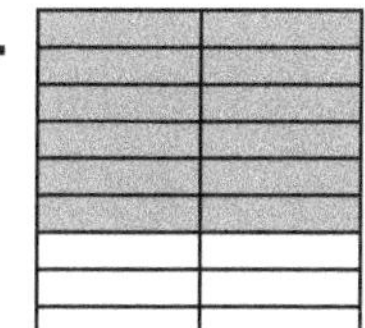

C.

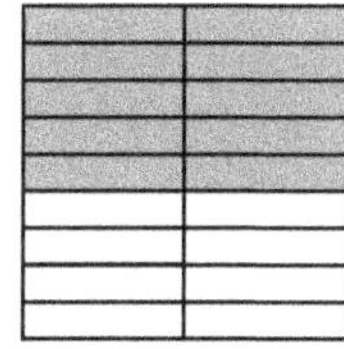

D.

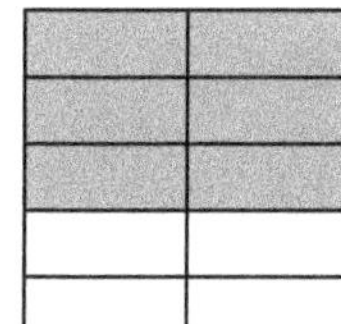

4. What fraction is shaded in the picture?

A. $\frac{2}{6}$ **B.** $\frac{8}{10}$

C. $\frac{2}{3}$ **D.** $\frac{4}{8}$

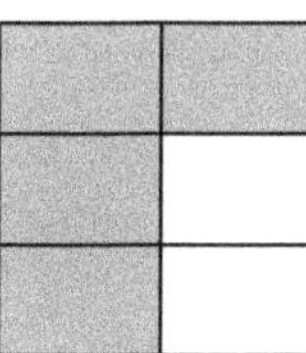

5. What fraction is shaded in the picture?

A. $\frac{2}{3}$ **B.** $\frac{3}{6}$

C. $\frac{3}{2}$ **D.** $\frac{3}{9}$

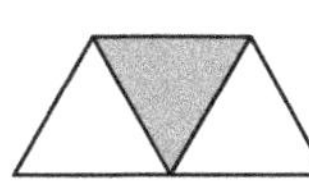

6. Which fraction is greater than $\frac{5}{9}$?

A. $\frac{7}{13}$ **B.** $\frac{6}{10}$ **C.** $\frac{3}{7}$ **D.** $\frac{4}{8}$

Test Yourself Page 2

7. Which fraction is less than $\frac{8}{10}$?

   A. $\frac{4}{5}$ **B.** $\frac{8}{9}$ **C.** $\frac{7}{9}$ **D.** $\frac{10}{12}$

8. What is $\frac{14}{8}$ as a mixed number?

   A. $2\frac{6}{8}$ **B.** $2\frac{4}{6}$ **C.** $1\frac{4}{6}$ **D.** $1\frac{6}{8}$

9. What is $\frac{17}{13}$ as a mixed number?

   A. $1\frac{13}{17}$ **B.** $2\frac{4}{17}$ **C.** $1\frac{4}{13}$ **D.** $2\frac{4}{13}$

10. What is $2\frac{3}{5}$ as an improper fraction?

    A. $\frac{13}{5}$ **B.** $\frac{10}{5}$ **C.** $\frac{10}{3}$ **D.** $\frac{8}{5}$

11. What is $5\frac{4}{7}$ as an improper fraction?

    A. $\frac{35}{4}$ **B.** $\frac{54}{7}$ **C.** $\frac{39}{7}$ **D.** $\frac{39}{4}$

12. Which decimal represents the part that is shaded?

    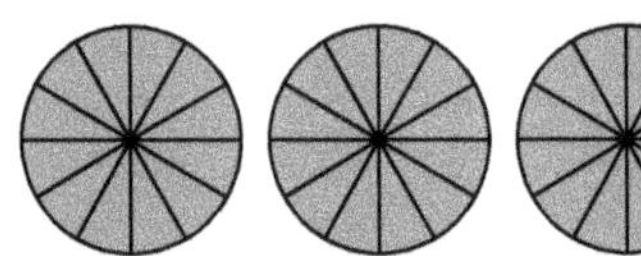

    A. 3.5 **B.** 5.3 **C.** 3.05 **D.** 5.03

13. What is the decimal equivalent of $\frac{15}{20}$?

    A. 0.15 **B.** 0.65 **C.** 0.75 **D.** 0.55

14. What is $\frac{17}{20}$ as a decimal?

    A. 0.83 **B.** 0.73 **C.** 0.75 **D.** 0.85

15. What is 0.14 as a fraction?

    A. $\frac{14}{10}$ **B.** $\frac{7}{10}$ **C.** $1\frac{4}{10}$ **D.** $\frac{14}{100}$

16. Raj and Milo play on the same soccer team. Each game is 60 min long. Raj plays $\frac{1}{3}$ of a game. Milo plays $\frac{5}{6}$ of a game. How many more minutes does Milo play than Raj?

    A. 20 min **B.** 35 min **C.** 30 min **D.** 25 min

Using Probability Language

Use probability language to describe predictions.

1. Make a check mark under the probability word that would apply for each sentence. For some sentences, more than one probability word may apply. Explain the reason for your choice.
   a) Today is Wednesday.
   b) It will rain today.
   c) The teacher is in the classroom.
   d) The temperature is 1°C and it might snow.
   e) People go on vacation in the summer.
   f) You can travel to another planet in a rocket.

At-Home Help

Probability words are used to describe how likely it is that an event will happen.

Examples of probability words are
- certain
- likely
- more probable
- less probable
- impossible

	Impossible	Less probable	More probable	Certain	Reason
a)					
b)					
c)					
d)					
e)					
f)					

2. Which event from Question 1 did you find most difficult to decide the probability? Explain.

____

3. Give an example of an event that would fit each probability word.
   a) impossible _______________________
   b) more probable _______________________
   c) certain _______________________
   d) less probable _______________________

Predicting Probabilities

Predict the probability of events and test your predictions.

Letters	Value of each letter
AEIOU	1
LNRST	2
BCDFGHKMPVWY	3
JQXZ	4

At-Home Help

It is possible to predict the probability of an event by repeating an experiment several times.

The results of the experiment can help you think about why the results happened. You can also use the results to predict the probability of other events that are related.

1. Use the information in the table above. Predict how likely each event is.

   a) picking three letters and getting a value of 12

   b) picking a 3-point letter before picking a 1-point letter

   c) picking four consonants before picking any vowels

2. Test each prediction in Question 1. Explain your results.

   a) ______________________________

   ____

   b) ______________________________

   ____

   c) ______________________________

   ____

3. Write the letters from your first and last name on separate pieces of paper. Place them into the same bag or container. Predict how likely each event is. Test your predictions. Remember to place each letter back into the bag after each draw. Explain what you found out.

   a) on the first draw, picking a vowel instead of a consonant

   ____

   ____

   b) on two draws, picking the first letter of your name before any other letter

   ____

   ____

Probabilities as Fractions

Express the likelihood of an event as a fraction.

You rolled two dice 10 times and recorded the sum of the numbers you got on each roll.

My rolls
12
4
5
10
5
3
7
10
5
9

At-Home Help

When probabilities are written as fractions, the numerator represents the number of likely events, and the denominator represents the total number of events.

For example, if you rolled a die 10 times and you got a 4 three times, the total number of events would be 10, because the die was rolled 10 times. The number of likely events in this case would be 3, because you got a 4 three times. So the probability of you rolling a 4 was $\frac{3}{10}$.

1. Write the probability of each event as a fraction.

   a) getting 5 ________ **b)** getting an even number ________

   c) getting a number below 7 ________ **d)** getting a number above 9 ________

2. **a)** Write the names of 6 different sports on separate pieces of paper. Place them in a bag or container.

   ____

   b) What is the probability of choosing a sport beginning with letter S? Carry out an experiment. Pick one sport from the bag and record your results. Repeat the experiment 10 times. Write the probability as a fraction.

   ____

   c) Carry out another experiment to find the probability of choosing a sport that has only two syllables. Repeat the experiment 10 times. Write the probability as a fraction.

   ____

Modelling Probability Problems

Conduct probability experiments.

1. Stefan performed an experiment. He flipped a coin 20 times. The first 10 times he saw heads.

   a) Predict the results of the last 10 flips. Write a fraction for your prediction. Explain your prediction.

   Prediction ____________________ Fraction ______________

   Reason

   ____

   b) Now flip a coin 10 times and record your results in the table. Write your results as a fraction.

Flip of coin	Heads	Tails
1		
2		
3		
4		
5		
6		
7		
8		
9		
10		

At-Home Help

It is possible to predict the probability that an event will happen. To test the prediction, you can do an experiment and record the results in a table.

The results of the experiment can be written as fractions to show probabilities.

Sometimes the results do not match the predictions.

For example, there is a 1 in 2 chance of getting heads when flipping a coin. So the predicted probability is $\frac{1}{2}$.

If you flipped the coin 10 times and got heads 6 times, then the probability of getting heads in the experiment was $\frac{6}{10}$.

2. Write the names of girls and boys on small pieces of paper. Make sure there are 8 names in total. Place the names in a bag or container. Conduct 2 experiments for each part. How many names of girls and boys might give you these results?

   a) picking a girl's name is more probable

   ____

   b) picking a boy's name is very probable

   ____

   c) picking a girl's name is very improbable but not impossible

   ____

Using Tree Diagrams

Use tree diagrams to record the outcomes of an experiment.

1. Play the game Rock, Paper, Scissors 6 times with a partner at home.
   Keep a tally of the results using a tree diagram.

2. Students choose their pizza slices to eat for lunch. The cost depends upon the type of crust and the number of toppings.

   Crust: thin, thick
   Toppings: pepperoni, mushroom

   a) Draw a tree diagram to show all possible pizza slice combinations.

   b) How many different types of pizza slices could you buy? ________________

   c) Imagine that only one slice is left of each type of pizza, and that you choose a slice by pointing with your eyes closed. Which event is more probable, you choosing a pizza slice with one topping or a slice with two toppings? Record your answer as a fraction. Explain.

   ____

   ____

At-Home Help

Tree diagrams are pictures that show all possible combinations for a particular choice.

For example:
A bag has two sizes of marbles. Each size of marble comes in three colours: red, green, and black. There is only one marble of each size and colour. If you were to pick a marble, the choices would be

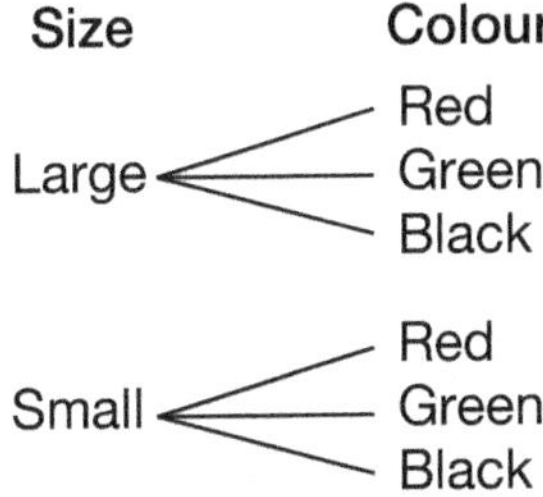

The total number of marbles is 6, and two marbles are red. So the probability of picking a marble that is red is $\frac{2}{6}$.

Solve Problems by Considering All Possibilities

Think about all of the possibilities when solving a problem.

You roll a die and get a number. Then you roll the die again and multiply the first number by the second number. You get 2 bonus points if you make a correct prediction about the product *before* rolling the die the second time.

At-Home Help

To solve a probability problem, start by listing all possibilities. It is easier if you organize the possibilities in a tree diagram or chart.

Look at your diagram and decide what predictions are reasonable.

You can test your predictions by doing an experiment.

1. **a)** You play one game and roll a 4 on the first roll. Use a tree diagram to list all possible products.

   b) You play another game and roll a 3 on the first roll. Use a tree diagram to list all possible products.

   c) Based on your tree diagrams, which prediction should you make if you roll 4 on the first roll? Explain.

   ____

   ____

2. Imagine you roll a die 10 times, and record the number you get on each roll. If you were to multiply each number you got by 3, which numbers must you roll to always get a product that is an even number?

Test Yourself

Circle the correct answer.

1. What is the correct order in which to place these probability words?

   A. certain, less probable, impossible, likely, more probable, unlikely

   B. less probable, more probable, likely, unlikely, certain, impossible

   C. impossible, unlikely, less probable, likely, more probable, certain

   D. certain, likely, more probable, less probable, unlikely, impossible

2. Which event is impossible?

   A. It will rain tomorrow.

   B. In Canada, winter is warmer than summer.

   C. We will have a test in math soon.

   D. The school year ends in June.

3. Which event is certain?

   A. I will go to a movie soon. **B.** I will sleep 8 hours tonight.

   C. Earth orbits around the sun. **D.** All trees will grow this season.

4. Which probability word would best describe this event?

   It will rain 1 out of 7 days this week.

   A. certain **B.** less probable **C.** more probable **D.** impossible

5. Which probability word would best describe this event?

   All students in a class are boys.

   A. certain **B.** less probable **C.** more probable **D.** impossible

6. When Twyla rolled a pair of dice 10 times, these numbers appeared: 10, 6, 9, 10, 5, 3, 6, 4, 6, and 9. What was the probability of Twyla rolling a 6?

   A. $\frac{4}{10}$ **B.** $\frac{4}{6}$ **C.** $\frac{3}{6}$ **D.** $\frac{3}{10}$

7. Look at Question 6. What was the probability of Twyla rolling an even number?

   A. $\frac{6}{10}$ **B.** $\frac{4}{10}$ **C.** $\frac{5}{10}$ **D.** $\frac{7}{10}$

Test Yourself Page 2

8. Look at Question 6. What was the probability of Twyla rolling a number below 5?

   A. $\frac{2}{5}$ **B.** $\frac{1}{4}$ **C.** $\frac{2}{10}$ **D.** $\frac{5}{10}$

9. Imagine that all the dessert choices on the menu were written on separate pieces of paper, and these papers were put in a bag. You choose one dessert choice from the bag without looking. What would be the probability of choosing a dessert with chocolate?

   A. $\frac{2}{8}$ **B.** $\frac{3}{8}$

   C. $\frac{6}{10}$ **D.** $\frac{6}{15}$

10. Which tree diagram represents the dessert choices in Question 9?

A.

Type	Flavour
Cake	Chocolate, Apple, Blueberry
Ice cream	Vanilla, Chocolate
Pie	Lemon, Strawberry, Apple

B.

Type	Flavour
Cake	Blueberry, Chocolate, Raspberry
Ice cream	Vanilla, Chocolate, Blueberry
Pie	Strawberry, Lemon, Apple

C.

Type	Flavour
Cake	Chocolate, Raspberry
Ice cream	Vanilla, Chocolate
Pie	Strawberry, Lemon, Apple

D.

Type	Flavour
Cake	Blueberry, Chocolate, Raspberry
Ice cream	Vanilla, Chocolate
Pie	Strawberry, Lemon, Apple

Tiling an Area

Tile an area using software.

1. How many congruent shapes will tile this area? Use Geometer's Sketchpad or the grid below.

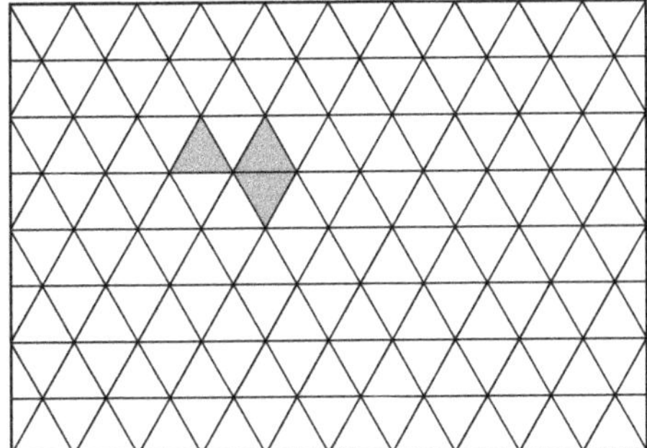

_____________ congruent shapes

2. Tile the area below with this shape 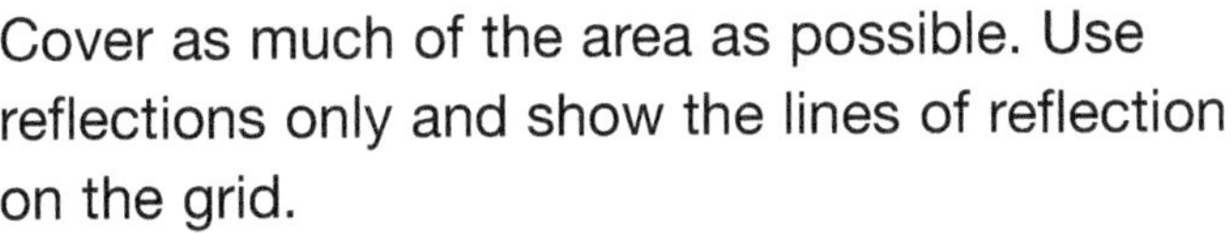 .

Cover as much of the area as possible. Use reflections only and show the lines of reflection on the grid.

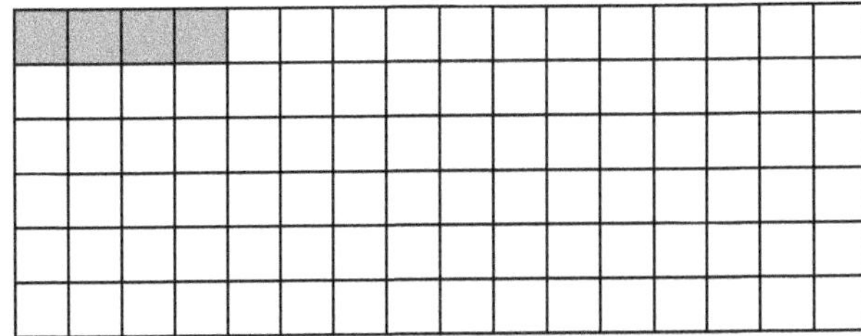

3. How would you move this shape ▭ to tile the lightly shaded area below?

Circle the correct answer.

translate 4 squares left

rotate 90° clockwise

translate 2 squares right and 1 square down

reflect about the horizontal

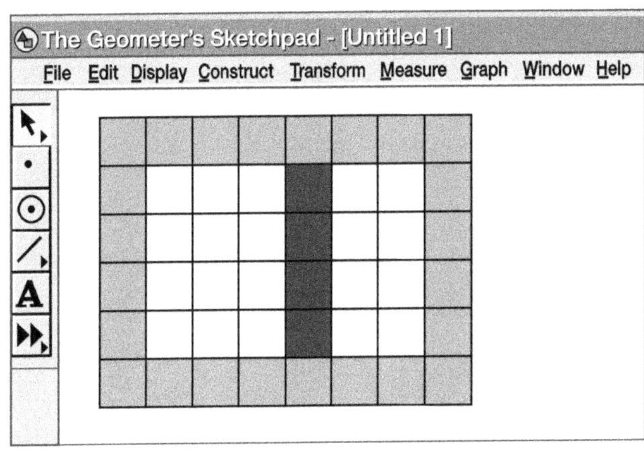

At-Home Help

Congruent means the same shape and size.

To tile an area, use repeated congruent shapes. There should be no gaps and no overlaps.

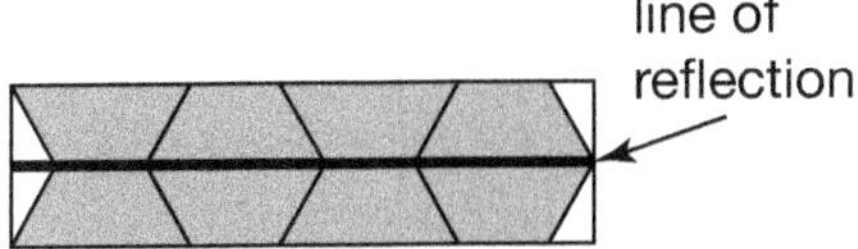

A **line of reflection** is a line in which a shape is reflected. Both shapes are identical in size and shape, but one appears flipped.

For example, in the picture above, there is a horizontal line of reflection.

Describing Tiling Patterns

Describe tiling patterns.

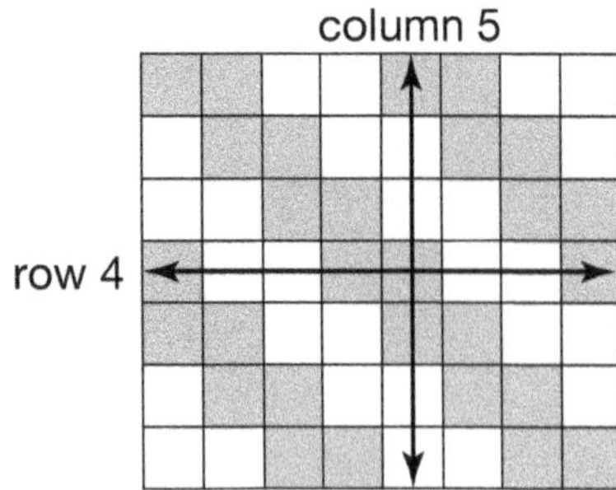

At-Home Help

A **tiling pattern** is a pattern of repeated congruent shapes that fit together with no gaps and no overlaps.

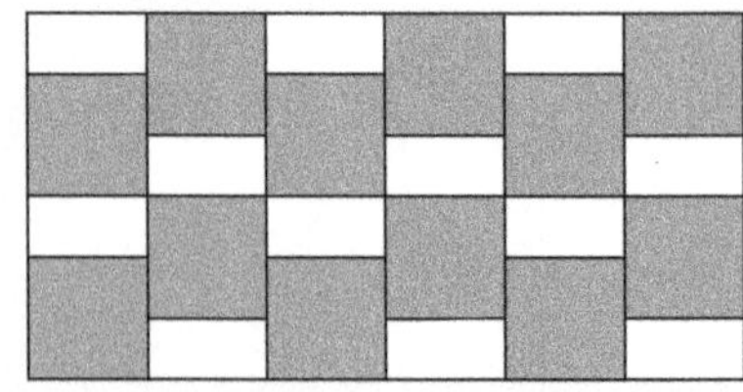

A **pattern rule** describes how you can reproduce a pattern.

For example, the pattern rule for the first column in the picture above is:

Start with 1 white rectangle, then 1 shaded square, 1 white rectangle, and 1 shaded square.

1. Which columns have different pattern rules? How do you know?

____

____

____

____

____

2. Write a pattern rule for columns 5 and 7. How are the pattern rules the same? How are they different?

____

____

____

____

____

3. Record the number of white and shaded tiles in each column. Use the table below.

Column	White tiles	Shaded tiles
1		
2		
3		
4		
5		
6		
7		
8		

Extending Tiling Patterns

Write a pattern rule to extend a pattern.

1. Which pattern rule best describes the first row of this tiling pattern? Circle the correct answer.

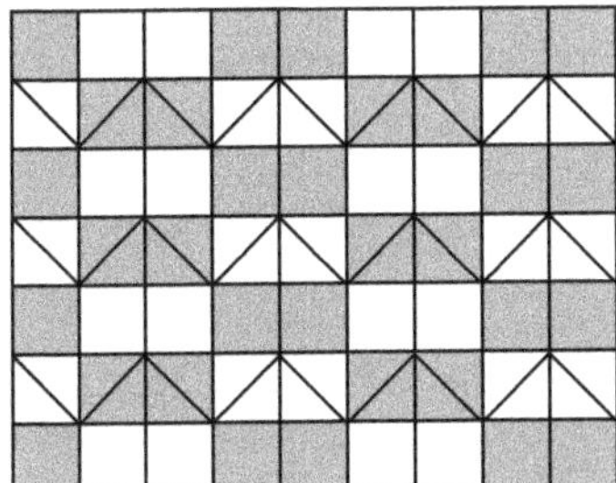

Start with 1 shaded tile, then alternate 1 white tile and 1 shaded tile.

Start with 1 white tile, then alternate 2 shaded tiles and 2 white tiles 4 times.

Start with 1 shaded tile, then alternate 2 white tiles and 2 shaded tiles 2 times.

Start with 1 white tile, then alternate 2 shaded tiles and 2 white tiles.

At-Home Help

A **pattern rule** states the starting point of a pattern, a description of the attributes that change, and the number of repetitions.

For example, the pattern rule for the first row is start with 1 shaded tile, then alternate 2 white tiles and 3 shaded tiles 3 times, and end with 2 white tiles.

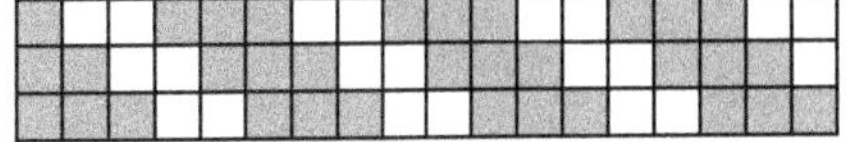

2. Look at the tiling pattern in Question 1. Write a pattern rule for any column.

____

____

3. Write a pattern rule for a row on this rug based on the letter F.

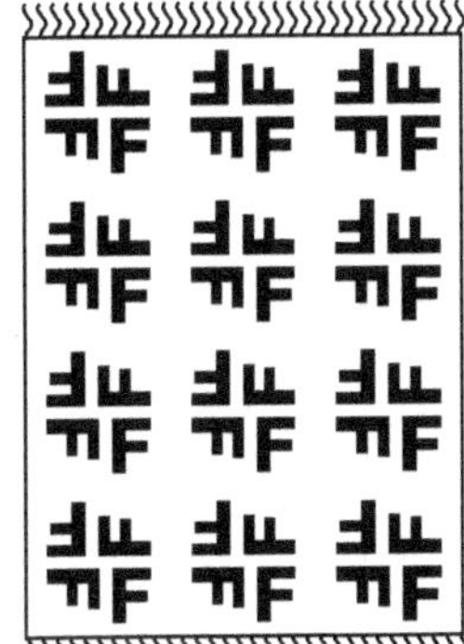

____

____

____

____

Translating Shapes on Grids

Identify the rule for translating a shape.

1. Which statement best describes this translation? Circle the correct answer.

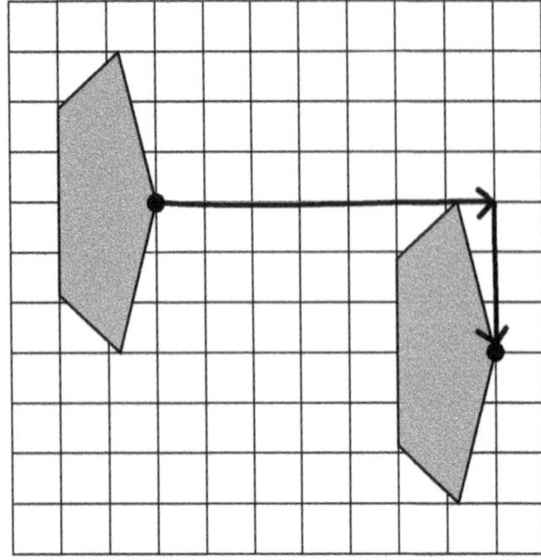

right 6 squares, down 3 squares

left 7 squares, up 4 squares

right 7 squares, down 3 squares

right 6 squares, down 2 squares

At-Home Help

A **translation** is a movement in a straight line. It can be left, right, up, or down.

For example, the translation shown is left 3 squares and down 5 squares.

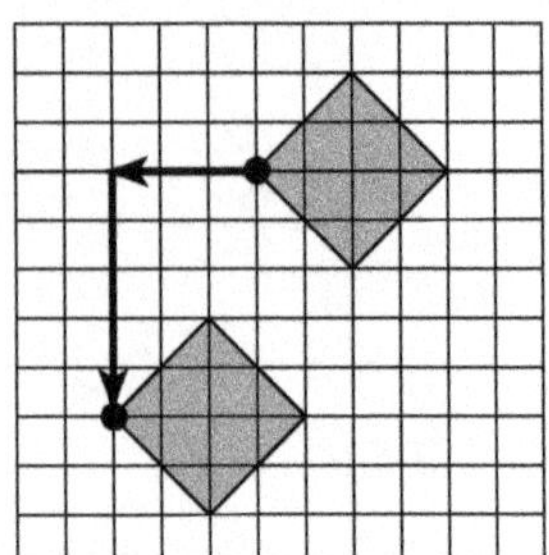

2. Greg wrote rules to describe the translation of a shape. Follow Greg's steps in the box.

   Show the result of each translation on the grid.

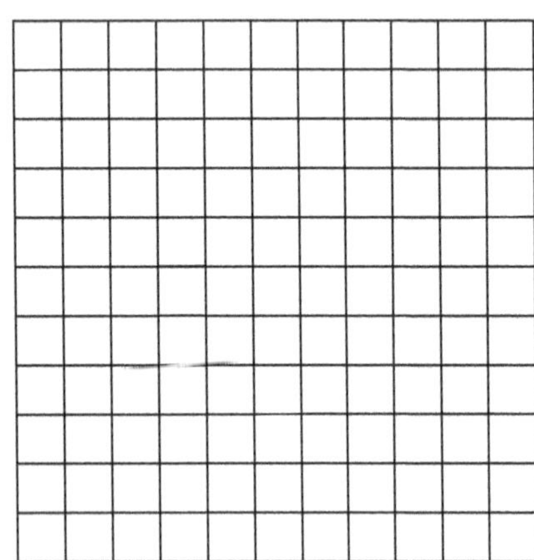

Start with a T-shape.

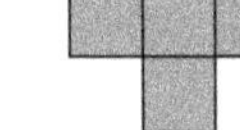

Step 1: right 6, down 2
Step 2: left 3, up 2
Step 3: left 3, down 2
Step 4: right 4, up 5
Step 5: up 2
Step 6: left 4

Rotating Shapes

Rotate shapes in a pattern.

You will need a protractor and a ruler.

1. Which rotation rule was used? Circle the correct answer.

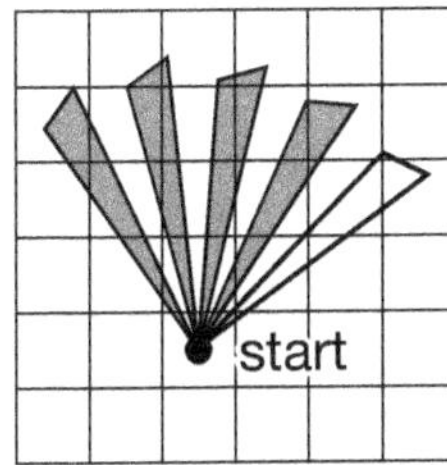

Rotate 20° counterclockwise 4 times.

Rotate 25° counterclockwise 4 times.

Rotate 20° counterclockwise 5 times.

Rotate 25° counterclockwise 5 times.

2. Chandra's Rotation Rule
Choose a vertex on the shape to be the centre of rotation. Rotate 25° counterclockwise 10 times.

Draw the logo using the rotation rule. Label the centre of rotation. Label the angle of rotation showing the direction.

3. A shape was rotated to create this logo.

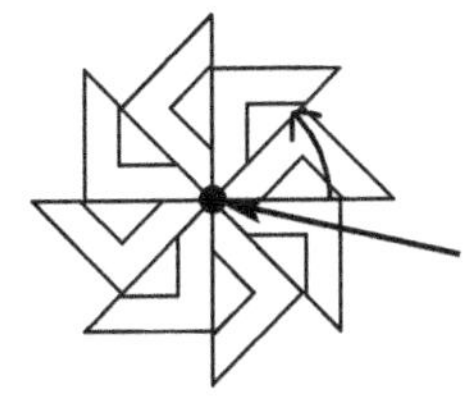

a) Identify the centre of rotation. Label it on the logo.

b) What is the angle of rotation? Label it on the logo. ____________________

c) What is a possible direction of each rotation? Label it on the logo.

____

At-Home Help

A **rotation** in 2-D is a turn about a point called the **centre of rotation**. When describing a rotation, remember to include both the angle and direction.

For example, this shape was rotated 90° counterclockwise.

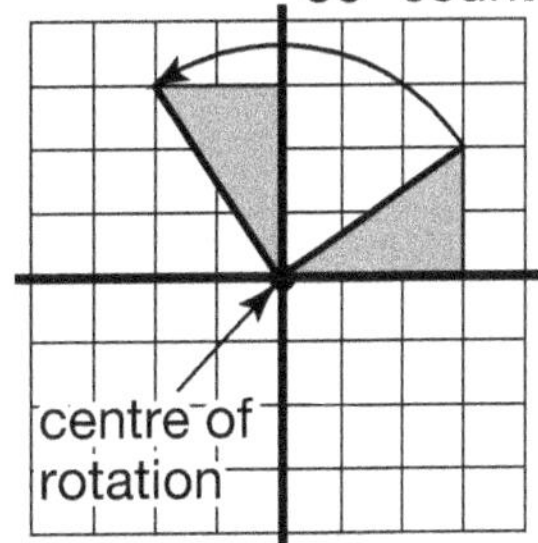

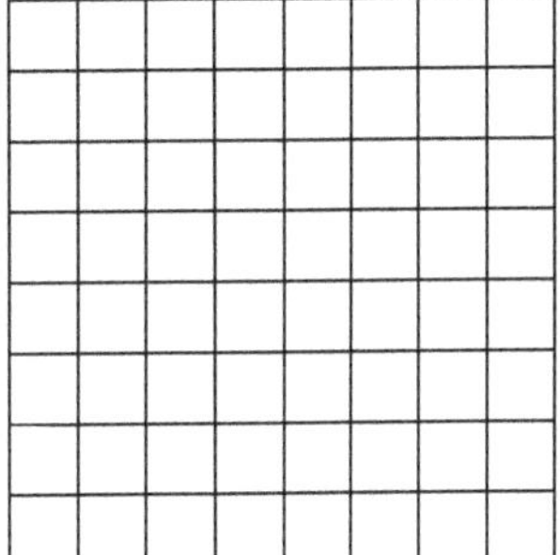

Communicate About Transformations

Describe transformations using math language.

You will need a protractor and a ruler.

1. Name the transformation used to create shapes A, B, and C from the black shape.

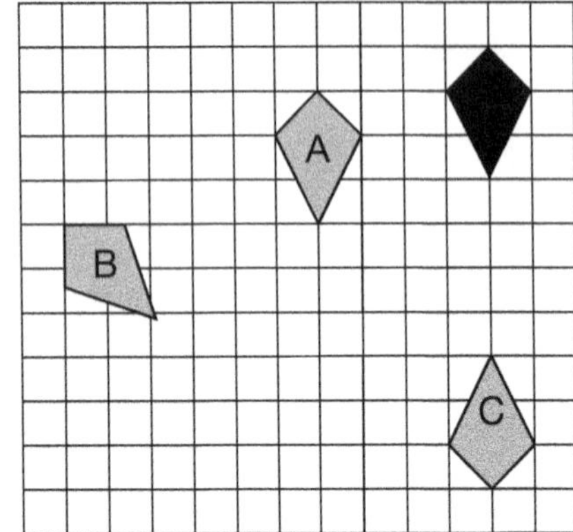

a) shape A ______________________

b) shape B ______________________

c) shape C ______________________

At-Home Help

Transformations can change the position, orientation, and size of a shape.

Translations and rotations change the position of a shape but not its orientation.

Reflections change both the position and orientation of a shape.

When describing transformations, remember to use the Communication Checklist.

Communication Checklist

☑ Did you use math language?
☑ Did you include diagrams?
☑ Did you show the right amount of detail?

2. Look at the picture in Question 1. What kind of transformation is each student describing? Identify the shape by its letter. Explain how you know.

a) Isabelle: My transformation changed the orientation of the shape.

____

____

b) Zev: My transformation changed the position of every point on the shape.

____

____

____

3. a) Copy the diagram on grid paper. Reflect it in the darker line.

b) Describe the effect of the reflection.

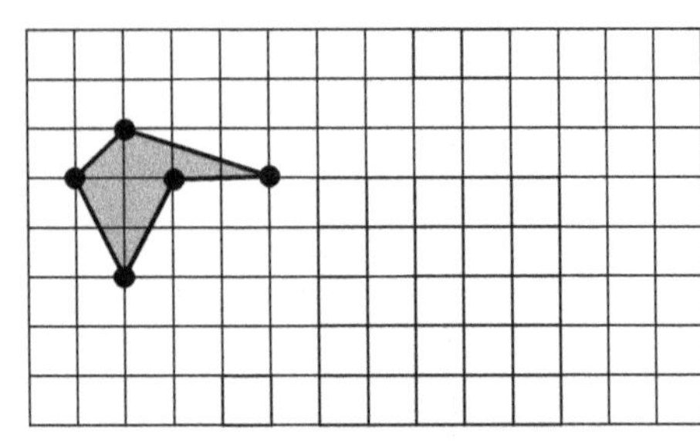

Modelling Congruence with Transformations

Show congruence using transformations.

You will need a protractor and a ruler.

1. Circle the congruent shapes. Explain how you know. Use transformation language.

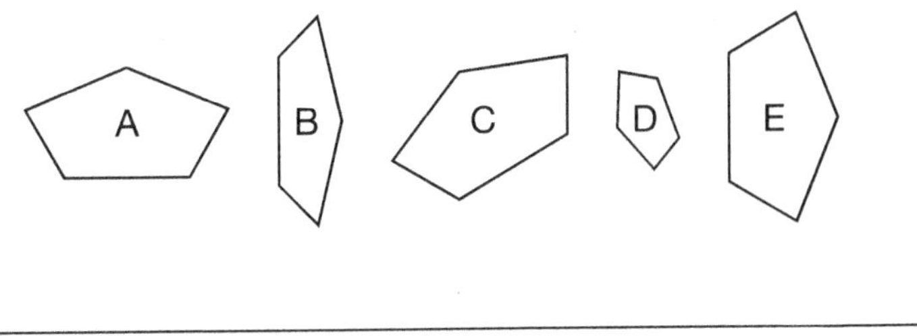

____

____

At-Home Help

Congruent means the same shape and size. Congruent shapes may be translated, rotated, or reflected.

For example, all three triangles are congruent.

2.

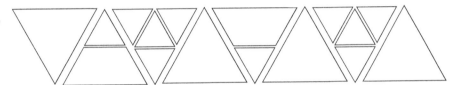

a) Identify all sets of congruent shapes. Use the letters A, B, and C to show shapes that are congruent.

b) Describe the shape in each set.

____

____

____

c) Choose one set of congruent shapes. Describe the transformations you used to show congruence.

____

____

____

____

____

Exploring Similarity

Identify similar figures using transformations.

You will need a ruler.

1. Two shapes were made using elastics. Why are these shapes similar?

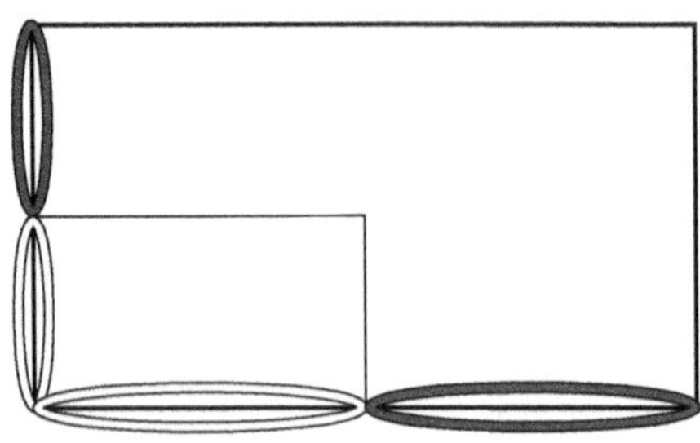

2. Yvette began to enlarge this triangle using elastics.

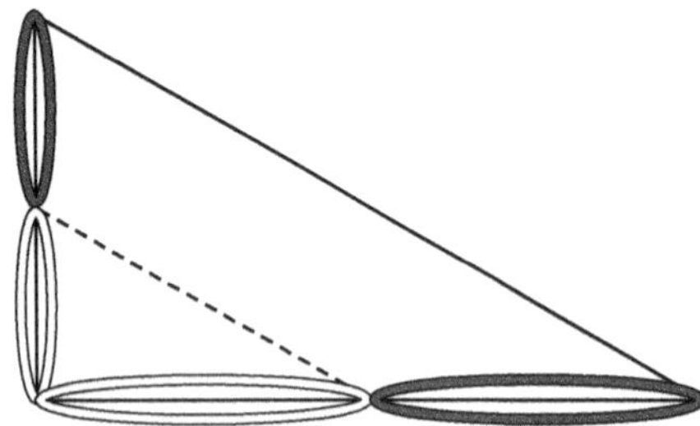

Draw the enlarged similar triangle.

3. What does a smaller similar triangle look like? Draw it.

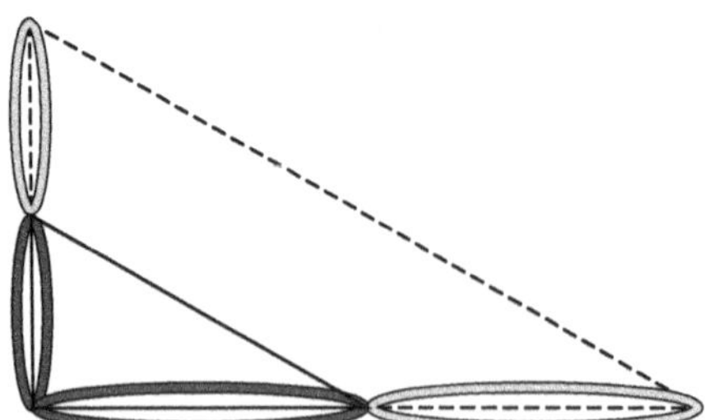

At-Home Help

Similar means the same shape but a different size.

For example, both trapezoids are similar.

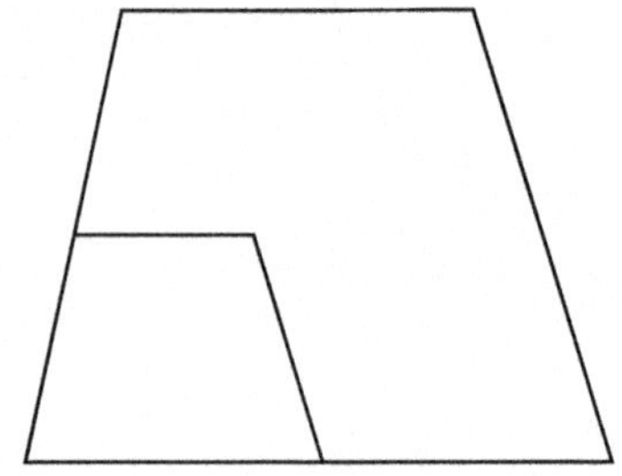

Test Yourself

Circle the correct answer.

1. How would you move this shape to tile the lightly shaded area below?

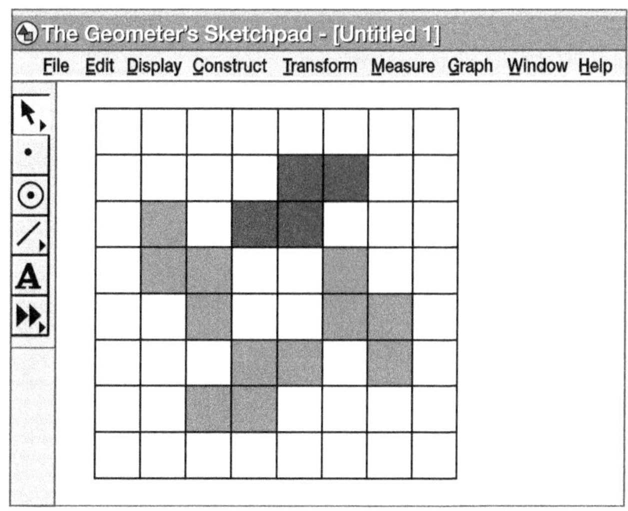

A. translate down 3 squares and left 2 squares

B. rotate 90° clockwise

C. translate right 2 squares and down 3 squares

D. reflect in a horizontal line

2. Which rows have a different pattern rule?

A. rows 1 and 5

B. rows 2 and 6

C. rows 3 and 7

D. rows 4 and 5

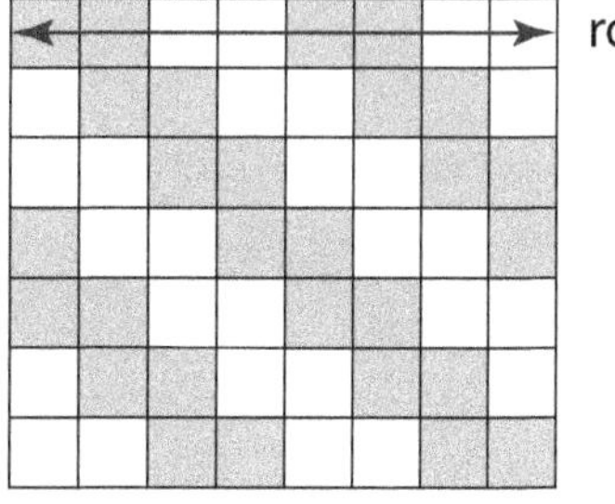

row 1

Test Yourself Page 2

3. Which statement best describes the translation shown?

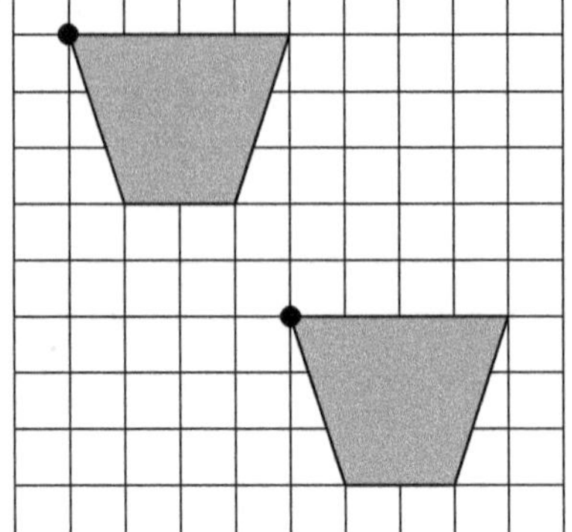

A. translate right 6 squares and down 4 squares

B. translate right 5 squares and down 4 squares

C. translate left 5 squares and up 4 squares

D. translate left 4 squares and up 5 squares

4. Which rotation rule was used to create the logo?

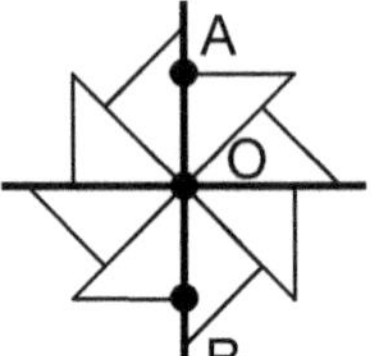

A. Rotate 30° counterclockwise about B 5 times.

B. Rotate 45° counterclockwise about O 7 times.

C. Rotate 45° counterclockwise about A 5 times.

D. Rotate 30° counterclockwise about O 7 times.

5. Which shapes are congruent and how do you know?

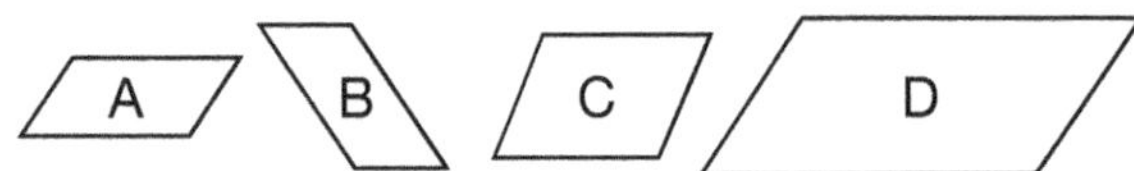

A. Translate A to C and A covers C exactly.

B. Rotate A to B and A covers B exactly.

C. Reflect A to D and A covers D exactly.

D. Translate A to B and A covers B exactly.

6. Look at the picture in Question 5. Which shapes are similar and how do you know?

A. C is twice as large as B.

B. C is twice as tall as A.

C. D is twice as large as A.

D. D is twice as tall as B.

Page 1

2-D Patterns

Use models and t-charts to record, extend, and make predictions about number patterns.

Look at design 1 of the capital letter F. It has been made from 10 dots.

design 1 design 2 design 3

At-Home Help

A **2-D pattern** has a length and a width.

For example, these shapes form a 2-D pattern.

□ ○ □ ○ □ ○

A **t-chart** has 2 columns. The data in both columns are related.

For example: As the number of songs increases by 1, the number of minutes of practice increases by 15 minutes.

Number of songs	Number of minutes of practice
1	10
2	25
3	40

1. How many dots are needed to complete design 4?
   22 dots
2. Predict the number of dots needed to complete design 5.
   Suggested answer: 26 dots
3. Draw design 4 and design 5.
   design 4 design 5
4. Complete the t-chart to show the pattern.

Letter design	Number of dots
1	10
2	14
3	18
4	22
5	26

5. If you had a total of 50 dots, what design number would the letter F be?
   design 11

Page 2

Patterns in Tables

Create tables to display, predict, and extend patterns.

Apple crisp is a great recipe to make for many different sized groups. The recipe in the chart is complete for one class and partially complete for two classes.

Apple Crisp Recipe

Number of classes	Number of apples	Amount of butter (mL)	Amount of brown sugar (mL)
1	24	150	200
2	48	300	400
3	72	450	600
4	96	600	800
5	120	750	1000

At-Home Help

A **table** usually has two or more columns of data. Each column has its own heading and is related to the other columns.

For example:

Number of times I make the recipe	Number of cups of water	Number of scoops of crystals	Number of people served
1	5	3	4
2			

1. Complete the recipe for all of the classes in the chart.
2. What pattern rules did you use to complete the table?
   Each amount of food increases by the amount needed to make one class recipe.
   e.g., Number of apples: Start at 24 and increase by 24 each time
3. If you bought 200 apples, what is the greatest number of classes that could have apple crisp? Explain your thinking using numbers.
   8 classes. Add 24 apples to each of the next recipes.
   6 classes: 120 + 24 = 144 apples
   7 classes: 144 + 24 = 168 apples
   8 classes: 168 + 24 = 192 apples
   9 classes: 192 + 24 = 216 apples (too many apples)
4. **a)** If one and one half classes wanted apple crisp, explain how you would calculate the amount of each ingredient.
   Take the amount for one recipe and add half of that amount.

   b) Calculate the amounts. Show your work.
   24 + 12 = 36 apples, 150 + 75 = 225 mL butter, and 200 + 100 = 300 mL brown sugar

Page 3

Solve Problems Using Patterns

Goal **Identify patterns to solve problems.**

1. What pattern could you use to add these numbers? Write a number sentence to show the pattern.

   1 + 2 + 3 + 4 + … + 37 + 38 + 39 + 40

   Paired numbers as shown sum to 41.

   1 + 40 = 41, 2 + 39 = 41, 3 + 38 = 41, 4 + 37 = 41, …

2. Use a pattern to add these numbers. Show your work.

   15 + 25 + 35 + 45 + 55 + 65 + 75 + 85

   Paired numbers as shown sum to 100.
   (15 + 85) + (25 + 75) + (35 + 65) + (45 + 55)
   = 100 + 100 + 100 + 100
   = 400

3. Glynis is stacking boxes of candles for a store display.

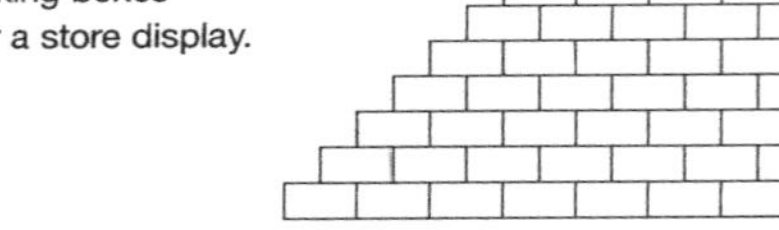

a) Make a plan that uses a pattern to find the number of boxes in the stack. Use number sentences and words.

   Paired rows as shown have a total of 11 boxes in each pair.

   1 + 10 = 11, 2 + 9 = 11, 3 + 8 = 11, 4 + 7 = 11, 5 + 6 = 11

b) Use your plan to find the total number of boxes in the stack. 55 boxes

c) How many boxes would there be in a stack that has 16 boxes in the bottom row? Explain your answer using number sentences and words.

   136 boxes. Pairing rows as before gives a total of 17 boxes in each pair.

   1 + 16 = 17, 2 + 15 = 17, 3 + 14 = 17, 4 + 13 = 17, 5 + 12 = 17, 6 + 11 = 17, 7 + 10 = 17, 8 + 9 = 17

   8 groups of 17 = 8 x 17 or 136

At-Home Help

Pairing numbers can help you find sums more easily. Try to find pairs that add up to the same number.

For example, to add

1 + 3 + 5 + 7 + 9 + 11

notice that 1 + 11, 3 + 9, and 5 + 7 all add up to 12.

sum = (1 + 11) + (3 + 9) + (5 + 7)
= 12 + 12 + 12
= 36

Page 4

3-D Patterns

Goal **Create a 3-D pattern and make predictions about its growth.**

Look at the stack of boxes in Question 3 on page 3.

1. Determine how each stack is made from the one before. Then complete the table to show how many layers of boxes there will be if there are 210 boxes in total.

Number of layers	Number of new boxes	Total number of boxes
1	1	1
2	2	2 + 1 = 3
3	3	3 + 3 = 6
4	4	4 + 6 = 10
5	5	5 + 10 = 15
6	6	6 + 15 = 21
7	7	7 + 21 = 28
8	8	8 + 28 = 36
9	9	9 + 36 = 45
10	10	10 + 45 = 55
11	11	11 + 55 = 66
12	12	12 + 66 = 78
13	13	13 + 78 = 91
14	14	14 + 91 = 105
15	15	15 + 105 = 120
16	16	16 + 120 = 136
17	17	17 + 136 = 153
18	18	18 + 153 = 171
19	19	19 + 171 = 190
20	20	20 + 190 = 210

2. Explain what pattern you used to calculate your answer.

   number of layers = number of new boxes

   total number of boxes = number of new boxes + previous total number of boxes

At-Home Help

A **3-D pattern** has a length, a width, and a height.

For example, these cubes form a 3-D pattern.

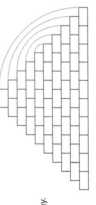

Organizing numbers in a table helps you see patterns.

For example:

Number of layers	Number of new boxes	Total number of boxes
1	1	1
2	3	3 + 1 = 4
3	5	5 + 4 = 9
4	7	7 + 9 = 16

total number of boxes
= number of new boxes
+ total number of boxes in the line above

Page 5

Number Patterns in Spreadsheets

Goal **Create and identify patterns in spreadsheets.**

Yoshi is starting a new spreadsheet for a school sale of used equipment that includes small beanbags, medium hula hoops, and large basketballs.

	A	B	C	D
1	Sports equipment sale prices			
2	Number of items	Small	Medium	Large
3	1	$1.20	$2.40	$4.40
4	2	$2.40	$4.80	$8.80
5	3	$3.60	$7.20	$13.20
6	4	$4.80	$9.60	$17.60
7	5	$6.00	$12.00	$22.00
8	6	$7.20	$14.40	$26.40
9	7	$8.40	$16.80	$30.80
10	8	$9.60	$19.20	$35.20

At-Home Help

Spreadsheets are columns of data that are related. Each number in a spreadsheet has its own cell. To extend the numbers in a column, use one or more operations.

For example:
cost of 3 red shirts in cell
B5 = B3 + B4, or B5 = B3 × A5
total cost in cell D3 = B3 + C3

	A	B	C	D
1	Shirt prices			
2	Number of shirts	Red	Green	Total cost
3	1	$10.00	$15.00	$25.00
4	2	$20.00	$30.00	$50.00
5	3	$30.00	$45.00	$75.00

1. Complete the spreadsheet.
2. Write a pattern rule for column B by looking at the numbers in that column. Then write a pattern rule for columns C and D.
   Start at $1.20 and add $1.20 to each number going down column B. Start at $2.40 and add $2.40 to each number going down column C. Start at $4.40 and add $4.40 to each number going down column D. OR Multiply the number at the top of each column by the number of items.
3. Calculate the total cost. Show your work.
   a) 6 small items and total cost
   6 x $1.20 = $7.20
   b) 3 small items, 2 medium items, and 7 large items and total cost
   3 x $1.20 = $3.60, 2 x $2.40 = $4.80, 7 x $4.40 = $30.80
   $3.60 + $4.80 + $30.80 = $39.20
   c) 10 items of each size and total cost
   10 x $1.20 = $12.00, 10 x $2.40 = $24.00, 10 x $4.40 = $44.00
   $12.00 + $24.00 + $44.00 = $80.00
4. How can you get the answer in cell C5 from other cells?
   C5 = C3 x A5 OR C5 = C3 + C4

Page 6

Test Yourself

Circle the correct answer.

Use the table to answer Questions 1 and 2.

Number of teams	Number of players
1	4
2	8
3	16
4	32
5	64

1. What is the pattern in the second column of the table?
   A. The numbers increase by 4.
   (B. The numbers double.**)** (circled)
   C. The numbers increase by 3.
   D. The numbers increase by 2.
2. How many players would there be if there were 7 teams?
   (A. 256**)** (circled) **B.** 212 **C.** 128 **D.** 246
3. Which table shows column 1 increasing by multiplying by 3 and column 2 doubling?

A.

1	8
3	10
9	12
12	14

B.

1	4
3	8
6	16
12	32

C.

1	2
2	6
4	18
8	54

D. (circled)

1	1
3	2
9	4
27	8

4. What are the next 2 numbers in this pattern?
   29, 30, 32, 35, 39, 44, ______, ______
   A. 50 and 55 **B.** 49 and 55 **(C.** 50 and 57**)** (circled) **D.** 49 and 57

Page 7

Test Yourself Page 2

5. Soccer teams go through a lot of equipment in one season. What numbers would complete the last row of this table?

Number of teams	Number of soccer nets	Number of soccer balls
1	2	5
3	6	15
5	10	25
?	?	?

A. 7, 14, 30 **B.** 7, 14, 35 **C.** 6, 15, 30 **D.** 7, 15, 35

6. What will be the number of Xs in design 4 and design 7?

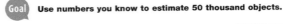

design 1

X X X
X   X

design 2

X X X X
X   X
X   X

design 3

X X X X X
X   X
X   X
X   X

A. 19 and 13 **B.** 23 and 14 **C.** 14 and 23 **D.** 13 and 19

Use this spreadsheet to answer Questions 7 and 8.

	A	B	C	D
1	Cost of Cans			
2	Number of Cans	Small	Medium	Large
3	1	$0.50	$2.00	$3.25
4	2	$1.00	$4.00	$6.50
5	3	$1.50	$6.00	$9.75

7. What would be the total cost of 4 cans of each size?

A. $22.50 **B.** $24.00 **C.** $23.50 **D.** $23.00

8. What is the pattern rule for column C?

A. Start at $2.00 and add $0.50 to each number going down column C.

B. Start at $2.00 and add $2.00 to each number going down column C.

C. Start at $2.00 and add $3.25 to each number going down column C.

D. Start at $2.00 and add $1.00 to each number going down column C.

Page 8

Estimating 50 Thousand

Use numbers you know to estimate 50 thousand objects.

1. Make a list of items in your home that you can count to 100.
Suggested answer: cereal, coins, marbles, paper, candies, paper clips, etc. You must be able to count the items.

2. Choose one item from your list. Count 2 sets of 100 and put them in a pile. *Pile should contain 200 items.*

3. How many of those piles would make a quantity of 1000 items? Show your work.
5 piles. 200 + 200 + 200 + 200 + 200 = 1000

4. How many piles of 1000 would make a quantity of 50 thousand items? Show your work.
50 piles. Adding 1000 items 50 times gives 50 thousand.

At-Home Help

To estimate 50 thousand, use familiar objects in smaller quantities.

For example: Use 100 nickels. Put them in a pile in a shoebox. About how many piles of 100 will fill the shoebox?

This answer can be used to estimate the number of boxes needed for 10 thousand nickels.

This new answer can be used to estimate the number of boxes needed for 50 thousand nickels.

5. Estimate what 50 thousand of those items would look like. How would you describe it to a friend?
Suggested answer:
50 thousand paper clips would fit into about 7 shoe boxes.

6. Use another way to estimate 50 thousand of the same item. Describe your method in detail.
Suggested answer: Count 500 items at a time and estimate how many piles of that amount would make 50 thousand items.

7. Choose another item from your list. Estimate what 50 thousand of these items would look like.
See answer to Question 5.

Page 9

Reading and Writing Numbers

Goal **Read, write, and model five-digit numbers.**

1. A file on your computer is 15 827 bytes long.
   a) Write this number in words.
   fifteen thousand eight hundred twenty-seven
   b) Write this number in expanded form.
   10 000 + 5000 + 800 + 20 + 7
   c) Draw a representation of 15 827 using base ten blocks.

Ten thousands	Thousands	Hundreds	Tens	Ones

At-Home Help

Numbers can be represented in different ways.

For example, sixteen thousand eight hundred fifty-four is

16 854 in **standard form,**

10 000 + 6000 + 800 + 50 + 4 in **expanded form,** and

using base ten blocks

2. Write each number in words and in expanded form.
   a) 35 247 thirty-five thousand two hundred forty-seven
   30 000 + 5000 + 200 + 40 + 7
   b) 40 409 forty thousand four hundred nine
   40 000 + 400 + 9
   c) 10 000 more than 50 030 sixty thousand thirty
   60 000 + 30
   d) 1000 less than 70 007 sixty-nine thousand seven
   60 000 + 9000 + 7

3. Write each number in standard form.
   a) fifty thousand eleven 50 011 **b)** 50 000 + 8000 + 60 + 3 58 063

Page 10

Renaming Numbers

Goal **Rename numbers with up to five digits.**

Suppose an ice cream company created the largest milkshake ever made. The company made a milkshake that would fill 24 382 one-litre containers.

1. Find five different combinations of full containers that would hold this milkshake. Show your work and record your answers in the table below.

V 10 000 L W 1000 L X 100 L Y 10 L Z 1 L

Suggested answer:

Container V 10 000 L	Container W 1000 L	Container X 100 L	Container Y 10 L	Container Z 1 L
2	4	3	8	2
0	24	0	38	2
2	0	43	7	12
2	3	13	5	32
1	14	3	0	82
2	4	2	18	2

At-Home Help

Numbers can be named many different ways.

For example, 22 712 can be named
- 2 ten thousands 2 thousands 7 hundreds 1 ten 2 ones
- 22 thousands 7 hundreds 12 ones
- 227 hundreds 12 ones
- 2 ten thousands 27 hundreds 1 ten 2 ones
- 22 thousands 71 tens 2 ones

... and many more combinations of thousands, hundreds, tens, and ones.

2. Draw 2 representations of 24 382 using base ten blocks.

Ten thousands	Thousands	Hundreds	Tens	Ones

Page 11

Comparing and Ordering Numbers

Goal **Compare and order numbers with up to five digits.**

1.

Blue Jays' opponents	Average attendance in Toronto	Average attendance at opponent's stadium
Orioles	20 572	27 955
Devil Rays	20 459	9048
Expos	31 571	12 782
Yankees	27 205	33 916
Angels	20 106	41 088

a) Which teams had a greater attendance when in their home stadium?

Orioles, Yankees, and Angels

b) Show the attendance of three games on the number line.

20 106   20 459   20 572

20 100   20 200   20 300   20 400   20 500   20 600

At-Home Help

When comparing and ordering numbers up to five digits, compare the digits in this order:

- ten thousand
- thousand
- hundred
- ten
- one

You can also compare and order numbers by their positions on a number line.

Inequality signs $<$ and $>$ show that one number is greater than another.

For example, $8 > 5$ is read "eight is greater than five."

$5 < 8$ is read "five is less than eight."

2. Complete each number sentence using $<$ or $>$.

a) 20 899 __>__ 20 100   **c)** 45 072 __<__ 47 072   **e)** 90 000 __>__ 89 999

b) 3687 __>__ 3675   **d)** 24 531 __>__ 23 154   **f)** 19 560 __<__ 20 650

3. Order each group of numbers from greatest to least using inequality signs.

a) 14 532   8927   41 536   50 001

50 001 > 41 536 > 14 532 > 8927

b) 67 013   6713   67 130   67 103

67 130 > 67 103 > 67 013 > 6713

Page 12

Rounding Numbers

Goal **Round numbers to the nearest ten thousand, thousand, and hundred.**

A doughnut machine has a counter to record the number of doughnuts made in a day. Yesterday the count was 36 471.

1. Round the number of doughnuts to the nearest hundred. Explain your answer.

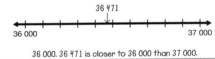

36 471

36 400   36 500

36 500. 36 471 is closer to 36 500 than 36 400.

At-Home Help

Numbers can be **rounded** to the nearest hundred, thousand, and ten thousand.

For example, 85 354 rounded

- to the nearest hundred is 85 400
- to the nearest thousand is 85 000
- to the nearest ten thousand is 90 000

A number line helps with rounding.

2. Round the number of doughnuts to the nearest thousand. Explain your answer.

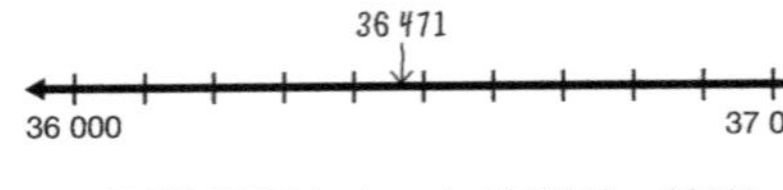

36 000. 36 471 is closer to 36 000 than 37 000.

3. Use the number line to round the number of doughnuts to the nearest ten thousand. Explain your answer.

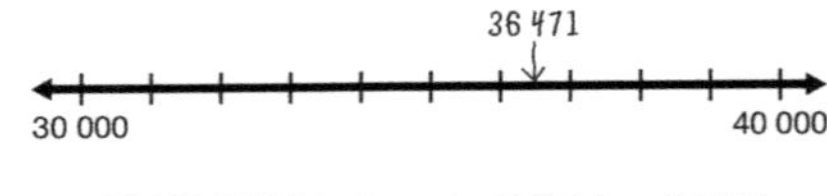

40 000. 36 471 is closer to 40 000 than 30 000.

4. Round each number to the nearest hundred, thousand, and ten thousand.

a) 45 632	**b)** 60 119	**c)** 75 456
45 600	60 100	75 500
46 000	60 000	75 000
50 000	60 000	80 000

Page 13

Communicate About Numbers in the Media

Evaluate the use of numbers in the media.

Gen is doing a science project on Canada geese. She found this information on a Web page.

> The Canada goose is well known for its V-shaped migratory flight pattern and characteristic honk.
>
> There are 11 geographical species, some with populations well over a million, and some with barely over one thousand.
>
> In 1991 there were 63 581 Canada geese in the United Kingdom.
>
> The largest goose is the giant, with a wingspan of more than 2 m and a mass under 10 kg. The smallest is the so-called "cackling" goose, which has a mass of only 1–2 kg.
>
> Between 1983 and 2000, the size of the urban wintering flock in Wichita grew from 1623 birds to over 15 000!

At-Home Help

Numbers are reported in the media to give information. These are some guidelines for reporting numbers.

- When reporting a large number, use a rounded number instead of an exact number.
- When rounding, round to the most appropriate place value.
- Use ranges so that a reader can tell the difference between least and greatest values.

Communication Checklist

☑ Did you explain your thinking?
☑ Did you use math language?
☑ Did you include the right amount of detail?

1. What numbers on the Web page do you find confusing?
   A range of numbers for populations is more useful than saying over a million, or barely over one thousand. Population in the United Kingdom could have been rounded to the nearest hundred. Size of wingspan and mass of the giant are not clear; over 2 m could be any number greater than 2, just as under 10 kg could be any number less than 10.
2. Are all the numbers described in the same way?
   No, some numbers are exact and some are rounded. Other numbers are estimates.
3. Do you agree with how the numbers 1623 and 15 000 are represented?
   Populations in Wichita should have been rounded to the same place value. 1623 should have been reported as about 1600, and 15 000 should have been rounded to the nearest hundred as well.
4. Where would you like to see a range given?
   Ranges would be useful for the populations of the 11 geographical species, and for the wingspan and mass of the giant.

Page 14

Decimal Hundredths

Read, write, and represent decimal hundredths.

1. In gym class, students practised long jump in the sandpit. Paige recorded her friends' jumps in a chart.

Long jump distances	
Sean	1.27 m
Dan	0.96 m
Lisa	1.36 m

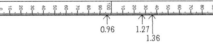

At-Home Help

The number 1.35 is read "one and thirty-five hundredths."

This number can be represented on a metre stick number line.

1.35

a) Use words to represent each distance.
   1.27: one and twenty-seven hundredths of a metre, or one metre and twenty-seven centimetres
   0.96: ninety-six hundredths of a metre, or ninety-six centimetres
   1.36: one and thirty-six hundredths of a metre, or one metre and thirty-six centimetres

b) Mark each distance on the metre stick number line.

0 10 20 30 40 50 60 70 80 90 100 10 20 30 40 50 60 70 80 90 100

0.96 1.27 1.36

2. Write each decimal number in standard form.
   a) six and seven hundredths 6.07
   b) five and ten hundredths 5.10
   c) fourteen and fifteen hundredths 14.15
   d) twenty-six hundredths 0.26
3. Write a decimal number in standard form to fit each description.
   a) 1 tenth greater than 4.16 4.26
   b) 1 greater than 4.16 5.16
   c) 1 hundredth greater than 4.16 4.17
4. Sally's best long jump distance is 1.63 m. Write in words how you would read her distance.
   one and sixty-three hundredths of a metre, or one metre and sixty-three centimetres

Page 15

Exploring Equivalent Decimals

Goal **Rename a decimal tenth as a decimal hundredth.**

1. Write a decimal tenth to describe the part of the grid that is shaded.
   0.6

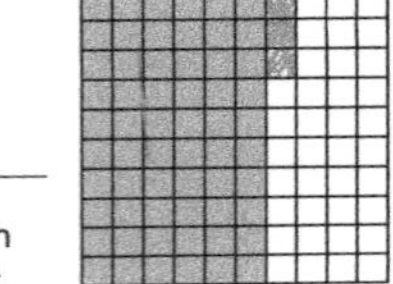

2. Write a decimal hundredth to describe the same part.
   0.60

3. Shade in three more squares on the grid.
4. Write a decimal number for the total shaded part.
   0.63
5. Write two ways to read this decimal number.
   sixty-three hundredths
   or six tenths three hundredths

At-Home Help

Some decimal numbers can be read as tenths or hundredths.

For example, 0.30 can be read as
- "three tenths zero hundredths" or
- "thirty hundredths"

0.30 can be represented by the shaded part on this decimal grid.

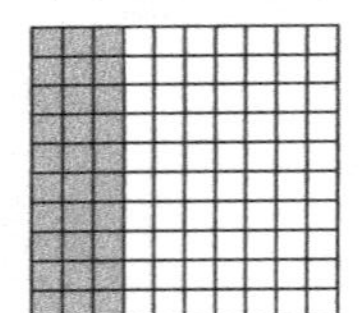

6. Show each decimal number on a grid by shading the appropriate squares.

   a) 0.70 **b)** 0.34 **c)** 0.07

7. Which of these decimal hundredths can be expressed as decimal tenths? Give reasons for your choice.

   0.70 0.07 0.77 0.17

   0.70. It is the only number that has a 0 in the hundredths place value.
   All the other numbers have a 7 in the hundredths place value.

Page 16

Rounding Decimals

Goal **Interpret rounded decimals, and round decimals to the nearest whole and to the nearest tenth.**

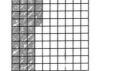

1. Sarah rounded the length of her room to the nearest tenth of a metre. The length is 3.5 m.

   3.4 3.5 3.6

   a) Write the numbers that round up from 3.4 to 3.5.
   If the number has a hundredth decimal place,
   it can be: 3.45, 3.46, 3.47, 3.48, and 3.49.

   b) Write the numbers that round down to 3.5.
   If the number has a hundredth decimal place,
   it can be: 3.50, 3.51, 3.52, 3.53, and 3.54.

At-Home Help

Decimal numbers can be rounded to the nearest whole number and the nearest tenth.

For example,
- 2.76 rounds up to 2.8
- 2.83 rounds down to 2.8

A number line helps with rounding.

2.76 2.83
2.7 2.8 2.9

Both 2.76 and 2.83 round up to 3.

2. Lori needs 4.47 m of ribbon for a school play.

   a) How much ribbon should she buy if ribbon is sold in lengths of whole metres?
   5 m

   b) How much ribbon should she buy if ribbon is sold in lengths of tenths of a metre?
   4.5 m

3. Round each number to the nearest whole number and the nearest tenth.

a) 3.65	**b)** 7.03	**c)** 0.79	**d)** 7.93
4	7	1	8
3.7	7.0	0.8	7.9

4. A gardener needs 8.74 m of hose to water a lawn.

   a) Round that length to the nearest tenth of a metre. 8.7 m

   b) Should he buy a hose of that length or a different length? Explain.
   He should buy a hose that is longer than 8.7 m, otherwise the hose will be too short.

5. A number rounded to the nearest tenth is 7.9. What might the number be? List three possibilities.
   If the number has a hundredth decimal place, it can be:
   7.85, 7.86, 7.87, 7.88, 7.89, 7.90, 7.91, 7.92, 7.93, or 7.94.

Comparing and Ordering Decimals

Goal **Compare and order numbers to decimal hundredths.**

1. Four members of the Sea Lions team competed in a relay race at a recent swim meet.

Swimmer	Stroke	Time
Zoe	Butterfly	2.54 s
Karilyn	Back	2.36 s
Andrea	Breast	2.75 s
Tanya	Freestyle	2.17 s

a) Who took the longest to swim her part of the race? What was her time?

Andrea, 2.75 s

b) Who swam the fastest? What was her time?

Tanya, 2.17 s

c) Order the times from shortest to longest.

2.17 s, 2.36 s, 2.54 s, 2.75 s

2. Draw a representation of Zoe's time using base ten blocks. Draw a hundreds block to represent 1.

Ones	Tenths	Hundredths
□ □	|||||	::

3. Complete each number sentence using < or >.

a) 3.94 _<_ 3.99 **b)** 46.03 _<_ 47.06 **c)** 20.80 _>_ 20.08

4. Order each group of numbers from least to greatest using inequality signs.

a) 0.23, 4.75, 6.35, 0.79, 4.57 *0.23 < 0.79 < 4.57 < 4.75 < 6.35*

b) 5.15, 1.55, 0.51, 15.01 *0.51 < 1.55 < 5.15 < 15.01*

c) 0.31, 0.13, 0.03, 0.01 *0.01 < 0.03 < 0.13 < 0.31*

d) 6.1, 6.5, 6.06, 6.75, 6 *6 < 6.06 < 6.1 < 6.5 < 6.75*

Counting Money

Goal **Estimate, count, read, and write money amounts to $1000.**

1.

At-Home Help

When counting money, first count the bills. Then count the coins.

For example:
The amount shown is $420.80.

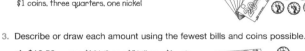

Different combinations of bills and coins can make the same amount.

a) Estimate the total. Explain your estimate.

Suggested answer: $620.

I counted the bills.

b) Count the amount. Record it.

$623.80

2. Describe or draw another set of coins and bills that make the same amount as in Question 1.

Suggested answer: six $100 bills, one $20 bill, three $1 coins, three quarters, one nickel

3. Describe or draw each amount using the fewest bills and coins possible.

a) $16.50 *one $10 bill, one $5 bill, one $1 coin, two quarters*

b) $281.30 *two $100 bills, one $50 bill, one $20 bill, one $10 bill, one $1 coin, one quarter, one nickel*

4. Describe or draw $281.30 using more bills and coins.

Suggested answer: five $50 bills, six $5 bills, one $1 coin, three dimes

Page 19

Test Yourself

Circle the correct answer.

1. Which container would you choose to hold 50 thousand nickels?

   A. 5 shoeboxes B. 5 lunchboxes C. 5 bathtubs D. 5 recycling boxes

2. Which representation is *not* the number 23 709?

   A. 20 000 + 3000 + 700 + 9

   B. 10 000 + 13 000 + 500 + 209

   C. 1 ten thousand + 13 thousand + 5 hundred + 20 tens + 9

   D. 10 000 less than 25 709

3. Which number sentence is incorrect?

   A. 20 899 < 28 100 B. 5697 > 5675

   C. 54 072 > 45 072 **D. 34 521 < 34 125**

4. Which number is rounded to the nearest hundred?

   A. 45 630 B. 75 000 **C. 61 300** D. 10 001

5. What would 89 605 rounded to the nearest thousand be?

   A. 89 000 B. 89 600 **C. 90 000** D. 90 600

6. Which number on the metre stick number line does the arrow point to?

   A. 1.60 B. 1.50 **C. 1.57** D. 1.55

7. Which description fits for the number 2.67?

   A. two and six tenths B. twenty-six and seven hundredths

   C. two hundred sixty-seven **D. two and sixty-seven hundredths**

8. Which number is 1 tenth greater than 2.67?

   A. 3.78 B. 2.78 C. 3.67 **D. 2.77**

9. What would 7.86 rounded to the nearest tenth be?

   A. 8.0 B. 7.8 C. 8.6 **D. 7.9**

Page 20

Evaluating Survey Results

Goal **Decide whether the results of a survey would likely apply to other groups of people.**

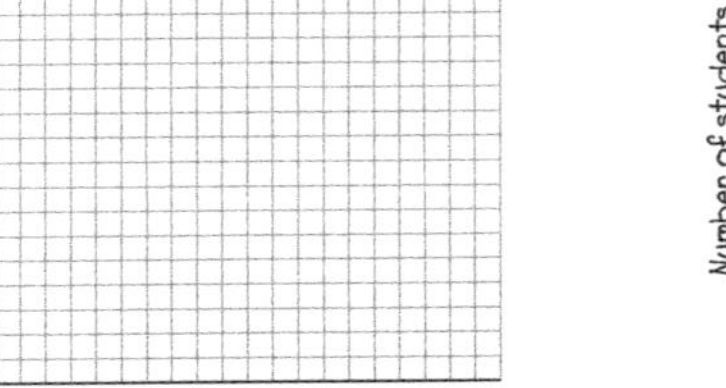

At-Home Help

Biased results are results of a survey that apply to one group but are not likely to apply to another group.

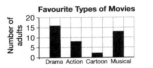

1. Which type of movie was the favourite for the adults surveyed? Explain why adults would prefer these movies.

   Suggested answer: Drama movies were the favourite because these movies usually have more involved plots, and more mature ideas or themes.

2. Explain why you think the overall results are accurate for this group of people.

   Suggested answer: Younger people prefer the other types of movies. Adults also prefer musicals which is why these movies rated high in the results. Cartoons are more suited to young children, and action movies to teenagers or young adults.

3. Would the results of this survey likely apply to students in a Grade 1 class? Explain.

   No, young children would not be interested in any of these types of movies except for cartoons.

4. Predict the results if your class were surveyed. Create a graph of your prediction.

   Suggested answer:

   Favourite Types of Movies

   Number of students: 0, 5, 10, 15, 20, 25, 30

   Drama, Action, Cartoon, Musical

   Type of movie

Page 21

Broken-Line Graphs

Goal **Make and use a broken-line graph to identify trends.**

1. **Monthly Precipitation in Toronto, Canada**

Precipitation (mm): 150, 125, 100, 75, 50, 25, 0

Jan. Feb. Mar. Apr. May Jun. Jul. Aug. Sep. Oct. Nov. Dec.

Month

At-Home Help

A **trend** in a graph refers to the general direction of data. The data can increase, decrease, or stay the same.

A **broken-line graph** is a graph in which data points are connected point by point.

What trends do you see in this broken-line graph?

Precipitation is greatest in winter and least in summer. From May to July, amount of precipitation decreases steadily. Amount of precipitation in July and August is the same. From August to December, amount of precipitation increases significantly.

2. Make a broken-line graph of monthly precipitation in Sydney, Australia.

Monthly Precipitation in Sydney, Australia (mm)

Jan.	Feb.	Mar.	Apr.	May	Jun.	Jul.	Aug.	Sept.	Oct.	Nov.	Dec.
10	15	40	70	75	40	35	15	60	50	20	10

Monthly Precipitation in Sydney, Australia

Precipitation (mm): 100, 90, 80, 70, 60, 50, 40, 30, 20, 10, 0

Jan. Feb. Mar. Apr. May Jun. Jul. Aug. Sep. Oct. Nov. Dec.

Month

3. Compare your broken-line graph to the graph in Question 1. How are they similar?

Both graphs show precipitation during the year. Also, both graphs show the same trend based on season: the greatest precipitation is in winter and the least in summer.

Page 22

Interpreting Circle Graphs

Goal **Calculate the number represented by each part of a circle graph.**

Thirty-two Grade 5 students answered a survey question about their favourite subject and most difficult subject. These circle graphs show the results.

Favourite Subject

Math, Gym, Reading, Science, Art

Most Difficult Subject

Math, Reading, Science

At-Home Help

A **circle graph** is a graph that displays data using a circle. Each section of the circle represents a data point. Circle graphs are used for data that represent parts of a whole.

For example, this circle graph shows the eye colour for a class of 24 students.

Eye Colour

green, brown, blue

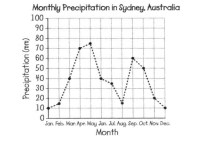

12 students have brown eyes. This number represents $\frac{1}{2}$ the class, so $\frac{1}{2}$ the circle represents brown.

6 students have green eyes. This number represents $\frac{1}{4}$ of the class, so $\frac{1}{4}$ of the circle represents green.

6 students have blue eyes. This number represents $\frac{1}{4}$ of the class, so $\frac{1}{4}$ of the circle represents blue.

1. What fraction represents each part in the Favourite Subject graph?

   Math $\frac{1}{4}$ Gym $\frac{1}{4}$ Art $\frac{1}{4}$

   Reading $\frac{1}{8}$ Science $\frac{1}{8}$

2. How many students are represented by each subject in the Favourite Subject graph?

   Math 8 Gym 8 Art 8

   Reading 4 Science 4

3. How many students are represented by each subject in the Most Difficult Subject graph?

   Math 16 Science 8 Reading 8

4. Suppose the survey applied to 40 students. How would your answers to Questions 2 and 3 change?

   Favourite Subject: Math 10, Gym 10, Art 10, Reading 5, Science 5

   Most Difficult Subject: Math 20, Science 10, Reading 10

Page 23

Bar Graphs with Intervals

Goal **Use the range to estimate the size of intervals to construct a bar graph.**

Akiko recorded the number of metres jumped during a triple jump. She collected data from 24 students in her class.

Metres jumped (triple jump)

15	18	4	12	10	6
10	20	15	7	17	10
9	13	5	8	16	12
14	19	3	15	11	13

1. What is the range of the data?

17 m (3 m to 20 m)

2. How many bars would you use if you made a bar graph of the data? Explain your choice based on the range. Include the intervals in your answer.

4. Since data go from 3 m to 20 m, use intervals of 5 m.

Intervals will be: 0–5, 6–10, 11–15, and 16–20.

3. **a)** Make a tally chart for the data.

Metres jumped (m)	Number of students
0–5	|||
6–10	卌 ||
11–15	卌 ||||
16–20	卌

b) Draw a bar graph using your tally chart.

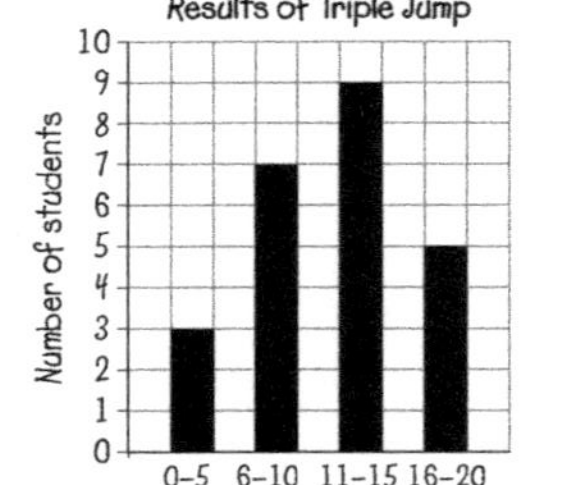

At-Home Help

Range is the spread of data. To find the range, look for the least and greatest data points.

For example, the range of the data is 53 to 80, which is 27 beats.

Heart Rates (beats in 1 min)

70	60	53
80	74	70
70	72	78

Before drawing some bar graphs, it is better to group data. **Intervals** refer to the size of the groups. All intervals should be the same size.

For example: Six students cycled between 0 and 4 km, and 3 students cycled between 5 and 9 km. The intervals on the graph are 0–4 and 5–9.

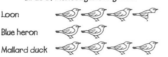

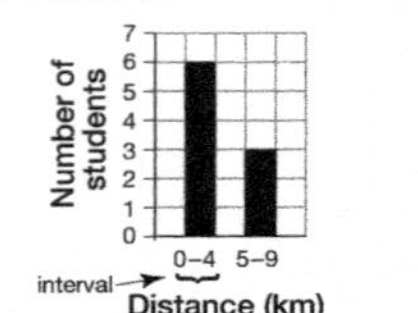

Page 24

Pictographs

Goal **Use whole and partial symbols to display data on a pictograph.**

Jose counted the number of birds on Memesagamesing Lake in Northern Ontario in July.

Type of bird	Number
Loon	75
Blue heron	40
Mallard duck	81
Cormorant	28

1. Draw a pictograph to show the data using whole and partial symbols. Make sure you show the scale.

Birds of Memesagamesing Lake

Loon

Blue heron

Mallard duck

Cormorant

= 20 birds

2. Explain how you decided on the number of whole and partial symbols to show the number of birds.

I didn't want to use too many symbols, so I used a whole symbol for 20 birds, half a symbol for 10 birds, and a quarter symbol for 5 birds.

3. Why are 81 and 28 difficult numbers to represent on the pictograph?

It is difficult to accurately represent 81 and 28 using whole or partial symbols.

For example, 81 is very close to 80 so 4 symbols can be used to represent this number.

Similarly, 28 is very close to 30 so $1\frac{1}{2}$ symbols can be used to represent this number.

4. What other scale could you use for the pictograph?

Suggested answer:  = 10 birds

At-Home Help

A **pictograph** is a graph that displays data using symbols. Each symbol represents a fixed number. Some data points can only be represented by using partial symbols.

For example, since 1 symbol represents 10 pies, 15 pies is represented with $1\frac{1}{2}$ symbols.

Types of Pies

Apple

Blueberry

Banana cream

Lemon meringue

= 10 pies

A **scale** on a pictograph shows the number represented by each symbol.

The scale for the pictograph above says that 1 symbol represents 10 pies.

Changing the Appearance of a Graph

Goal **Explain how changing the scale of a graph can affect its appearance.**

Drake made a graph to show the results of a survey about favourite desserts.

Favourite Desserts

Dessert	Number of people
Pie	150
Cake	127
Ice cream	106
Fruit cup	95

Favourite Desserts

Number of people: 0, 100, 200, 300

Pie, Cake, Ice cream, Fruit cup

Dessert

1. How does the scale affect the appearance of this graph?

   The scale makes the graph look like there is very little difference between the preferences for each dessert.

2. Make another bar graph with a different scale to make the difference between the bars appear more dramatic.

At-Home Help

The **scale** of a bar or line graph refers to the divisions on both the vertical and horizontal axes.

The scale of a graph can affect the appearance of data.

For example: The scale on the first graph goes from 0 to 200. This makes the difference between the bars not very clear.

The scale on the second graph goes from 0 to 20. The difference between the bars is very clear.

Favourite Colours

Number of people: 0, 25, 50, 75, 100, 125, 150, 175, 200

Red, Yellow, Blue, Green

Colour

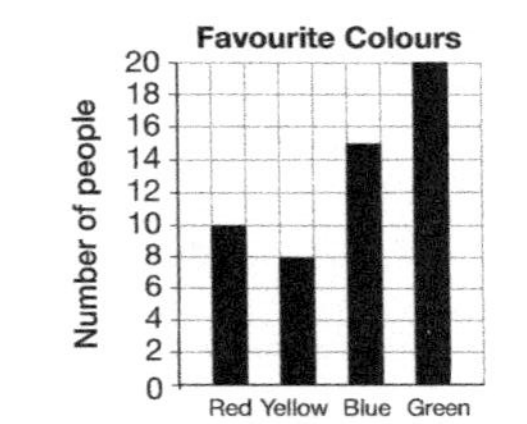

Graphing with Technology

Use graphing software to organize and display data.

Anton collected different types of materials for recycling. He was paid for each item he collected.

- 12 tins at 2¢ per tin
- 18 plastic containers at 5¢ per container
- 7 cardboard boxes at 10¢ per box
- 9 glass bottles at 15¢ per bottle

1. Organize the data using a table or spreadsheet.

	A	B	C	D	E
1	Number of items	Tin (2 ¢ each)	Plastic (5 ¢ each)	Cardboard (10 ¢ each)	Glass (15 ¢ each)
2	1	$0.02	$0.05	$0.10	$0.15
3	2	$0.04	$0.10	$0.20	$0.30
4	3	$0.06	$0.15	$0.30	$0.45
5	4	$0.08	$0.20	$0.40	$0.60
6	5	$0.10	$0.25	$0.50	$0.75
7	6	$0.12	$0.30	$0.60	$0.90
8	7	$0.14	$0.35	$0.70	$1.05
9	8	$0.16	$0.40		$1.20
10	9	$0.18	$0.45		$1.35
11	10	$0.20	$0.50		
12	11	$0.22	$0.55		
13	12	$0.24	$0.60		
14	13		$0.65		
15	14		$0.70		
16	15		$0.75		
17	16		$0.80		
18	17		$0.85		
19	18		$0.90		

2. Construct a graph of your choice that would represent the data well. Use paper and pencil or a spreadsheet.

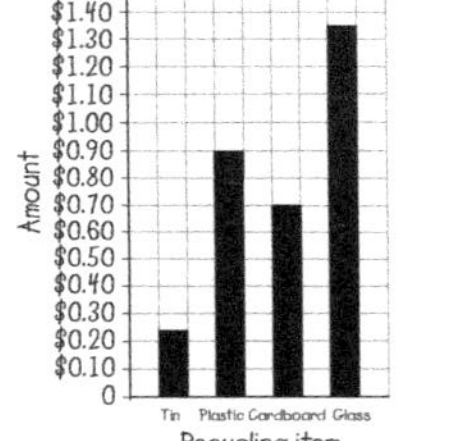

At-Home Help

A **spreadsheet** has columns and rows to organize data. Spreadsheets usually have columns of numbers that represent the result of math calculations.

Page 27

Mean and Mode

Calculate the mean and identify the mode of a set of data.

1. What is the mode of this group of numbers? Explain.

   6, 7, 4, 4, 9, 3, 2, 3, 7, 4, 9

   Mode = 4. This number appears most often.

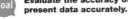

2. **a)** What is the mean of 6, 7, and 8?

   7

   b) What is the mean of 12, 14, and 16?

   14

   c) What do you notice about the mean of each group of numbers in Parts **a)** and **b)**?

   The mean is the middle number in both parts.

3. Calculate the mean and identify the mode of 32, 38, 33, and 33.

   mean = 34 mode = 33

4. Create a group of four numbers that has a mode of 4 and a mean of 5.

   Suggested answer: 4, 9, 4, 3

At-Home Help

Mean is the rearrangement of numbers to make equal shares.

For example, the mean of 0, 5, 1, 1, 3 is 2.

0 5 1 1 3

2 2 2 2 2

Mode is the number that occurs most often in a group of numbers.

For example, the mode of 0, 5, 1, 1, 3 is 1.

Page 28

Communicate About Graphs

Evaluate the accuracy of a graph and suggest ways to present data accurately.

Leo recorded the cross-country running times of each student in his class. He then drew a bar graph.

Time (min)

4	8	4	12	10	6
13	7	17	5	9	15
9	16	5	8	6	14
14	9	5	15	11	7

Leo's graph is not accurate.

Cross-Country Running Times

Time (min)

1. What is missing from the graph?

   The vertical axis has no label.

2. How is the graph not accurate? Use the Communication Checklist to help you.

   The intervals along the horizontal and vertical axes are not equal.

   The bars are not the same width.

3. Sketch a more accurate graph.

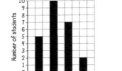

   Cross-Country Running Times

   Number of students

   Time (min)

At-Home Help

Graphs show information accurately if these points are followed.

- All graphs should have a title.
- On a bar graph or a line graph, the horizontal and vertical axes should be labelled.
- The intervals along the horizontal axis should be equal. Similarly, the intervals along the vertical axis should be equal.
- All bars on a bar graph should be the same width.
- On a pictograph, all data points should be represented by the same symbol. The overall size of the symbol should also be the same.
- On any graph, the scale should be appropriate for the data points.

Communication Checklist

☑ Did you check the scale?

☑ Did you include all of the data?

☑ Did you draw and label the graph correctly?

Page 29

Test Yourself

Circle the correct answer.

1. Paul surveyed 50 boys in his school. He asked them to list their favourite sport.

Sport	Number of boys
Bowling	5
Soccer	32
Curling	3
Cross country running	10

Which group would probably be close to the results of Paul's group?

A. senior citizens **B.** Grade 5 girls **C.** parents **D.** toddlers

2. What are the mode and mean of this group of numbers?

5, 4, 9, 7, 5, 6, 3, 1

A. 5 and 4 **B.** 4 and 5 **C.** 4 and 6 **D.** 5 and 5

3. What is the trend in this broken-line graph?

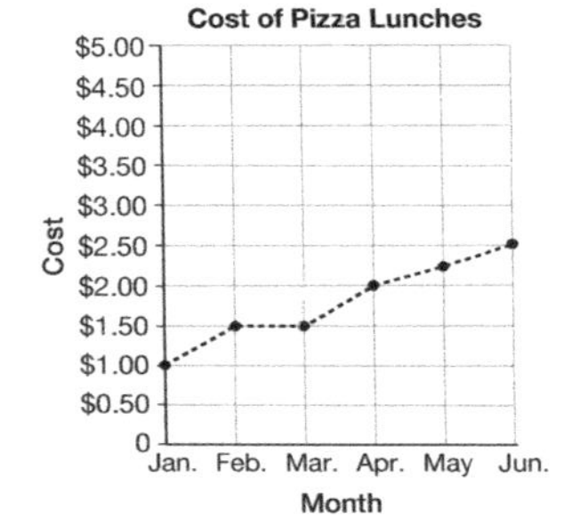

A. gradual decrease in cost **B.** no change in cost

C. gradual increase in cost **D.** steep increase in cost

Page 30

Test Yourself Page 2

Use these data to answer Questions 4, 5, and 6.

Time (min)

20	36	5	49	21	57	36
16	67	16	60	23	44	51
10	21	44	9	46	68	32
63	37	8	68	47	55	19

4. What is the range of the data?

A. 63 **B.** 61 **C.** 62 **D.** 64

5. What interval would be the best choice to make a bar graph?

A. 2 **B.** 5 **C.** 8 **D.** 15

6. How many numbers would be in the interval 31–45?

A. 4 **B.** 6 **C.** 5 **D.** 7

Use the pictograph to answer Questions 7 and 8.

100 students were surveyed about their favourite ride at the fair.

Favourite Rides

Ferris wheel ☐☐▯

Bumper cars ▯

Roller coaster ☐☐☐☐▫

Swing ☐▫

☐ = 12 students

7. What other scale could be used for this pictograph?

A. ☐ = 10 students **B.** ☐ = 16 students

C. ☐ = 15 students **D.** ☐ = 14 students

8. If the scale were changed to ☐ = 20 students, how would 65 students choosing the roller coaster be shown?

A. ☐☐ **B.** ☐☐▫ **C.** ☐☐☐▫ **D.** ☐☐▯

Page 31

Adding and Subtracting Using Mental Math

Use mental math strategies to add and subtract.

1. Use mental math to calculate each answer. Explain your strategy.
   a) 54 + 29 Round both numbers to nearest 5 before adding. Then adjust sum to get exact answer. 55 + 30 = 85, 85 − 2 = 83
   b) 88 + 32 Regroup numbers, then add. (88 + 2) + 30 = 120
   c) 100 − 48 Round second number to nearest 10 before subtracting. Then adjust difference to get exact answer. 100 − 50 = 50, 50 + 2 = 52
   d) 70 − 14 Regroup numbers, then subtract. (70 − 10) − 4 = 56
2. The Boston Marathon is a 42 km run. Aaron ran the marathon in 100 min.

   0 km 10 km 20 km
   0 min 20 min 40 min

   Use mental math to calculate Aaron's distance and time at each point during the 42 km run. Describe your strategy.

Distance	0 km	10 km	20 km	25 km	30 km	35 km	42 km
Time	0 min	20 min	40 min	55 min	70 min	85 min	100 min

Sample answer:
Aaron took 40 min to run 20 km during the first half of the run. Since there were 4 more points during the run, each point was about an extra 5 km. He did each 5 km in 15 min (60 ÷ 4 = 15).
I think he sped up at the end so he did 7 km in 15 min.

At-Home Help

Rounding is a mental math strategy for adding and subtracting numbers. When you round, you will likely need to adjust your answer to get the exact answer.

For example:

23 + 58 can be rounded to 20 + 60 = 80. 23 is 3 more than 20 and 58 is 2 less than 60. So adjust answer by adding 1. Answer is 81.

76 − 40 can be rounded to 80 − 40 = 40. 76 is 4 less than 80. So adjust answer by subtracting 4. Answer is 36.

Regrouping is another mental math strategy for adding and subtracting numbers. Regroup numbers into 5s or 10s to make calculations easier.

For example:

43 + 92 can be regrouped as (43 + 2) + 90. Answer is 45 + 90 = 135.

80−19 can be regrouped as (80 −10) − 9. Answer is 70 − 9 = 61.

Page 32

Estimating Sums and Differences

Estimate sums and differences and justify your strategy.

1. Estimate which calculations are reasonable. Explain how you estimated.
   a) 2997 + 1158 = 4155
   Reasonable because 3000 + 1100 = 4100, which is close to 4155.
   b) 6053 − 4802 = 2251
   Not reasonable because 6000 − 4800 = 1200, which is less than 2251.
   c) 8095 − 2559 = 5536
   Reasonable because 8100 − 2500 = 5600, which is close to 5536.
   d) 3273 + 897 + 4298 = 8238
   Not reasonable because 3300 + 900 + 4300 = 8500, which is greater than 8238.
2. The chart shows data for hockey players in a town.

Hockey players		Number of players
Boys	novice level	4854
	atom level	5013
Girls	novice level	3955
	atom level	2081

How many more hockey players are boys than girls? Estimate to check the reasonableness of your calculation. Show your work and justify your choice of estimation strategies.

Estimate		Actual answer	
Boys	4900 + 5000 = 9900	Boys	4854 + 5013 = 9867
Girls	4000 + 2100 = 6100	Girls	3955 + 2081 = 6036
Difference	9900 − 6100 = 3800	Difference	9867 − 6036 = 3831

I rounded the number of players to the nearest hundred before adding.
My answer of 3800 was very close to the actual answer of 3831.

At-Home Help

To check the reasonableness of a calculation, estimate the answer using one or more mental math strategies.

For example:

To check if 1198 +1510 + 1454 + 1354 = 8516 is reasonable, use rounding and regrouping. Then estimate the sum.

1200 +1500 + 1400 + (50 + 1350)
= 1200 + 1500 + 1400 + 1400
= 5500

So the sum 8516 is not reasonable.

Page 33

Adding Whole Numbers

Goal **Add 3 four-digit whole numbers using paper and pencil.**

1. Estimate and then add. Show your work.

Sample answers:

a) 2549 + 3288 + 7426

Estimate:	23
3000	140
3000	1 100
+ 7000	12 000
13 000	13 263

b) 5283 + 6094 + 846

Estimate:	13
5000	210
6000	1 000
+ 800	11 000
11 800	12 223

c) 7106 + 5882 + 4037

Estimate:	16 000
7000	900
6000	110
+ 4000	15
17 000	17 025

At-Home Help

When adding several whole numbers together, you can estimate the sum using rounding.

For example:

		Estimate
	1899	2000
	3045	3000
	+ 2357	+ 2000
Actual answer →	7301	7000

d) 1093 + 2764 + 898

Estimate:

1000 + 3000 + 900 + = 4900

1093
2764
+ 898
3000
1500
240
15
4755

e) 7549 + 3808 + 4261

Estimate:

7500 + 4000 + 4000 + = 15 500

7 549
3 808
+ 4 261
14 000
1 500
100
18
15 618

2. Seven students wrote stories, each with a different number of words. What 3 stories have a total between 7000 and 8000 words? Show your work.

Student	Number of words
Raj	2419
Sima	3256
Ben	3780
Cathy	2934
Bill	4087
Dan	2593
Kew	1806

Student	Estimated number of words
Raj	2400
Sima	3300
Ben	3800
Cathy	2900
Bill	4100
Dan	2600
Kew	1800

Possible combinations: Raj, Sima, Kew (7481 words)
Raj, Cathy, Dan (7946 words)
Raj, Cathy, Kew (7159 words)
Sima, Cathy, Kew (7996 words)
Sima, Dan, Kew (7655 words)
Cathy, Dan, Kew (7333 words)

Page 34

Solve Two-Step Problems

Goal **Select operations and solve two-step problems.**

You will need a calculator.

1. Rachel shot baskets each day for a period of 2 weeks. She shot a total of 2260 baskets. Rachel shot 100 more baskets each day during the last 3 days. How many shots per day did she take during the first week?

total number of baskets shot not including extras:
2260 – 300 = 1960 baskets

number of baskets shot per day during first week:
1960 ÷ 14 = 140 baskets

At-Home Help

When solving word problems, follow these steps.

- First write down what you are asked to find out.
- Then look at the information you are given.
- Decide what information is important.
- Make a plan.
- Choose operations that use the given information to solve the problem.
- Check if your answer is reasonable.

Remember to show all your work.

2. Mr. James is 49 years of age. His sister is 45 years of age. What is the difference in age in each of these units of time? Show your work.

a) months

49 – 45 = 4 years
4 x 12 = 48 months

b) weeks

49 – 45 = 4 years
4 x 52 = 208 weeks

c) days

49 – 45 = 4 years
4 x 365 = 1460 days

3. A school has a total of 1258 students. There are 297 primary students and 364 junior students. How many senior students are there?

297 + 364 = 661 primary and junior students
1258 – 661 = 597 senior students

Page 35

Communicate About a Choice of Calculation Method

Goal **Justify your choice of calculation method and explain each step in solving a problem.**

1. Marcus was at Youth Camp. He had a total of 3025 points that he could spend at the camp store. About how many points does he have left?

Camp store item	Cost in points
Candy	875
Ice cream	436
Chips	297
Drinks	980

Alana wrote this rough copy to solve the problem.

> I only need to estimate, because the problem asks "about" how many points are left.
> Marcus spent about 2600 points.
> He had about 3000 points in total.
> He should have about 400 points left.

Write a good copy. Use the Communication Checklist to help you.

I used mental math to round the numbers in the chart.
I then added the rounded numbers together to find out how much Marcus spent.
900 + 400 + 300 + 1000 = 2600 points
I rounded the total number of points to 3000.
I subtracted how much Marcus spent from his total points.
3000 − 2600 = 400
Marcus has about 400 points.

At-Home Help

When writing a solution to a word problem, first write a rough copy.
- If the problem does not ask for an exact answer, use estimation to find the answer.
- You can use rounding, regrouping, or any other mental math strategy.
- Check if your answer is reasonable.

Then write a good copy explaining all your steps.

Remember to show all your work.

Communication Checklist
☑ Did you explain your thinking?
☑ Did you show all the steps?
☑ Did you use math language?

2. Richard and his friends collected a total of 4548 old coins. The chart shows some of the coins.

Type of coin	Number of coins
Penny	789
Nickel	1516
Dime	934

a) Richard forgot to list quarters in the chart. About how many quarters were collected?

1300 quarters

b) About how many more pennies would be needed to match the number of nickels?

700 more pennies

Page 36

Adding Decimals

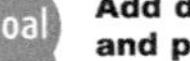

Goal **Add decimal tenths and hundredths using base ten blocks and pencil and paper.**

1. Estimate and then add. Show your work.

a) 8.3 + 5.7
Estimate: 8 + 6 = 14
14.0

b) 6.89 + 5.43
Estimate: 7 + 5 = 12
12.32

c) 5.16 + 3.87
Estimate: 5 + 4 = 9
9.03

d) 4.93 + 0.82 + 6.95
Estimate: 5 + 1 + 7 = 13
12.70

2. Estimate and then calculate the total distance. Show your work.

0.85 km and 5.28 km

Estimate	Actual answer
1 km	0.85 km
+ 5 km	+ 5.28 km
6 km	6.13 km

3. Dmitri added 2.78 and 5.49. He also added 278 and 549. He compared his answers.

a) Explain how the answers are the same.

The numbers being added in each case have identical digits. Also, both sums have identical digits.

b) Explain how the answers are different.

The position of the decimal point is not the same in both addition questions. This means that although the digits are identical, their corresponding place values are not.

At-Home Help

Decimal tenths and hundredths are added using the same rules as whole numbers.
- It is easier to add vertically if the decimal points are aligned.
- Add place values that are the same.
- If the sum of a place value is 10 or more, regroup using the next greater place value.
- Check your answer using estimation.

For example:

		Estimate
	1.76	2
	+ 0.45	+ 0
Actual answer →	2.21	2

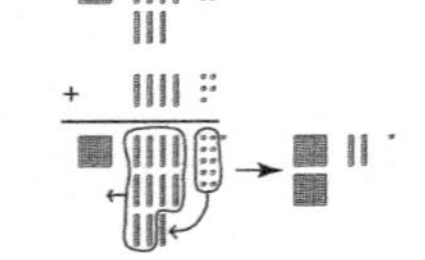

Page 37

Adding Money

Goal **Use various methods to calculate the cost of purchases.**

1. Estimate and then add. Show your work.

a) $23.65 + 19.88 + 14.63 = $58.16
Estimate: 20 + 20 + 15 = 55

b) $18.63 + 12.88 = $31.51
Estimate: 20 + 12 = 32

c) $52.64 + 0.86 + 8.29 = $61.79
Estimate: 50 + 1 + 10 = 61

d) $2.65 + $1.74
Estimate: 3 + 2 = 5
$2.65 + 1.74 = $4.39

e) $13.43 + $7.09
Estimate: 13 + 7 = 20
$13.43 + 7.09 = $20.52

f) $48.91 + $0.72
Estimate: 49 + 1 = 50
$48.91 + .72 = $49.63

At-Home Help

Adding money amounts is the same as adding decimal hundredths.

Use estimation to check your sums.

For example:

		Estimate
	$29.95	$30
	+ 35.95	+ 36
Actual answer →	$65.90	$66

2. **a)** Create a problem involving buying 2 or more video games. Solve your problem. Show your estimate and actual answer.

Name of video game	Cost
Hockey Super Stars	$26.50
World Cup Soccer	$23.78
Race Car Rally	$10.45
Wave Surfer	$9.99

Suggested answer: Mohammed bought birthday presents for his 2 brothers. He bought 1 Race Car Rally and 2 Wave Surfer games. How much did Mohammed spend on all the games?

Mohammed spent $30.43.

Estimate	Actual answer
$10	$10.45
+ 2(10)	9.99
	+ 9.99
$30	$30.43

b) Explain how you calculated your answer. Then check your answer.

Since Mohammed bought 2 games that are the same, I can multiply the cost of the game by 2.
Wave Surfer: 2 x $9.99 = $19.98
Then I find the sum. $10.45 + $19.98 = $30.43
Mohammed spent $30.43.

To check my answer, I round the cost of the video games and then estimate the sum.
Wave Surfer: 2 x $10 = $20
Total: $10 + $20 = $30
Mohammed spent about $30.

Page 38

Making Change

Goal **Calculate change from purchases.**

1. Calculate the total cost and the amount of change.

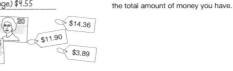

a) $12.94, $2.51

(cost) $15.45, (change) $4.55

b)

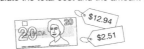

$14.36, $11.90, $3.89

(cost) $30.15, (change) $4.85

c)

$36.59, $18.71

(cost) $55.30, (change) $4.70

d)

$13.98, $39.07, $43.65

(cost) $96.70, (change) $3.30

At-Home Help

To calculate change from purchases, first find the total cost.

You can use estimation if you want to find the approximate cost.

Then subtract the total cost from the total amount of money you have.

2. You have been given $60 for your birthday.

Item	Cost
Shirt	$25.85
Binder	$15.99
Sunglasses	$9.43
Video game	$17.68
Book	$23.97

a) Choose 2 items you can buy. Calculate the total cost. Then choose 3 items and calculate the total cost. Show your work.

Suggested answers:

Items	Cost
shirt and binder	$25.85 + $15.99 = $41.84
binder, sunglasses, and video game	$15.99 + $9.43 + $17.68 = $43.10

b) How much change will you receive? Show your work.

(using suggested answers given)

Items	Change
shirt and binder	$60.00 – $41.84 = $18.16
binder, sunglasses, and video game	$60.00 – $43.10 = $16.90

Page 39

Subtracting Decimals

Goal **Use pencil and paper to subtract decimal tenths and hundredths.**

1. Estimate and then subtract. Show your work.

a) 9.85 − 7.14
Estimate: 10 − 7 = 3
2.71

b) 6.03 − 1.57
Estimate: 6 − 2 = 4
4.46

c) 7.00 − 4.96
Estimate: 7 − 5 = 2
2.04

d) 8.67 − 5.82
Estimate: 9 − 6 = 3
2.85

e) 7.6 − 3.8
Estimate: 8 − 4 = 4
3.8

f) 9.00 − 5.16
Estimate: 9 − 5 = 4
3.84

g) 25.34 − 5.79
Estimate: 25 − 6 = 19
19.55

2. In long jump, Benjamin jumped 4.85 m while his friend Dan jumped 5.62 m. How much farther did Dan jump than Benjamin?

0.77 m

3. Sofia got an answer of 3.75 when she subtracted 5.25 from a whole number. What is the whole number? Explain how you got your answer.

Add 3.75 and 5.25 to find the whole number, which is 9.

To recheck answer, subtract: 9.00 − 5.25 = 3.75

At-Home Help

Decimal tenths and hundredths are subtracted using the same rules as whole numbers.

- It is easier to subtract vertically if the decimal points are aligned.
- Subtract place values that are the same starting from the smallest place value.
- If you can't find the difference for a particular place value, regroup using the next greater place value.
- Check your answer using estimation.

For example:

	Actual answer →	Estimate
	3.00	3
−	0.75	1
	2.25	2

Page 40

Test Yourself

Circle the correct answer.

1. Which question would give an answer close to 2591?
   A. 3658 − 1149 **B.** 1468 + 1897 **(C.** 1255 + 1349**)** **D.** 4513 − 2928

2. Using estimation, which question has an answer between 1350 and 1450?
   A. 1046 + 829 **B.** 6391 − 4869 **(C.** 874 + 573**)** **D.** 2836 − 1264

3. Which calculation is correct?
   A. 1259 + 745 + 5567 = 7754
   B. 1259 + 745 + 5567 = 6747
   C. 1259 + 745 + 5567 = 6574
   (D. 1259 + 745 + 5567 = 7571**)**

4. Three transport trucks can move loads that total 4581 kg. Two of the trucks moved 2614 kg and 1088 kg. How much would you estimate the third truck moved?
   A. 780 kg **B.** 700 kg **(C.** 900 kg**)** **D.** 800 kg

5. What is the answer to 7246 − 3859?
   A. 4613 **(B.** 3387**)** **C.** 4631 **D.** 3287

6. Sima is 3655 days old. Mario's cousin is 298 days older than Sima. Mario is 189 days younger than his cousin. How many days old is Mario?
   (A. 3764 days**)** **B.** 3953 days **C.** 3466 days **D.** 3769 days

7. What is the total cost shown?

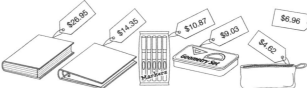

$26.95
$14.35
Markers $10.87
Geometry Set $9.03
$4.62
Pens $6.96

   A. $72.87 **B.** $67.78 **(C.** $72.78**)** **D.** $67.87

8. Tina gave the store clerk a $100 bill for all the items in Question 7. How much change would she receive?
   A. $32.78 **B.** $27.78 **C.** $32.22 **(D.** $27.22**)**

Page 41

Using Measurements to Describe Objects

Goal **Use logical reasoning to choose measurements.**

You will need a ruler marked in millimetres.

At-Home Help

Measurements can be used to describe objects. To solve measurement problems, use the clues given and your own knowledge.

1 cm = 10 mm
100 cm = 1 m
1000 mm = 1 m

Fill in the blanks with the correct measurements.

1. Anna's kitchen table seats __6__ people.
   It is __90__ cm wide, __1.5__ m long,
   and __750__ mm high.
   1.5 750 6 90

2. Tilo can cycle __10__ km in one hour. The library is 5 km from his home. It will take Tilo about __30__ min to cycle from home to the library. The speed limit for cars on city streets is __50__ km/h.
   This is __5__ times Tilo's speed.
   5 10 50 30

MAXIMUM
50
km/h

3. A box of crackers is __0.18__ m high, __6__ cm deep, and __140__ mm wide. The box holds about __70__ crackers.
   0.18 70 140 6

4. A new pencil is __0.2__ m long and __7__ mm wide.
   The eraser is __0.5__ cm long.

0 cm 5 10 15 20 25 30

   0.2 0.5 7

Page 42

Measuring Lengths

Goal **Relate metric units of length to each other.**

You will need a ruler marked in millimetres.

At-Home Help

When measuring objects, you may have to use tools that are available rather than ideal. You can use a 30 cm ruler to measure many lengths.

1 m = 100 cm
1 m = 1000 mm
1 cm = 10 mm

1. Describe how you can use a 30 cm ruler to measure ribbon for each length.
   a) 0.3 m Since 0.3 m = 30 cm, use ruler once.
   b) 105 cm Use ruler three times to get 90 cm, then add another 15 cm to get 105 cm.
   c) 750 mm Use ruler twice to get 60 cm, then add another 15 cm to get 75 cm or 750 mm.

2. Describe how to cut a piece of fabric 0.9 m long using a 30 cm ruler.
   Use ruler three times to get 90 cm or 0.9 m.

3. Draw each length.
   a) 112 mm
   b) a 0.3 m zigzag path

4. How can you calculate the thickness of one coin in millimetres? Use the information in the picture and a calculator.
   Height of 50 coins is 7 cm or 70 mm. So to find thickness of 1 coin, divide height of 50 coins by the number of coins.
   70 mm ÷ 50 = 1.4 mm Each coin is 1.4 mm thick.

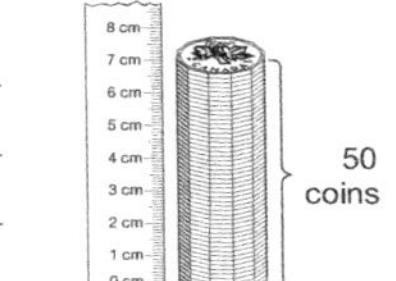

5. Two adjacent houses on a street are 1300 cm apart.
   a) Do you think the houses are in a rural or an urban area? Explain.
   Houses are in an urban area because 1300 cm or 13 m is not a great distance.
   b) What would be a better unit for describing the distance? Why?
   Metres would be a better unit because it is easier to write and visualize 13 m than 1300 cm.

Page 43

Measuring Circumference

Goal **Measure around circular objects.**

You will need a ruler marked in millimetres, and a tape measure.

1. Measure and record the width and circumference of each circle in centimetres. Complete the table.

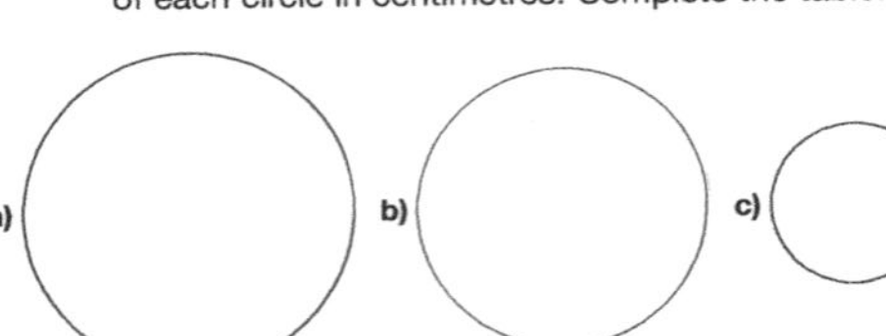

Circle	Width	Circumference
a)	4 cm	about 12.6 cm
b)	3.5 cm	about 11.0 cm
c)	2 cm	about 6.3 cm

At-Home Help

Circumference is the distance around a circle or circular object.

width

circumference

Circles have a particular relationship between width and circumference.

2. For each circle, is the circumference closer to two times, three times, or four times the width?

three times

3. Liam is practicing for a 400 m race. If he runs around a circular track with a width of 100 m, will he run as far as the race distance? Explain.

No, because three times 100 m is 300 m, which is less than 400 m.

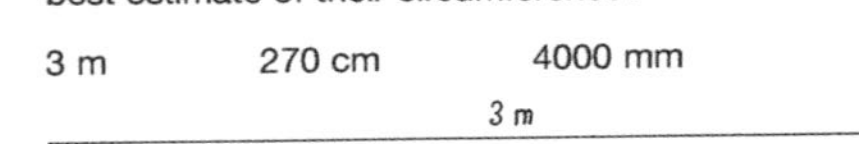

100 m

4. The hula hoops in the gym are 96 cm in width. What is the best estimate of their circumference?

3 m   270 cm   4000 mm

3 m

Page 44

Measuring Perimeter

 **Measure perimeter on a grid.**

You will need a metric ruler.

1. The initials for the Maple Leafs are shaded on the grid below. Estimate the perimeter. Check by measuring.

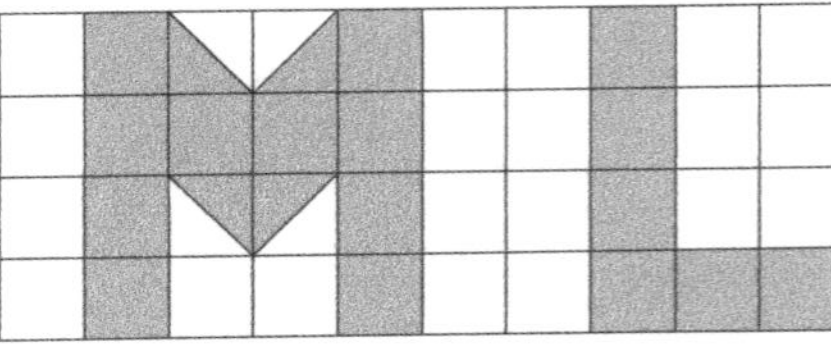

	Estimated perimeter	Actual perimeter
M	20 cm	21.2 cm
L	10 cm	14 cm
total	30 cm	35.2 cm

At-Home Help

Perimeter is the distance around an object. Using grid paper helps you measure the perimeter of irregular shapes. When the sides of shapes do not follow grid lines, use a ruler to measure the lengths accurately.

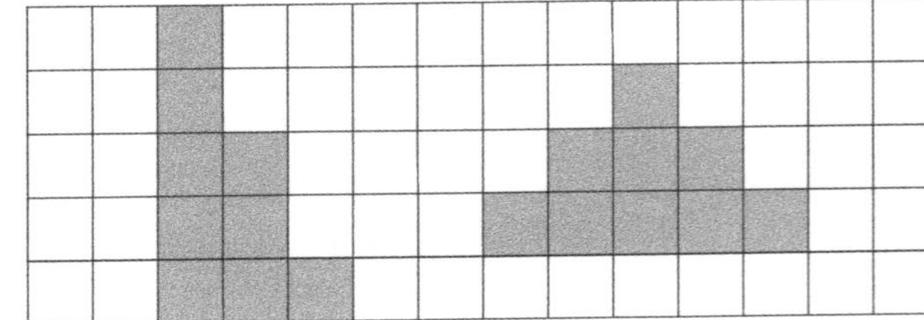

Perimeter is an outside measurement.

2. Use the grid to draw two different shapes each with a perimeter of 16 cm. Each shape must have more than 4 sides.

Suggested answer:

Page 45

Measuring the Perimeter of a Rectangle

Goal **Develop and use a rule for calculating the perimeter of a rectangle.**

1. Calculate the length of trim you would need to go around these blankets.

a) 2 m, 3 m

2 m + 3 m + 2 m + 3 m = 10 m or 2(2 m + 3 m) = 10 m

b) 90 cm, 140 cm

90 cm + 140 cm + 90 cm + 140 cm = 460 cm
or 2(90 cm + 140 cm) = 460 cm

At-Home Help

In a rectangle, opposite sides are the same length. The perimeter of a rectangle can be calculated by adding the length and width, and then doubling the sum.

7 m
5 m

For example:

perimeter of this rectangle
= two times (5 m + 7 m)
= two times (12 m)
= 24 m

2. Which rectangle has the greater perimeter? How much greater is it?

a) 7.5 cm by 6 cm **b)** 7 cm by 7 cm

Rectangle b) has the greater perimeter. It is 1 cm greater than a).

3. **a)** How will the perimeter of this rectangle change if you add 4 m to the width?

8 m
3 m

The perimeter will increase by 8 m.

b) How will the perimeter change if you divide the length in half?

The perimeter will decrease by 8 m.

4. To calculate the perimeter of a square, Sue multiplies the width by 4. Is her rule correct? Explain.

Yes. All the side lengths of a square are equal. Since perimeter is the distance around an object, multiplying the side length of a square by 4 gives the correct perimeter.

Page 46

Solve Problems Using Tables

Goal **Use tables to solve distance problems.**

1. Tom cycles 150 m in one minute. He multiplies this by 10 then makes a table of his distances and times.

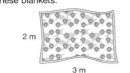

Distance (m)	Time (min)
1500	10
3000	20
4500	30
6000	40
7500	50
9000	60

Complete the table to estimate how long it will take Tom to cycle 8 km.

It will take Tom about 53 minutes to cycle 8 km.

At-Home Help

Organizing data in tables helps you see patterns. Using tables is an effective problem-solving strategy.

For example, as the distance increases by 1000 m, the time increases by 10 minutes.

Distance (m)	Time (min)
1000	10
2000	20
3000	30

2. Rosa can paddle her kayak at the rate of 1 km every 5 minutes. At this rate how far will she paddle in 1 hour? Make a table to help you.

Distance (km)	Time (min)
1	5
2	10
3	15
4	20
5	25
6	30
7	35
8	40
9	45
10	50
11	55
12	60

12 km

3. Tamara skates 120 m in one minute. Emma skates 1 km in 10 minutes. Create 2 tables to find out which girl can skate farther in 30 minutes. How much farther?

Suggested answer:

Tamara

Distance (m)	Time (min)
120	1
240	2
360	3
480	4
600	5
720	6
840	7
960	8
1080	9
1200	10

Emma

Distance (m)	Time (min)
1000	10

In 30 minutes, Tamara can skate 600 m farther.

Page 47

Measuring Time

 **Estimate and measure time to the nearest second.**

1. Juanita is making popcorn. Estimate and then calculate the time it took to make the popcorn.

start finish

I estimate the time to be Suggested answer: 3 min.

I calculate the time to be 2 min 30 s.

2. Kevin wonders how long the songs on the radio are. He noted the start and end times of one song. Estimate and then calculate the time.

start finish

I estimate the time to be Suggested answer: 4 min.

I calculate the time to be 4 min 11 s.

3. A ride at the amusement park has a sign saying: "Five minutes of thrills and spills!"

Yoshi noted the start time of 11:55:26 and the finish time of 12:00:12. Was the sign accurate? Explain.

The actual time on the ride is a little less than 5 min (4 min 46 s). Since signs usually do not list times in seconds and the ride is almost 5 min, the sign is accurate.

4. The school bell rings at 9:00:00. How much time is left before the bell?

9 min 27 s

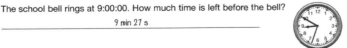

At-Home Help

This clock shows when the traffic light turned red.

This clock shows when the traffic light turned green.

The traffic light was red for 1 min 43 s. From 8:47:29 to 8:48:00 is 31 s. From 8:48:00 to 8:49:00 is 1 min. From 8:49:00 to 8:49:12 is 12 s. So the total time was 1 min 43 s.

Page 48

Recording Dates and Times

 **Write dates and times using numeric format.**

1. Colin's flight home landed on March 25, 2004, at 23 minutes 12 seconds after eight o'clock in the evening.

   Record the date and time in numeric format.

   2004-03-25 20:23:12

2. Colin departed three weeks before his return home at five minutes after noon.

   Record his departure time in numeric format.

   2004-03-04 12:05:00

3. Write each birth date and time in numeric format.

   a) July 18, 1999 at 3 minutes 15 seconds after midnight

   1999-07-18 00:03:15

   b) November 20, 2001 at 4 seconds after six thirty in the evening

   2001-11-20 18:30:04

4. The Internet Café charges $0.50 for each minute or part of a minute. How much should Sofie pay if she logs on at 16:48:33 and logs off at 17:00:26? Show your work.

   16:48:33 to 17:00:26 is almost 12 min
   50¢ x 12 = 600¢
   = $6.00

At-Home Help

When dates are recorded in numeric format, the year is recorded first, then a hyphen, then the month (using two digits), then another hyphen, then the day (using two digits).

For example, March 10, 2004 would be written as 2004-03-10.

The times on flight, train, and ship schedules are recorded using a 24 hour clock. The hour is written first, followed by a colon, then the minute(s), also followed by a colon, then the seconds (all numbers must have two digits).

On a 24 hour clock, noon is written as 12:00:00. On digital clocks, midnight is displayed as 00:00:00. All hours are written according to the number of hours after midnight.

For example, 1 p.m. is written as 13:00:00.

Test Yourself

Circle the correct answer.

1. A student desk is about ______ m high. It measures about ______ mm across and about ______ cm from front to back. What are the measurements?

A. 0.8, 650, 410 **B.** 80, 650, 41

C. 0.8, 65, 41 **D.** 0.8, 650, 41

2. What is the thickness of 1 card in mm? Use the information in the picture to help you.

15 cards
3 cm

A. 2 **B.** 30

C. 3 **D.** 20

3. The width of Adam's bicycle wheel is 0.6 m. What is the best estimate of the circumference of the wheel?

A. 60 cm **B.** 1.2 m **C.** 2.5 m **D.** 190 cm

4. What is the perimeter of this shape?

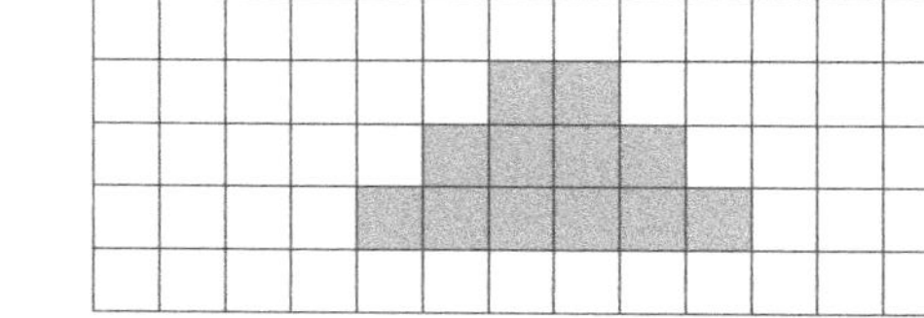

A. 14 cm **B.** 18 cm **C.** 12 cm **D.** 20 cm

5. A 7.5 cm by 6 cm photo is enlarged. The length and the width are doubled. What is the perimeter of the new photo?

A. 7.5 cm greater **B.** double the original perimeter

C. 12 cm greater **D.** 1.5 times the original perimeter

Test Yourself Page 2

6. Fiona rides her skateboard about 150 m in 1 minute. She made a table to track her distance and time. About how long will it take her to skateboard 4 km?

Distance (m)	Time (min)
1500	10
3000	20

A. 20 minutes

B. 23 minutes

C. 27 minutes

D. 30 minutes

7. Neil wants to synchronize the clocks in his home. When the radio announced it was exactly noon, three clocks in his home looked like this:

i

ii

iii

How must Neil correct the time on each clock?

A. (i) back 23 seconds, (ii) ahead 1 minute 44 seconds, (iii) back 2 minutes

B. (i) back 37 seconds, (ii) ahead 1 minute 44 seconds, (iii) back 2 minutes

C. (i) back 37 seconds, (ii) ahead 1 minute 16 seconds, (iii) back 2 minutes

D. (i) ahead 37 seconds, (ii) ahead 2 minutes 44 seconds, (iii) back 2 minutes

8. A hot air balloon will be launched at 40 minutes 30 seconds after 3 p.m. on Canada Day (July 1), 2017. How would the date and time of the launch be written in numeric format?

A. 2017-01-07 3:40:30 **B.** 2017-01-07 03:40:30

C. 2017-07-01 15:40:30 **D.** 2017-01-07 15:40:30

9. Which statement best describes circumference?

A. Circumference is the distance around a circle.

B. Circumference is the width of a circle.

C. Circumference is the distance around any object.

D. Circumference is the area of a circle.

Page 51

Multiplying Tens

Goal **Use number facts to multiply by tens.**

1. What number facts can you use to calculate these answers? Find the answers.

	Number fact	Answer
a) 40 × 30	4 x 3 = 12	1200
b) 50 × 70	5 x 7 = 35	3500
c) 60 × 20	6 x 2 = 12	1200
d) 90 × 80	9 x 8 = 72	7200

2. How can you use this array to calculate 30 × 60? Find the product.

1800. Use the array to multiply 3 x 6.

3. Use the array to multiply 40 × 20.

800

4. Calculate the area of each rectangle.

a) 40 cm, 50 cm

2000 square centimetres

b) 40 cm, 80 cm

3200 square centimetres

5. Calculate each product. Explain your thinking.

		Explanation
a) 30 × 60 =	1800	I used multiplication fact 3 x 6 = 18.
b) 70 × 40 =	2800	I used multiplication fact 7 x 4 = 28.

At-Home Help

A **product** is the answer to a multiplication question.

For example, 66 is the product of 11 × 6.

11 × 6 = 66

When you multiply tens, it is easier to use multiplication facts for the non-zero digits.

For example, to multiply 30 × 20 use the multiplication fact 3 × 2 = 6.

An array can help with multiplication.

30 × 20 = 600

Page 52

Estimating Products

Goal **Solve two-step problems and use estimation to check the reasonableness of a calculation.**

1. Estimate which calculations are reasonable. Explain how you estimated.

a) 224 × 8 = 1792

Reasonable because 220 x 10 = 2200, which is close to 1792.

b) 29 × 58 = 1200

Not reasonable because 30 x 60 = 1800, which is much greater than 1200.

c) 1475 × 99 = 213 425

Not reasonable because 1500 x 100 = 150 000, which is much less than 213 425.

d) 49 × 49 = 2401

Reasonable because 50 x 50 = 2500, which is close to 2401.

At-Home Help

To check the reasonableness of a multiplication, estimate the answer by rounding the numbers being multiplied to the nearest 10.

For example:

To check if 12 × 39 = 468 is reasonable, round 12 and 39 to the nearest ten. Then multiply.
10 × 40 = 400

So the product 468 is reasonable.

2. Trevor has 60 nickels and 50 dimes. He wants to know if he can buy a book that costs $11.55. How much more money does he need to buy the book? Explain how you solved the problem.

$3.55. I multiplied 60 x 5 and 50 x 10. I added the products together to get 800¢ or $8.00. Then I subtracted $8.00 from $11.55.

3. A group of 25 hockey players are having a contest to see who can sell the most chocolate bars. Each group of 5 players gets a box of 30 chocolate bars.

a) Calculate the greatest number of chocolate bars that can be sold. Show your work.

25 ÷ 5 = 5 groups
5 x 30 = 150 bars

b) Use estimation to show that your calculation in Part **a)** is reasonable. Explain your thinking.

Round 25 to 30.
30 ÷ 5 = 6 groups
My answer in Part a) is reasonable because 6 x 30 = 180 bars, which is close to 150 bars.

Page 53

Solve Problems Using Tree Diagrams

Goal **Use a tree diagram to solve combination problems.**

Norman is designing hats for his baseball team. The designs include 3 colours, 2 logos, and 3 styles.

Colour	Logo	Style
Blue	Maple leaf	Button with stitching
Red	Baseball bat and ball	Button with no stitching
Black		Smooth top

1. How many different baseball hats can Norman design? Use a tree diagram. 18 hats

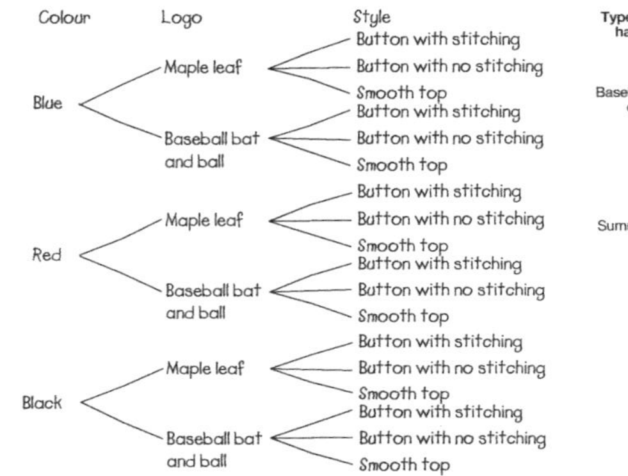

2. Create a tree diagram using 2 colours and 2 logos to get a total of 4 different hats.

Suggested answer:

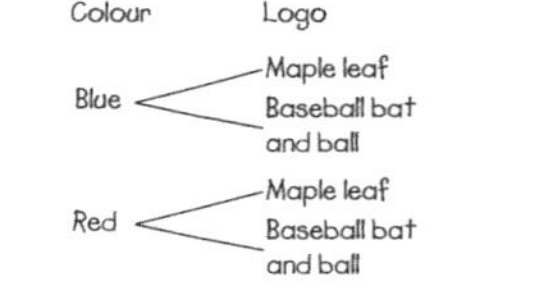

At-Home Help

To find the number of combinations of items in a problem, use a tree diagram to list all possibilities.

Choose one item and list all the combinations for it. Repeat this process for all items.

For example, if you have 3 types of hats, 2 fabrics, and 4 colours, then the total number of different hats you can make is 24.

Type of hat: Baseball cap, Summer hat, Fall hat
Fabric: Denim, Corduroy
Colour: Red, Green, Blue, Black

Page 54

Multiplying by Regrouping

Goal **Use mental math to multiply two two-digit numbers.**

1. Use each number line to calculate.

   a) $12 \times 14 =$ 168

   10×14=140 2×14=28

   0

   b) $15 \times 11 =$ 165

   10×11=110 5×11=55

   0

2. Use mental math to calculate.

   a) $12 \times 16 =$ 192

   b) $17 \times 11 =$ 187

3. Calculate.

   a) $11 \times 12 =$ 132

   b) $12 \times 18 =$ 216

   c) $15 \times 13 =$ 195

4. A roller coaster holds 15 people. How many people can go on the roller coaster in 22 rides?

   330 people

5. How many cobs of corn are in 19 dozen?

   228 cobs

At-Home Help

Regrouping is a mental math strategy for multiplying numbers. Regroup numbers into 10s to make calculations easier.

For example:

12×12 can be regrouped as $(10 + 2) \times 12$. $10 \times 12 = 120$ and $2 \times 12 = 24$.

10×12=120 2×12=24

0

$12 \times 12 = 120 + 24$
$= 144$

Page 55

Multiplying with Arrays

 **Multiply two-digit numbers.**

1. Calculate the number of cells in each table.
   a) 11 rows and 13 columns 143 cells
   b) 17 rows and 21 columns 357 cells
   c) 13 rows and 15 columns 195 cells

2. What multiplication question is represented by these base ten blocks? Calculate the product.
   a) 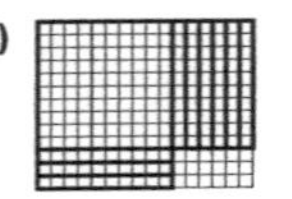 13 x 16 = 208
   b) 14 x 14 = 196
   c)  21 x 15 = 315

3. A quilt has 11 rows and 17 columns of squares. How many squares are on the quilt? 187 squares

4. Two quilts are made of square patches each measuring 1 dm by 1 dm. What is the area of each quilt?
   a) 14 rows and 18 columns 252 square decimetres
   b) 22 rows and 25 columns 550 square decimetres

Page 56

Dividing Hundreds by One-Digit Numbers

 **Use division facts to divide hundreds.**

1. What division facts can you use to calculate these answers? Find the answers.

	Division fact	Answer
a) 800 ÷ 2	8 ÷ 2 = 4	400
b) 1500 ÷ 5	15 ÷ 5 = 3	300
c) 1200 ÷ 3	12 ÷ 3 = 4	400
d) 2800 ÷ 7	28 ÷ 7 = 4	400
e) 3600 ÷ 4	36 ÷ 4 = 9	900
f) 4200 ÷ 6	42 ÷ 6 = 7	700

2. Explain how using 16 ÷ 4 can help you divide 1600 by 4.
   16 ÷ 4 = 4 so 1600 ÷ 4 = 400.

3. Explain how multiplication can help you check your answer to Question 2.
   400 x 4 = 1600, which is the number to be divided in Question 2.

4. An 1800 m track is divided equally into 6 shorter runs. Use a division fact to predict the length of each short run.
   300 m. Division fact is 18 ÷ 6 = 3.

At-Home Help

To divide hundreds by one digit, it is easier to use division facts for the non-zero digits.

For example, to divide 1200 ÷ 2 use the division fact 12 ÷ 2 = 6.

An array can help with division.

1200 ÷ 2 = 600

You can also check your answer using multiplication.

600 × 2 = 1200

Page 57

Estimating Quotients

Goal **Overestimate and underestimate when dividing.**

1. Overestimate each division. Show the numbers you used to estimate.

	Overestimate
a) 1427 ÷ 5	1500 ÷ 5 = 300
b) 8)2394	2400 ÷ 8 = 300
c) 3)1713	1800 ÷ 3 = 600
d) 5406 ÷ 7	5600 ÷ 7 = 800

2. Underestimate each division. Show the numbers you used to estimate.

	Underestimate
a) 1135 ÷ 2	1000 ÷ 2 = 500
b) 1303 ÷ 4	1200 ÷ 4 = 300
c) 2645 ÷ 3	2400 ÷ 3 = 800
d) 4495 ÷ 6	4200 ÷ 6 = 700

3. For each question, is it more accurate to overestimate or underestimate? Explain.

a) 2914 ÷ 5 Overestimate because 2914 is closer to 3000 than 2500.

b) 3759 ÷ 6 Underestimate because 3759 is closer to 3600 than 4200.

4. Estimate to solve the problem. Explain your thinking.

The total attendance at 2 hockey games in March was 9498 people. Approximately what was the average attendance at each game?

10 000 ÷ 2 = 5000 people. I overestimated because 9498 is closer to 10 000 than 8000.

At-Home Help

A **quotient** is the answer to a division question.

For example, 8 is the quotient of 48 ÷ 6.

48 ÷ 6 = 8

To do some calculations, it is easier to overestimate and underestimate. The actual answer will be somewhere between both estimates.

With other calculations, either an overestimate or an underestimate gives a fairly accurate answer.

For example, 4753 ÷ 6 would be 4800 ÷ 6 = 800 as an overestimate. 800 is fairly accurate because 4753 is closer to 4800 than 4200.

1095 ÷ 2 would be 1000 ÷ 2 = 500 as an underestimate. 500 is fairly accurate because 1095 is closer to 1000 than 1200.

4539 ÷ 6 would be 4200 ÷ 6 = 700 as an underestimate and 4800 ÷ 6 = 800 as an overestimate. The actual answer is about 750, or halfway between 700 and 800.

Page 58

Dividing Greater Numbers

Goal **Divide a four-digit number by a one-digit number.**

1. Estimate and then divide. Show your work.

	Estimate	Answer
a) 2641 ÷ 2	2600 ÷ 2 = 1300	1320 R1
b) 3)2001	2100 ÷ 3 = 700	667
c) 6)3517	3600 ÷ 6 = 600	586 R1
d) 2134 ÷ 9	1800 ÷ 9 = 200	237 R1
e) 6)1604	1800 ÷ 6 = 300	267 R2
f) 4395 ÷ 5	4500 ÷ 5 = 900	879

At-Home Help

To divide some numbers, you may need to regroup first.

2. Check two of the answers in Question 1 using multiplication and addition.

Suggested answer:
Part a): 1320 x 2 = 2640, 2640 + 1 = 2641
Part e): 267 x 6 = 1602, 1602 + 2 = 1604

3. Eight dolphins in a pod each have about the same mass. Their total mass is about 1195 kg. What is the approximate mass of each dolphin?

about 149 kg

4. Four trucks are ready to transport the 8 dolphins to a marine centre. Each truck can carry 225 kg. Can the trucks carry all the dolphins in one trip? Explain.

1195 kg ÷ 4 = 298 R3
298 kg > 225 kg
So, the dolphins have more mass than the trucks can carry.

Page 59

Choosing Multiplication and Division Methods

Goal **Choose and justify a calculation method.**

Answer each question using the information given. Explain why you chose multiplication or division.

Did you know...
- the giant Canada goose has a mass of 7 kg
- it flies at a maximum altitude of 245 m from the ground
- it takes 30 days to hatch one nest of eggs
- it can fly about 40 km in 1 hour
- it can fly for about 16 hours each day

At-Home Help

To decide whether to multiply or divide in a problem, look to see if any totals are given.

For example, if the total cost of several items having the same value is given and the problem asks you to find the cost of each item, you need to divide.

If you are asked to find a total, you need to multiply.

For example, if you are given the volume of juice per bottle and the number of bottles, you can find the total volume by multiplying.

1. What would be the mass of a flock of 65 geese?
   455 kg. Use multiplication because the mass of one goose is given and you want to know the total mass of 65 geese.
2. How many hours would the geese have flown in 12 days?
   192 h. Use multiplication because the number of hours one goose flies per day is given and you want to know the total number of hours flown in 12 days.
3. How many days would the geese fly if they flew for a total of 592 hours?
   37 days. Use division because the total hours over several days is given and you want to know the number of days.
4. How many days would a goose sit on 15 nests of eggs?
   450 days. Use multiplication because the number of days a goose sits per nest is given and you want to know the total number of days needed for 15 nests.
5. Three geese fly at different altitudes from the ground. They are equal distances apart. Approximately what are the 3 different altitudes from the ground?
   Sample answer: about 83 m, 164 m, and 245 m. Use division because the total altitude above ground is given and you want to know the individual altitudes.

Page 60

Test Yourself

Circle the correct answer.

1. What is the product of 50×40?
   A. 900 **B.** 200 **C.** 2000 (circled) **D.** 9000
2. What is the product of 90×30?
   A. 1200 **B.** 2700 (circled) **C.** 120 **D.** 270
3. What is the product of 600×60?
   A. 1200 **B.** 3600 **C.** 12 000 **D.** 36 000 (circled)
4. Which estimate is most reasonable for 26×18?
   A. 550 **B.** 450 (circled) **C.** 750 **D.** 600
5. Which estimate is most reasonable for 38×35?
   A. 900 **B.** 1050 **C.** 1100 **D.** 1200 (circled)
6. What is the product of 8×257?
   A. 2056 (circled) **B.** 1656 **C.** 2165 **D.** 2065
7. What is the product of 94×62?
   A. 5688 **B.** 5628 **C.** 5828 (circled) **D.** 5288
8. What is the area of this rectangle?
   A. 1611 square metres
   B. 1161 square metres (circled)
   C. 1616 square metres
   D. 1116 square metres

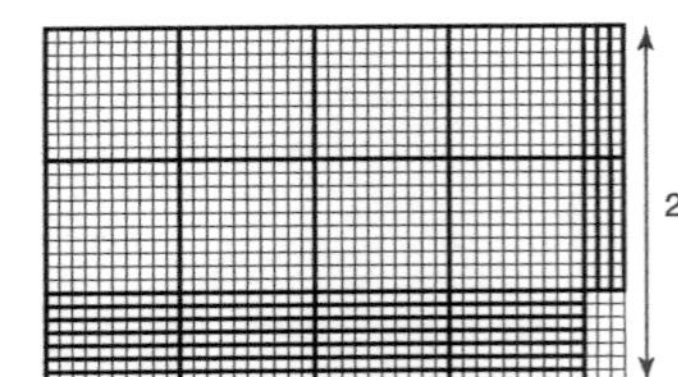

Page 61

Test Yourself Page 2

9. What is the answer to 7396 ÷ 4?

A. 1489 (B. 1849) C. 1949 D. 1889

10. What is the answer to 4508 ÷ 8?

A. 563 R1 B. 562 R3 C. 562 R4 (D. 563 R4)

11. What are the missing numbers from top to bottom?

```
  57
 ×4?
 3?2
2???
????
```

A. 4, 6, 280, 2822 (B. 6, 4, 280, 2622) C. 6, 4, 260, 2822 D. 4, 6, 260, 2622

12. Tiles are to be placed on a kitchen wall. They are in 18 rows and 14 columns. How many tiles are needed?

A. 254 tiles B. 245 tiles (C. 252 tiles) D. 225 tiles

13. The area of a rectangular room is 63 square metres. The longest side is 9 m long. What is the perimeter of the room?

(A. 32 m) B. 30 m C. 31 m D. 33 m

14. A square room has a perimeter of 164 m. What is its area?

A. 1861 square metres B. 1600 square metres
C. 328 square metres (D. 1681 square metres)

Page 62

Constructing Symmetrical Shapes

Construct 2-D shapes with one line of symmetry.

1.

a) Use symmetry to complete the picture.

b) Describe the method you used. Check for symmetry.

Suggested answer: I used a grid to draw a congruent half on the other side of the line of symmetry. I checked for congruence with a transparent mirror.

2.

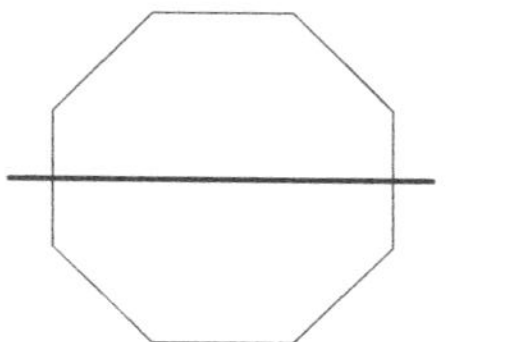

a) Use a different method from Question 1 to complete the picture.

b) Describe the method you used. Check for symmetry and describe your method.

Suggested answer: I chose several points on the given half. For each point, I measured the distance to the line of symmetry, making sure distance was at right angles to the line of symmetry. I measured the same distance from the line of symmetry to the other side and marked a point. I repeated this for all other points. Then I joined the new points to complete the picture. I folded the picture to check for symmetry.

At-Home Help

A line of symmetry may be horizontal or vertical.

To complete a picture that has a line of symmetry, use one of these two ways.

- Use a grid to draw a congruent half on the other side of the line of symmetry.
- Find matching points by measuring the distance from several points on the given half to the line of symmetry. Make sure distance is at right angles to line of symmetry. Then join all new points to make a congruent half.

Check for symmetry by using one of these two ways.

- Fold the completed picture along the line of symmetry to see if both halves match exactly.
- Use a transparent mirror to check for congruence of both halves.

Page 63

Constructing Triangles

Goal **Draw triangles with given side lengths and angle measures.**

You will need a ruler and a protractor.

1. Draw a triangle with side lengths of 3 cm and 6 cm. The angle between these two sides is 75°.

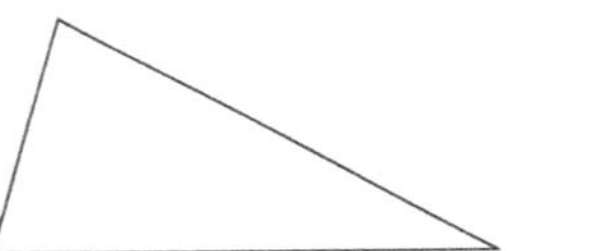

At-Home Help

You can draw a triangle if you know the measure of
- only one angle and one side
- two angles and one side without specifying where the side is
- two sides and one angle without specifying where the angle is

There is only one solution if two side lengths and one angle are given, and the angle location is known.

2. Draw two different triangles that each have one side length of 6 cm and angles of 125° and 25°.

Suggested answer:

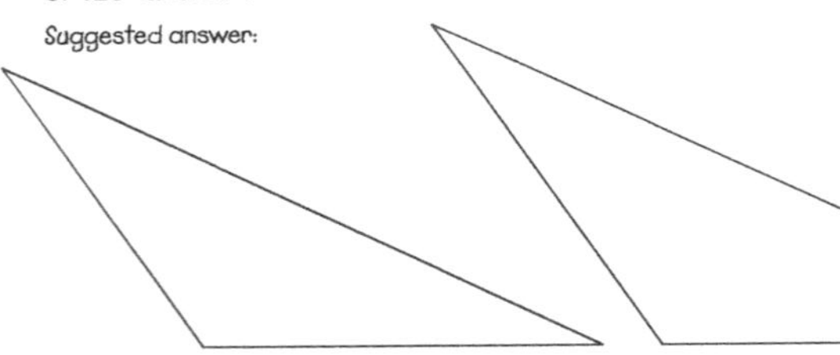

3. Draw three different triangles that each have one side length of 5 cm and an angle of 60°.

Suggested answer:

Page 64

Classifying Triangles by Angles

Goal **Investigate angle measures in triangles.**

You will need a protractor.

1.

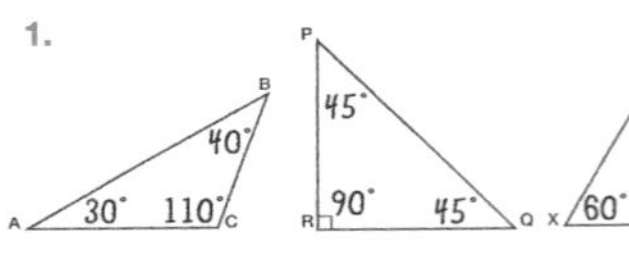

a) Measure and label all the angles in the triangles.

b) Classify the triangles. Give reasons for your answers.

Triangle ABC is *obtuse-angled*.

Reason: *One angle is obtuse.*

Triangle PQR is *right-angled*.

Reason: *One angle is 90°.*

Triangle XYZ is *acute-angled*.

Reason: *All angles are acute.*

At-Home Help

A **right-angled triangle** has one right angle.

A **right angle** measures 90°.

An **obtuse-angled triangle** has one obtuse angle.

An **obtuse angle** measures greater than 90°.

120°

An **acute-angled triangle** has only acute angles.

An **acute angle** measures less than 90°.

60° 60° 60°

2. **a)** What type of triangle has an angle that measures 100° and an angle that measures 50°? Give your reasons.

obtuse-angled triangle

100° is an obtuse angle.

b) What type of triangle has an angle that measures 60° and an angle that measures 90°? Give your reasons.

right-angled triangle

90° is a right angle.

Page 65

Classifying Triangles by Side Lengths

Goal **Investigate side lengths of triangles.**

You will need a ruler.

1.

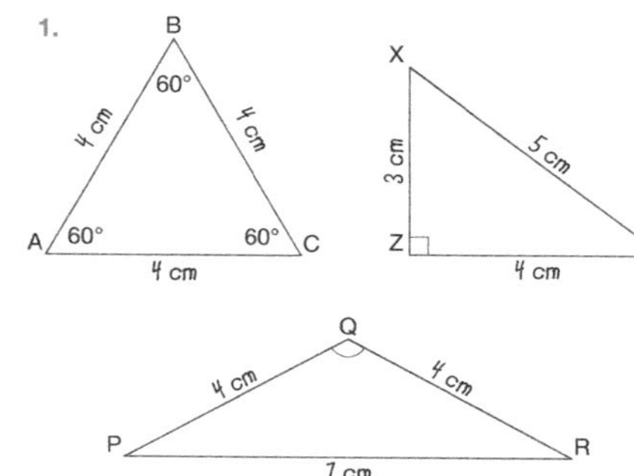

a) Measure and label all the side lengths of the triangles.

b) Classify the triangles according to their side lengths. Give your reasons.

Triangle ABC is equilateral.

Reason: All side lengths are equal.

Triangle PQR is isosceles.

Reason: Two side lengths are equal.

Triangle XYZ is scalene.

Reason: All side lengths are different.

2. Classify the triangles according to their angle measures and side lengths. Example: Triangle KLM is an obtuse-angled scalene triangle.

a) Triangle ABC is an acute-angled equilateral triangle.

b) Triangle PQR is an obtuse-angled isosceles triangle.

c) Triangle XYZ is a right-angled scalene triangle.

At-Home Help

An **equilateral triangle** has all sides of equal length.

An **isosceles triangle** has two sides of equal length.

A **scalene triangle** has all sides of different length.

Page 66

Measuring Angles in Polygons

Goal **Identify and classify regular polygons by their angle measures.**

1. Match these shapes with the angle clues below. Name each shape.

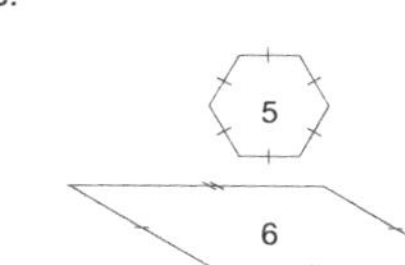

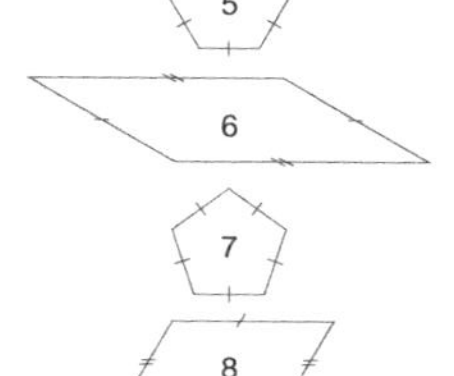

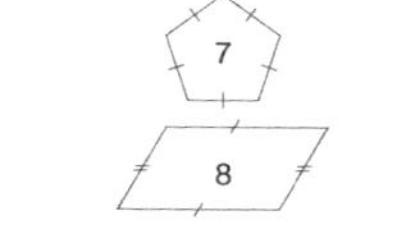

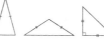

a) 100°, 100°, 80°, 80° trapezoid (shape 1)

b) 120°, 120°, 60°, 60° parallelogram (shape 8)

c) 60°, 60°, 60° equilateral triangle (shape 3)

d) 90°, 90°, 90°, 90° square (shape 4)

e) 30°, 30°, 150°, 150° parallelogram (shape 6)

2. Write angle clues for the remaining polygons. Match the shapes with your angle clues. Name each shape.

Angle clue: 108°, 108°, 108°, 108°, 108° Shape: pentagon (shape 7)

Angle clue: 120°, 120°, 120°, 120°, 120°, 120° Shape: hexagon (shape 5)

Angle clue: 135°, 135°, 135°, 135°, 135°, 135°, 135°, 135° Shape: octagon (shape 2)

3. Without measuring, predict the size of angle A. Use what you know about the relationship between the number of sides and angle measures in a regular polygon.

Angle A will be less than 135° but greater than 120°.

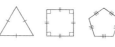

At-Home Help

A **regular polygon** is a polygon with equal angle measures and equal side lengths.

Regular polygons are identified by the number of sides.

The angle measure in a regular polygon increases as the number of sides increases.

For example: Each angle in a regular hexagon is greater than each angle in a square, because a hexagon has 6 sides while a square has only 4 sides.

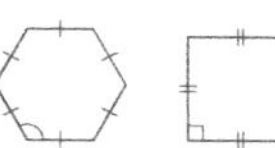

Page 67

Properties of Polygons

 **Investigate properties of geometric shapes.**

1. Match the polygons with the property riddles below.

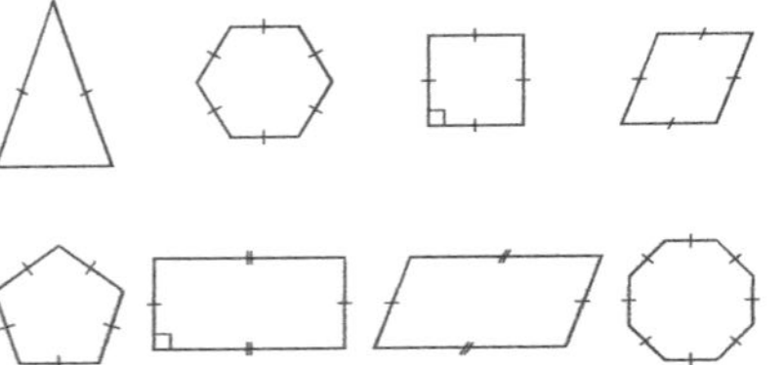

At-Home Help

The **properties** of a shape are the features that describe it.

For example:

The properties of a regular hexagon are 6 equal sides, 6 equal angles (all obtuse), 3 pairs of parallel sides, and 6 lines of symmetry.

Because no other shape shares all the same properties, a shape can be identified by its properties.

a) I have no parallel sides.
All my sides are equal in length.
All my angles are equal.
I have 5 lines of symmetry.
Who am I?
pentagon

b) I have 3 pairs of parallel sides.
All my sides are equal in length.
All my angles are obtuse.
I have 6 lines of symmetry.
Who am I?
hexagon

c) I have 2 pairs of parallel sides.
All my sides are equal in length.
I have 2 pairs of equal angles.
I have 2 lines of symmetry.
Who am I?
rhombus

d) I have 2 pairs of parallel sides.
My opposite sides are equal in length.
All my angles are equal in size.
I have 2 lines of symmetry.
Who am I?
rectangle

2. Write property riddles for two of the remaining polygons. Write about parallel sides, side lengths, angle measures, and lines of symmetry. Name each polygon.

a) Suggested answer:
I have 4 pairs of parallel sides.
All my sides are equal in length.
All my angles are equal.
I have 8 lines of symmetry.
Who am I? octagon

b) Suggested answer:
I have no parallel sides.
I have 2 sides that are equal in length.
Two of my angles are equal.
I have 1 line of symmetry.
Who am I? isosceles triangle

Page 68

Sorting Polygons

 **Sort and classify polygons by sides, angles, and vertices.**

1. Use a Venn diagram to sort these shapes using two of the properties below.
   - number of sides
   - number of angles
   - number of vertices
   - number of lines of symmetry
   - parallel sides
   - equal side lengths
   - equal angles
   - kinds of angles

Suggested answer:

All angles equal | At least 2 parallel sides

At-Home Help

Polygons can be sorted based on
- number of sides
- number of angles
- number of vertices
- number of lines of symmetry
- parallel sides
- equal side lengths
- equal angles
- kinds of angles

In a polygon, the number of angles and the number of vertices are equal to the number of sides.

An **irregular polygon** is a polygon with different angle measures and different side lengths.

For example:

A **Venn diagram** is a drawing with overlapping circles inside a rectangle. This type of diagram is helpful when sorting shapes or numbers.

2. Are there any shapes inside both circles? If so, what properties do these shapes have in common?
(using suggested answer given) octagon, hexagon, square, and rectangle
All these shapes have all angles equal and at least 2 parallel sides.

3. Are there any shapes outside both circles? If so, why are they placed there?
(using suggested answer given) isosceles triangle
This shape has neither all angles equal nor at least 2 parallel sides.

Page 69

Communicate About Shapes

Use math language to describe geometric ideas.

1.

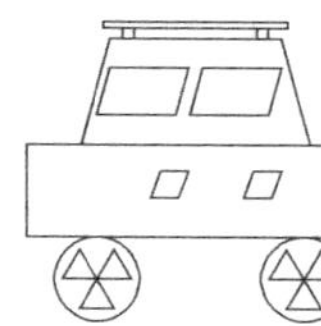

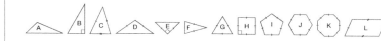

At-Home Help

To describe how to draw a picture made of polygons, remember to use the Communication Checklist.

The true test of whether or not your directions are clear is if someone else can reproduce the picture exactly.

Communication Checklist

☑ Did you show the right amount of detail?

☑ Did you use math language?

☑ Did you include only necessary information?

a) Write directions for a friend to draw the picture shown.

Suggested answer:

The body of the car is made up of a trapezoid at the top.

The bottom part of the body of the car is a rectangle.

There are 2 windows in the top part of the car. They are shaped like parallelograms.

There is 1 door handle below each window in the rectangular body of the car.

The door handles are rhombuses.

There is a roof rack shaped like a thin rectangle. The rectangle rests on two small squares, which are on top of the body of the car.

There are 2 wheels, which are circles.

There are 3 triangles inside each wheel.

b) Use the Communication Checklist to identify the strengths of your directions. List them.

Suggested answer: I used math language for all the polygons.

I included all the details, but did not include unnecessary information such as colours,

and exact measurements of lengths and angles.

2. If possible, test your directions by having your parent use them to draw the picture.

Page 70

Test Yourself

Circle the correct answer.

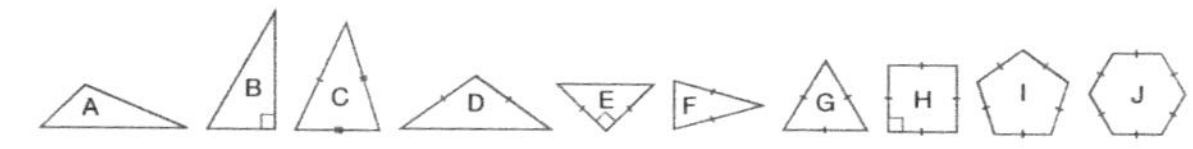

1. Which triangle has no lines of symmetry?

   (**A.** shape A) **B.** shape D **C.** shape F **D.** shape G

2. Which shape is a regular polygon?

   A. shape B **B.** shape C (**C.** shape K) **D.** shape E

3. Which shape has no parallel sides?

   A. shape J **B.** shape L **C.** shape H (**D.** shape I)

4. Which shape has 2 pairs of equal angles?

   (**A.** shape L) **B.** shape D **C.** shape H **D.** shape K

5. Which shape has no obtuse angles?

   A. shape A **B.** shape K **C.** shape L (**D.** shape E)

6. Which shape is a right-angled isosceles triangle?

   A. shape B **B.** shape F (**C.** shape E) **D.** shape D

7. Which shape has only acute angles?

   A. shape L **B.** shape H (**C.** shape C) **D.** shape K

8. Which shape is a scalene triangle?

   A. shape G (**B.** shape A) **C.** shape D **D.** shape F

9. Which shape is an irregular polygon?

   (**A.** shape L) **B.** shape H **C.** shape J **D.** shape I

10. Which shape is symmetrical?

   A. shape B **B.** shape L **C.** shape C (**D.** shape D)

Areas of Polygons

Goal **Estimate and measure the area of polygons.**

1. A hockey team chose this logo for their uniforms.

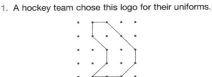

   a) Estimate the area in square units.
   Suggested answer: 8 square units

   b) Measure the area in square units.
   7.5 square units

2. For each polygon, estimate and then measure the area in square units.

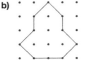

	Estimated area	Measured area
a)	*Suggested answer: 11 square units*	*11.5 square units*
b)	*Suggested answer: 10 square units*	*9 square units*
c)	*Suggested answer: 10 square units*	*9.5 square units*

At-Home Help

A grid is like an area ruler. Each full square on the grid has an area of 1 square unit. Many shapes drawn on grids can be divided into squares and right-angled triangles.

For example:

In this shape, there are 5 full squares (lightly shaded) and 2 half squares (darkly shaded). So the total area is 6 square units.

Areas of Irregular 2-D Shapes

Goal **Develop methods to measure the areas of irregular 2-D shapes.**

Find the area of this tulip shape to the nearest square unit using each of the methods below.

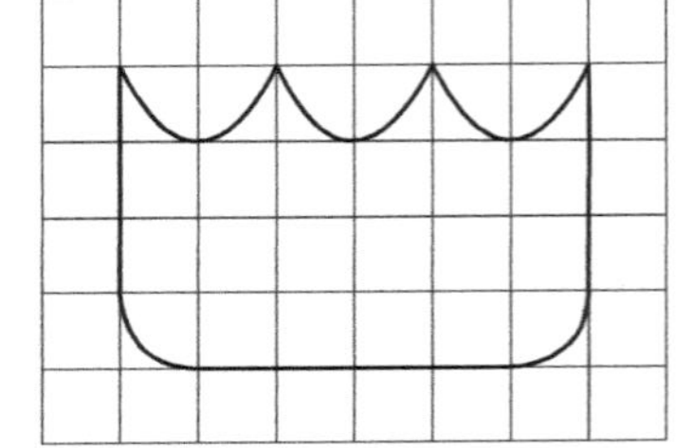

1. Count the full squares. For part squares, if less than half a square is covered, round down. If more than half a square is covered, round up.

Full squares	Part squares	Total area
16	*2*	*18 square units*

2. Count the full squares. For part squares, count how many squares you could make by putting together the part squares.

Full squares	Part squares	Total area
16	*3*	*19 square units*

3. Count the full squares. For part squares, count only those that are half or more.

Full squares	Part squares	Total area
16	*2*	*18 square units*

At-Home Help

A grid is useful when measuring the area of an irregular 2-D shape to the nearest square unit.

On centimetre grid paper, each full square has an area of 1 square centimetre. Part squares that cover less than half a square can be rounded down. Part squares that cover more than half a square can be counted as 1 full square. Part squares can also be grouped to make up about 1 full square.

For example:

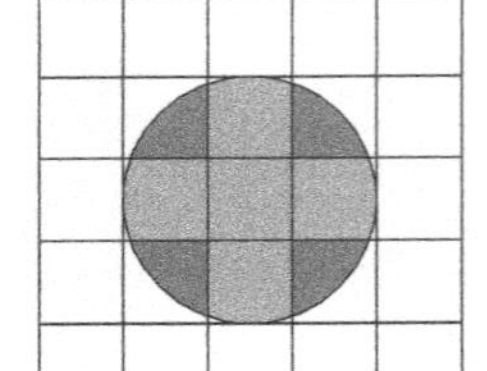

This circle covers 5 full or almost full squares (lightly shaded). There are 4 remaining part squares (darkly shaded), which can be grouped to give about 2 more full squares. So the total area of the circle is about 7 square units.

Relating Perimeter and Area of Rectangles

Goal **Explore relationships among side lengths, perimeter, and area of rectangles.**

Camille has 20 cm of decorative tape to put around the perimeter of a bookmark.

1. Sketch all possible rectangles she can design with a perimeter of 20 cm.

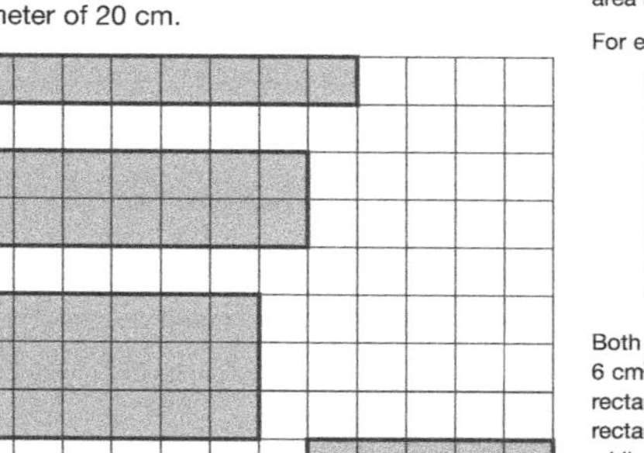

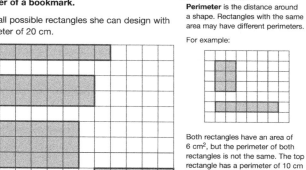

2. Calculate the area of each rectangle in Question 1. Record your answers in the table.

Length of side 1 (cm)	Length of side 2 (cm)	Area (cm^2)
1 cm	9 cm	9 cm^2
2 cm	8 cm	16 cm^2
3 cm	7 cm	21 cm^2
4 cm	6 cm	24 cm^2
5 cm	5 cm	25 cm^2

3. How are the areas and the shapes of the rectangles related?

The areas of the rectangles increase as side length 1 gets close to side length 2. This means that the areas increase as the rectangles get close to becoming a square.

At-Home Help

Perimeter is the distance around a shape. Rectangles with the same area may have different perimeters.

For example:

Both rectangles have an area of 6 cm^2, but the perimeter of both rectangles is not the same. The top rectangle has a perimeter of 10 cm while the bottom rectangle has a perimeter of 14 cm.

Rectangles with the same perimeter may have different areas.

Both rectangles have a perimeter of 16 cm, but the area of both rectangles is not the same. The top rectangle has an area of 12 cm^2 while the bottom rectangle has an area of 7 cm^2.

Perimeter is an outside measurement while area is an inside measurement.

Area Rule for Rectangles

Goal **Develop and explain a rule for calculating the area of a rectangle.**

1. Jasmine is choosing address labels. Calculate each area. Use the rule for area of a rectangle. Show your work.

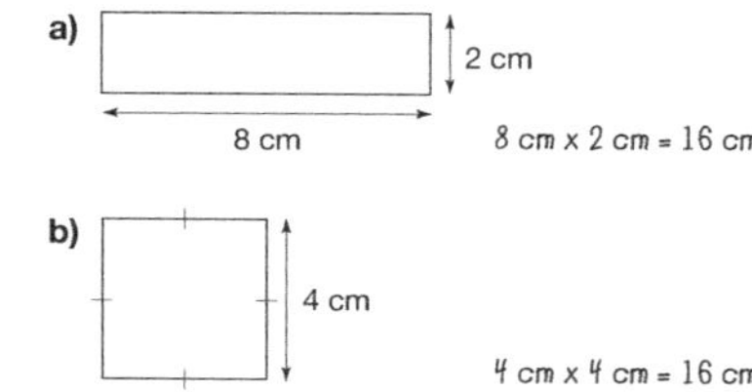

2. Calculate the area of each rectangle. Use the rule for area of a rectangle. Show your work.

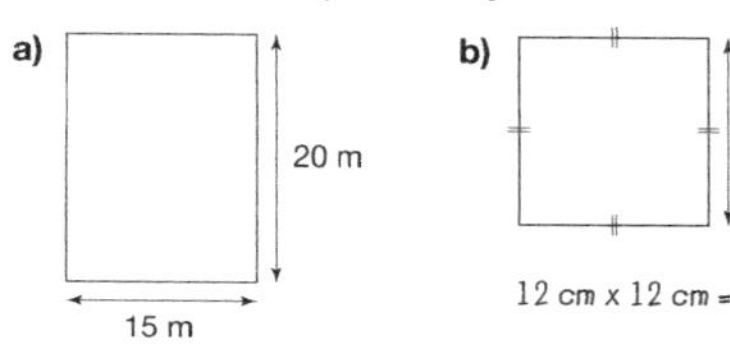

3. Nancy is using 1 cm^2 tiles to make rectangular coasters. Each tile costs $0.15. Which coaster will cost the most? Explain.

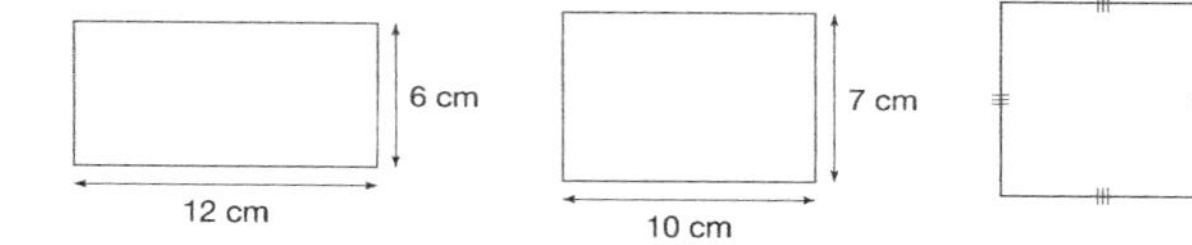

6 cm by 12 cm rectangle. This shape has the greatest area (72 cm^2).

At-Home Help

The area of a rectangle, when viewed on a grid, is like a multiplication array.

3 cm

5 cm

For example, this rectangle has a width of 3 cm and a length of 5 cm. The area of the rectangle can be found by multiplying the length by the width.

5 cm × 3 cm = 15 cm^2

The general rule for the area of a rectangle is

area = length × width

Page 75

Solve Problems by Solving Simpler Problems

Solve problems by breaking them into smaller parts.

1. Alain's parents are purchasing new flooring for their living room. The flooring costs $20 for each square metre.

   How much will the flooring cost before taxes?

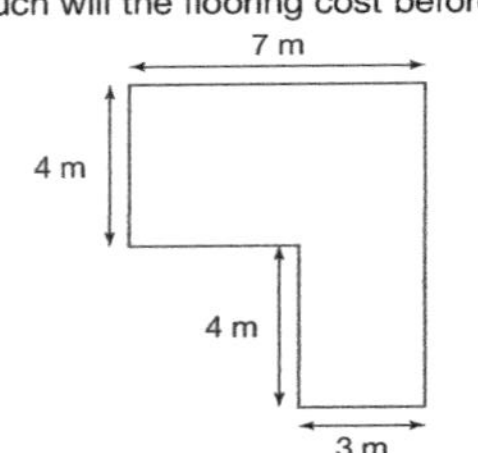

Scale 1 cm = 4 m

   a) Calculate the area by dividing the shape into two parts. Use 2 different sets of rectangles. Did you get the same answer? Explain why or why not.

   40 m². The area was the same for both sets of rectangles because the size of the room did not change. $4 \times 7 + 4 \times 3 = 40$ $4 \times 4 + 8 \times 3 = 40$

   b) Calculate the cost of the flooring. $800

2. A photograph is 12 cm by 16 cm. It has a mount that is 3 cm wide all around it. What is the area of the mount? Show your work.

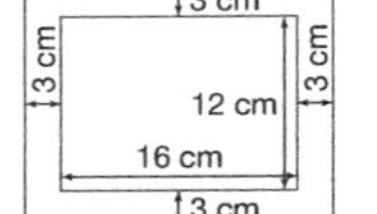

(area of photo and mount) 22 cm x 18 cm = 396 cm²
(area of photo) 16 cm x 12 cm = 192 cm²
(area of mount) 396 cm² − 192 cm² = 204 cm²

At-Home Help

The area of a complex shape can sometimes be found by dividing it into several smaller parts. The total area is then equal to the sum of the areas of the smaller parts.

For example, the area of this shape can be calculated two ways.

area = area of 2 cm by 2 cm square + area of 6 cm by 3 cm rectangle
$= 2 \times 2 + 6 \times 3$
$= 4 + 18$
$= 22\ cm^2$

or area = area of 5 cm by 2 cm rectangle + area of 4 cm by 3 cm rectangle
$= 5 \times 2 + 4 \times 3$
$= 10 + 12$
$= 22\ cm^2$

Page 76

Modelling Area

Model area using an appropriate scale.

1. Jasleen's parents are planning a community garden. The dimensions are 20 m by 16 m. They want to make a scale model of the garden on centimetre grid paper.

   a) Choose an appropriate scale. Explain your choice.

   Suggested scale: 1 cm = 4 m

   Using this scale, the garden can easily fit on the grid. The model of the garden will be 5 cm by 4 cm.

   b) Model the garden. Include the scale.

   Suggested model:

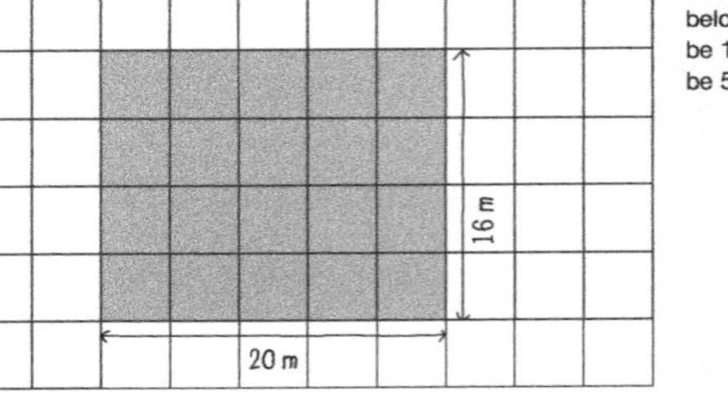

Scale 1 cm = 4 m

   c) What is the area of the garden? Include the units.

   320 m²

   d) What is the area of the model? Include the units.

   (using suggested model) 20 cm²

2. Would you measure each area in square kilometres, square metres, square centimetres, or square millimetres?

   a) a restaurant square metres

   b) a function key on a calculator square millimetres or square centimetres

   c) a country square kilometres

   d) a postcard square centimetres

At-Home Help

Large objects, such as floor plans, towns, and buildings, can be modelled using a scale. A **scale model** may be larger or smaller than the real object but must be the same shape. A scale model is similar to the real object.

When choosing a scale, consider the size of the object and the space you have available for the model.

For example, to draw a model of a 20 m by 12 m patio on the grid below, an appropriate scale would be 1 cm = 4 m. The model will then be 5 cm (20 ÷ 4) by 3 cm (12 ÷ 4).

20 m
12 m
Scale 1 cm = 4 m

Remember to always include the scale on your model.

Page 77

Coordinate Grids

Use coordinate pairs to identify and describe locations on a grid.

1. Ari drew this logo on a coordinate grid.

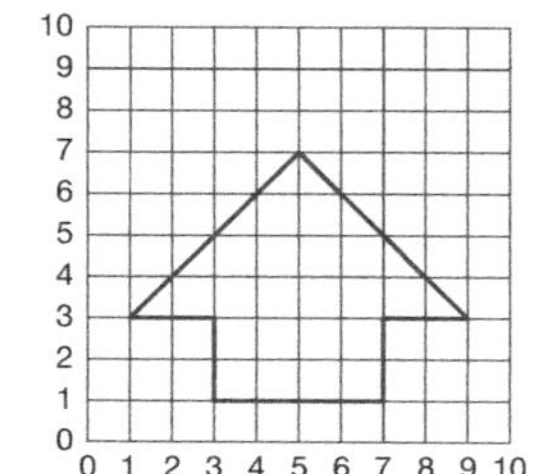

a) What points on the grid could you use to describe the logo? Write the coordinates for each point.

(1, 3), (3, 3), (3, 1), (7, 1), (7, 3), (9, 3), and (5, 7)

b) Write instructions for drawing the logo from these points.

Plot the points in Part a), then join the points with straight lines to form a closed polygon.

At-Home Help

A **coordinate grid** is a grid with each horizontal and vertical line numbered in order. **Coordinates** identify locations on a coordinate grid, and are sets of numbers that describe where a vertical and a horizontal line meet. The coordinate from the horizontal axis is always written first.

For example, the vertices of the triangle below have coordinates (3, 1), (7, 8), and (10, 2).

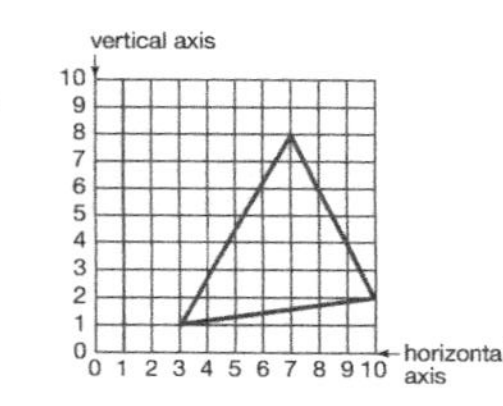

2. Ken started drawing the initial of his first name on a coordinate grid.

a) Name the coordinates he has used so far.

(1, 1), (1, 9), and (7, 9)

b) Write the coordinates he would need to finish the letter K. Mark these points on the grid and finish the initial.

Suggested answer: (1, 5) and (7, 1)

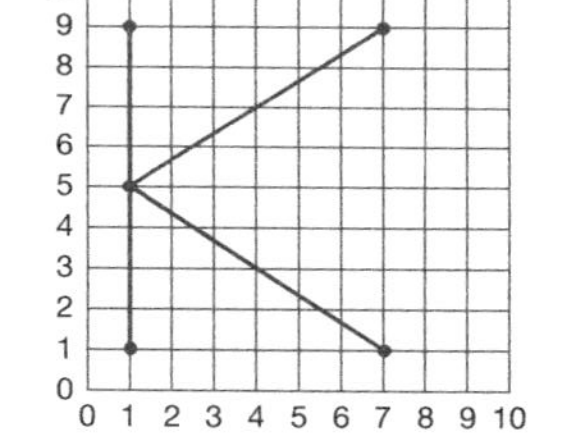

Page 78

Test Yourself

Circle the correct answer.

1. What is the area of each shape in square units?

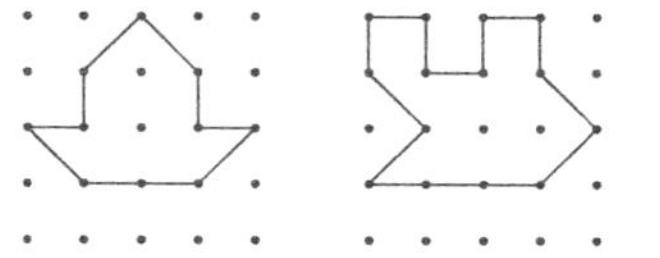

A. 6 square units, 8 square units (circled)
B. 7 square units, 7 square units
C. 8 square units, 6 square units
D. 9 square units, 8.5 square units

2. What is the area of each shape to the nearest square centimetre?

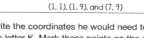

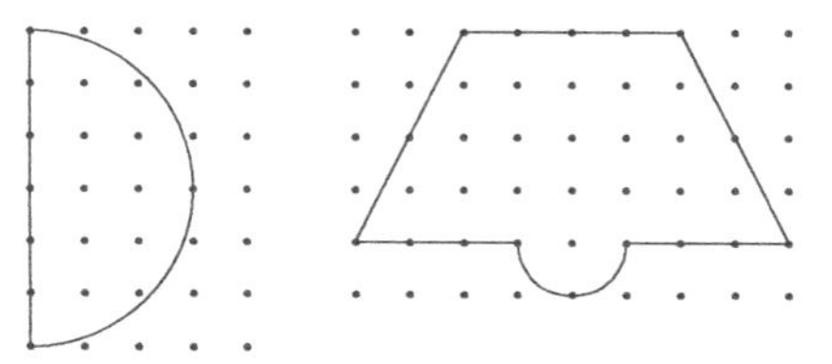

A. 11 cm^2, 24 cm^2
B. 14 cm^2, 26 cm^2 (circled)
C. 17 cm^2, 24 cm^2
D. 18 cm^2, 28 cm^2

3. Pat made a rectangle using square stickers. The stickers are 1 cm^2. The perimeter of the rectangle is 22 cm. Of all the rectangles Pat could have made, what are the dimensions of the rectangle with the smallest area and the rectangle with the largest area?

A. 2 cm by 9 cm, 4 cm by 7 cm
B. 3 cm by 8 cm, 4 cm by 7 cm
C. 4 cm by 7 cm, 5 cm by 6 cm
D. 1 cm by 10 cm, 5 cm by 6 cm (circled)

4. A rectangle has an area of 48 cm^2. What dimensions would give the shortest perimeter?

A. 6 cm by 6 cm
B. 6 cm by 8 cm (circled)
C. 4 cm by 12 cm
D. 2 cm by 24 cm

Page 79

Test Yourself Page 2

5. What is the area of each rectangle?

A. 648 cm^2, 24 cm^2 **B.** 648 m^2, 135 km^2 (circled)

C. 108 cm^2, 135 cm^2 **D.** 108 m^2, 24 km^2

6. A zoo has the shape of an 18 km by 12 km rectangle. A scale model of the zoo is shown below. What are the areas of the zoo and the model?

A. 60 km^2, 24 cm^2

B. 60 km^2, 20 cm^2

C. 216 km^2, 20 cm^2

D. 216 km^2, 24 cm^2 (circled)

7. What coordinates would describe this shape?

A. (7, 5), (5, 8), (3, 8), (1, 5), (3, 2), and (5, 2)

B. (5, 7), (8, 5), (8, 3), (1, 5), (3, 2), and (5, 2)

C. (5, 7), (8, 5), (8, 3), (5, 1), (2, 3), and (2, 5) (circled)

D. (5, 7), (5, 8), (3, 8), (1, 5), (3, 2) and (5, 2)

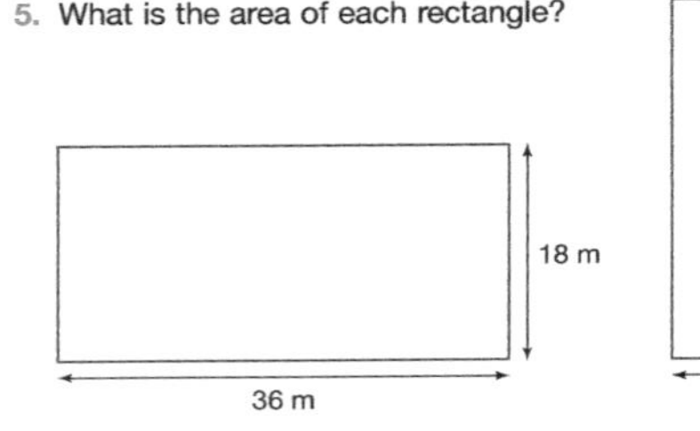

Page 80

Estimating Products

Goal **Estimate products of decimal numbers using whole numbers.**

1. Each team banner uses 1.9 m of fabric. The fabric costs \$7.99 for each metre.

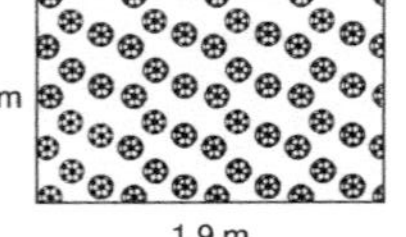

At-Home Help

To estimate decimal products, round each decimal to the nearest whole number. To get a closer estimate
- add a little if you rounded down
- subtract a little if you rounded up

For example:
To calculate 3.7 × 5.1, round 3.7 up to 4 and 5.1 down to 5.
Estimated answer is 4 × 5 = 20.

5.1 is closer to 5 than 3.7 is to 4. So to get a closer estimate, subtract a little from 20. Closer estimate is 20 − 2 = 18.

a) Estimate the number of metres needed for 30 banners.
Suggested answer: 60 m

b) Estimate the cost of fabric for 30 banners.
Suggested answer: \$480

c) Calculate the cost of fabric for 30 banners using a calculator. Explain why your estimate was higher or lower than the exact amount.
(actual cost) \$455.43 Suggested answer: \$480.00 was high because the amount of fabric was rounded up to 2 m and the cost was rounded up to \$8.00.

2. Trim for the perimeter of each banner costs \$2.89 for each metre. Each banner measures 1.2 m by 1.9 m. About how much will the trim cost for one banner? *\$18*

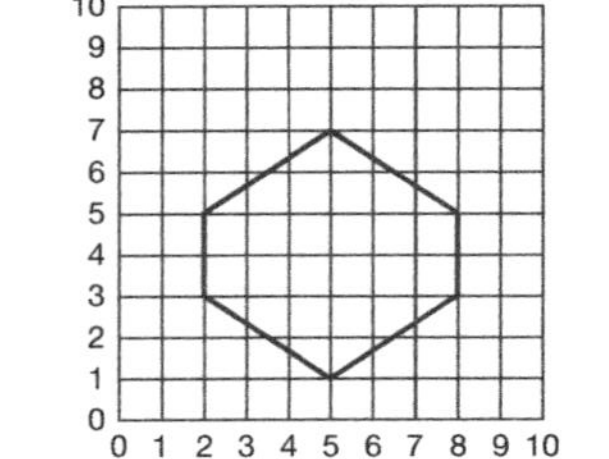

3. Estimate each product using whole numbers.

a) 8 × 2.6 *Suggested answer: 20*

b) 7.5 × 1.2 *Suggested answer: 9*

c) 5.1 × \$4.49 *Suggested answer: \$23*

Multiplying by 10 or 100

Multiply decimal tenths and hundredths by 10 and 100.

1. A math text is 2.5 cm thick. How high would a stack of 10 math texts be?

   25 cm

At-Home Help

When you multiply a decimal number by 10, the digit in the tenths place moves to the ones place.

For example:
6.8 × 10 = 68

Similarly, when multiplying a decimal number by 100, the digits in the tenths and hundredths places increase in place value.

For example:
4.57 × 100 = 457

2. A box of pencils is 19.5 cm long.

   a) How long would 10 boxes placed end to end be?

   195 cm or 1.95 m

   b) How long would 100 boxes placed end to end be?

   1950 cm or 19.5 m

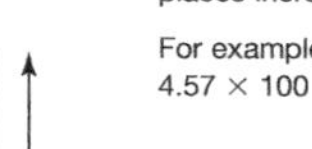
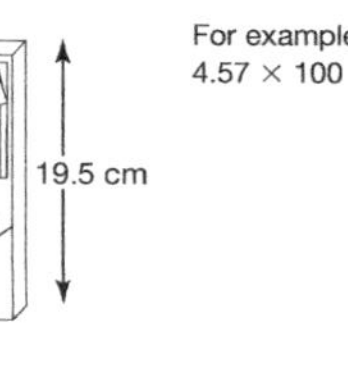

3. A package of tennis balls costs $3.79.

   a) What is the cost of 100 packages? *$379.00*

   b) What is the cost of 10 packages? *$37.90*

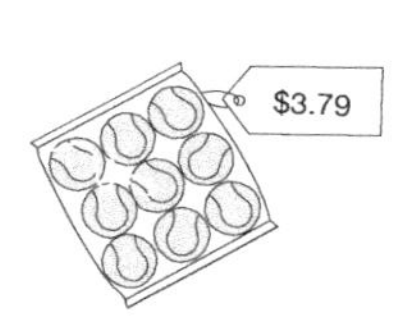

4. The mass of a package of tennis balls is 0.45 kg. What would the mass of 10 and 100 boxes be? Circle the correct answer.

   45 kg, 450 kg   (4.5 kg, 45 kg)   4.5 g, 45 g   0.45 kg, 4.5 kg

Multiplying Tenths by Whole Numbers

Multiply decimal tenths by whole numbers using drawings and symbols.

You will need a ruler or tape measure.

1. The mass of a stapler is 0.2 kg. What is the mass of 9 staplers?

   1.8 kg

2. Mrs. Gulliver used four 1.7 m pieces of border for a bulletin board. How many metres did she use?

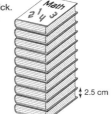

   1.7 m

   She used 6.8m.

At-Home Help

When you multiply a whole number by a decimal tenth, it is like multiplying two whole numbers except you have to put in the decimal point because it is tenths.

For example:
57 × 2 = 114
5.7 × 2 = 11.4

3. Rajiv lined up six loonies. Each loonie is 2.5 cm wide. How long is the line of loonies?

   15 cm

4. Bianca drinks 0.7 L of milk each day. How much milk does she drink in one week? *4.9 L*

5. Measure the width of this workbook to the nearest tenth of a centimetre. How long would 6 workbooks be if they were put together side by side? *21.3 cm x 6 = 127.8 cm*

Page 83

Multiplying Hundredths by Whole Numbers

Multiply decimal hundredths by whole numbers using models, drawings, and symbols.

1. Neela ordered 4 tickets. Each ticket cost $4.75.

   a) Calculate the total cost. $19.00

   b) How could you have predicted that the cost was less than $20.00? Explain.

   Suggested answer: The price of one ticket is less than $5.00, and $5 x 4 = $20. So the exact cost must be less than $20.00.

2. Multiply.

   a) 3.43 × 5   *17.15*   **b)** 6.26 × 2   *12.52*

3. Evan cycled 6.68 km. Nadia rode twice as far on her bike. How do you know that Nadia rode more than 13 km?

   Nadia rode twice as far as Evan. 6 x 2 = 12, 6.5 x 2 = 13, so 6.68 x 2 is more than 13.

At-Home Help

When you multiply a whole number by a decimal hundredth, it is like multiplying two whole numbers except you have to put in the decimal point because it is hundredths.

For example:
675 × 3 = 2025
6.75 × 3 = 20.25

Page 84

Communicate About Estimation Strategies

Explain estimation strategies to determine if a solution is reasonable.

1. Each Canadian dollar is worth $0.76 US. Estimate the cost in US dollars of a software package priced at $30.00 Canadian. Explain your thinking.

   Sample answer: between $21 and $24, or about $22

   $30 Canadian = 30 x 0.76 US

   30 x 0.7 = 21   30 x 0.8 = 24

2. Use the exchange rate in Question 1. Estimate the cost in US dollars of adult and child admission to the Toronto Zoo. Admission costs in Canadian dollars are $18.00 for adults and $12.00 for children. Explain how you estimated. *Suggested answer:*

   Adult admission is about $ *14* US.

   Child admission is about $ *8* US.

   Round 18 to 20 and 0.76 to 0.7

   20 x 0.7 = 14

   Round 12 to 10 and 0.76 to 0.8

   10 x 0.8 = 8

At-Home Help

Use the Communication Checklist when explaining and justifying your estimation strategies. You may round or group numbers to make your explanations more clear. You may also want to use models to justify your answer.

For example, to estimate 1.79 × 8, you may say: "I round 1.79 to 2, then I multiply 2 × 8 = 16. I know my estimate is a bit high because I rounded up."

Communication Checklist
☑ Did you show all your steps?
☑ Did you use a model?
☑ Did you explain your thinking?

3. One euro is worth about $1.67 Canadian. Tim estimates that a book that costs 25 euros would cost about $30.00 Canadian. Explain how you would decide if this estimate makes sense.

   Suggested answer: The estimate does not make sense because it is very low. If the book was 10 euros, then it would cost $16.70 Canadian. But the book costs 25 euros, so the cost is at least $16 + $16 + $8, which is a lot more than $30.

4. A can of apple juice contains 1.36 L of juice. Serina bought 9 cans of juice. What is the best estimate of the amount of juice she bought? Circle the correct answer.

   (12 L)   14 L   9 L   18 L

Page 85

Choosing a Multiplication Method

Goal **Justify the choice of a multiplication method.**

1. If you know the cost of 10 tiles, how can you calculate the cost of 100 tiles?

Multiply the cost of 10 tiles by 10.

2. If you know how much water to add to 1 can of juice concentrate, how can you calculate how much to add to 2 cans?

Multiply amount of water by 2.

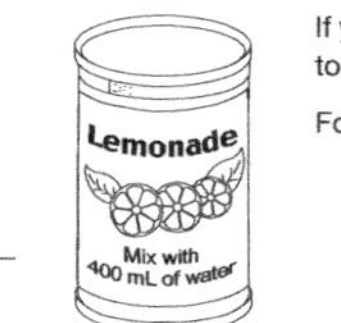

At-Home Help

If numbers are simple in a question, you can use mental math. Multiplying by 10 or 100, or multiplying one-digit numbers, can be done mentally.

For example, $7.00 × 8 = $56.00.

If you can multiply numbers without a lot of regrouping, use pencil and paper.

For example, $5.20 × 7 = $36.40.

If you have to use a lot of regrouping to multiply, use a calculator.

For example, $6.47 × 12 = $77.64.

3. Calculate the cost of 5 kg of each fruit.

apples $2.29/kg
bananas $1.10/kg
stawberries $4.00/kg
oranges $1.87/kg

a) Which calculation(s) would you do mentally? Explain your thinking.

strawberries. It is easy to multiply $4.00/kg by 5 mentally.

b) Which calculation(s) would you do with pencil and paper? Explain your thinking.

bananas. It is not difficult to multiply $1.10/kg by 5 with pencil and paper. There is no regrouping.

c) Which calculation(s) would you do with a calculator? Explain your thinking.

apples and oranges. Multiplying $2.29/kg by 5 and $1.87/kg by 5 would involve several regroupings, so it is easier to use a calculator.

Page 86

Test Yourself

Circle the correct answer.

1. What whole numbers would be best to estimate the product of 5.7 × $3.35?

A. 5 × $3 **B.** 5 × $4 **(C.** 6 × $3**)** **D.** 6 × $4

2. Fabric for a flag costs $7.69 for each metre. The flag is 6.3 m long. Vanessa estimated the cost by multiplying 6 × $8 = $48. How would you describe her estimate?

A. very high **B.** very low **(C.** close**)** **D.** high

3. You multiply a decimal number by 10 and the product is 55. What is the decimal number?

(A. 5.5**)** **B.** 55 **C.** 55.5 **D.** 0.55

4. An insect's image is 1.4 cm in length. It is enlarged to 100 times that length. What is the enlarged length?

A. 14 cm **(B.** 140 cm**)** **C.** 14 m **D.** 1.4 cm

5. A hundreds block represents 1. What multiplication question is modelled here?

(A. 1.7 × 4 = 6.8**)**
B. 1.7 × 4 = 5.8
C. 4 × 1.7 = 8.6
D. 4 × 1.7 = 68

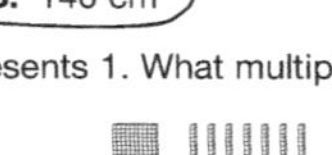

6. A hundreds block represents 1. This arrangement models a multiplication question. It can also show a related multiplication question. What are the two questions?

A. 4 × 3.5 and 2 × 8
B. 4 × 3.5 and 7 × 8
C. 4 × 3.5 and 4 × 7
(D. 4 × 3.5 and 2 × 7**)**

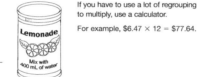

Page 87

Test Yourself Page 2

7. A binder costs $3.69 and a package of paper costs $1.49. Megan buys 3 binders and 4 packages of paper. What is the total cost before taxes?

   A. $11.07 B. $19.23 (C. $17.03) D. $5.96

8. Serge cycles 0.15 km each minute. How far will he cycle in 12 minutes?

   A. 18 km (B. 1.8 km) C. 180 km D. 1.5 km

9. Serge has to cycle 5 km. He cycles at a rate of 0.15 km/min. About how long will it take him to cycle 5 km?

   A. about 15 min B. about 60 min (C. about 30 min) D. about 1.5 h

10. Ed has to calculate these products. He wants to do the calculations efficiently.

    (i) 6.17 × 11 (ii) 4.10 × 5 (iii) $5.32 × 2 (iv) $8.00 × 8

    What methods should Ed use?

    (A. (i) a calculator, (ii) pencil and paper, (iii) pencil and paper, (iv) mentally)

    B. (i) mentally, (ii) a calculator, (iii) pencil and paper, (iv) a calculator

    C. (i) pencil and paper, (ii) a calculator, (iii) mentally, (iv) mentally

    D. (i) pencil and paper, (ii) mentally, (iii) mentally, (iv) a calculator

11. A package of stickers costs $3.69. How can you calculate how much 5 packages cost?

    A. Multiply $3.69 by 10.

    B. Divide $3.69 by 10.

    (C. Multiply $3.69 by 5.)

    D. Divide $3.69 by 5.

Page 88

Estimating Quotients

Estimate quotients when dividing decimal numbers.

Heather is wrapping gifts. She has 5.25 m of ribbon.

At-Home Help

A **quotient** is the answer to a division question.

For example, 2 is the quotient of 14 ÷ 7.

14 ÷ 7 = 2

When you divide a decimal number by a whole number, it is easier to estimate the answer if you round the decimal to the nearest whole number.

For example, to estimate the answer to 8.8 ÷ 4, you may round 8.8 to 9.

9 ÷ 4 is about 2.

1. Heather wants to use this ribbon for 2 gifts. Estimate the length she will use for each gift.

   Suggested answer: about 2.5 m

2. She wants to use this ribbon for 3 gifts. Estimate the length she will use for each gift.

   Suggested answer: about 1.75 m

3. How could you use your answer to Question 1 to estimate the length needed for 4 gifts?

   Divide answer to Question 1 by 2.

4. The shortest length of ribbon Heather can use to decorate a gift is about 0.5 m. Does she have enough ribbon to decorate 10 gifts?

   Yes.

Page 89

Dividing by 10

Goal **Use regrouping to divide decimal numbers by 10.**

1. Craig wants to calculate the length of his running stride. He ran 14.6 m in 10 strides.

   a) Calculate the length of Craig's stride.

   Craig's stride is 1.46 m long.

   b) Use multiplication to check your answer to Part **a)**. 1.46 m x 10 = 14.6 m

At-Home Help

When you divide any number by 10, the quotient has the same digits as the dividend but each digit moves to the next lower place value.

For example, using whole numbers, 350 ÷ 10 = 35. The 3 hundreds in 350 become 3 tens, the 5 tens become 5 ones, and the 0 ones become 0 tenths.

Using decimal numbers, 67.8 ÷ 10 = 6.78. The 6 tens become 6 ones, the 7 ones become 7 tenths, and the 8 tenths become 8 hundredths.

2. A patio is 4.4 m long. It is divided into 10 equal sections for placing flower pots. How wide is each section?

   0.44 m or 44 cm

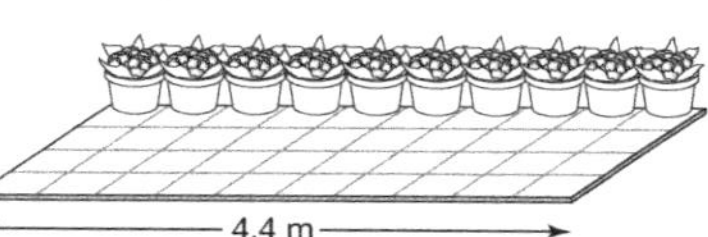

3. A bike rack has sections to park 10 bikes. What is the width of each section if the bike rack is 6.5 m long?

   0.65 m or 65 cm

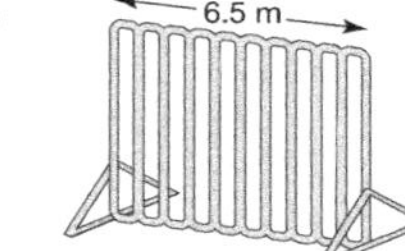

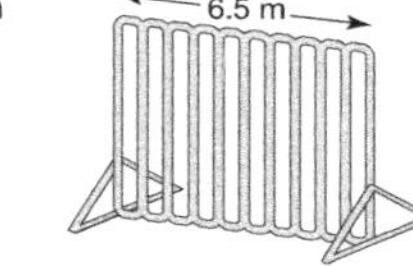

4. Calculate.

   a) 23 ÷ 10 — 2.3
   b) 16.9 ÷ 10 — 1.69
   c) 66.2 ÷ 10 — 6.62
   d) $10\overline{)44.4}$ — 4.44
   e) $10\overline{)239.7}$ — 23.97
   f) $10\overline{)263.1}$ — 26.31

Page 90

Calculating a Decimal Quotient

Goal **Express quotients as decimal numbers to tenths or hundredths.**

1. Graciela has 6 kg of strawberries to divide equally into 8 bags. Calculate the mass of each bag to 2 decimal places. Show your work.

   0.75 kg
   8)6.00 kg
   5.6
   0.40
   0.40
   0.00

At-Home Help

When you divide numbers, it is sometimes possible to find a quotient to the nearest tenth or hundredth. This is done by regrouping the remaining ones to tenths and any remaining tenths to hundredths.

For example:

   2.75
   4)11.00
   8
   3.0
   2.8
   0.**20**
   0.20
   0.00

When 3 ones remain, regroup as 30 tenths.

When 2 tenths remain, regroup as 20 hundredths.

11 ÷ 4 to the nearest hundredth is 2.75.

2. What will be the mass of each bag if the scale measures mass to tenths of a kilogram?

   a) 7 kg divided into 2 bags 3.5 kg
   b) 4 kg divided into 8 bags 0.5 kg

3. Calculate to 2 decimal places.

   a) 14 ÷ 8 — 1.75
   b) 12 ÷ 5 — 2.40
   c) 4 ÷ 5 — 0.80
   d) 2 ÷ 8 — 0.25

4. Jacob wants to cut a 22 m length of string into 8 equal pieces. Calculate the length of each piece to 2 decimal places.

   2.75 m

Dividing Decimals by Whole Numbers

Divide a decimal by a one-digit whole number using models and symbols.

1. Sam's garden is 1.5 m by 6 m. He divided it into 4 equal sections.

   a) Estimate the area of each section. Show your work.

   Suggested answer: about 3 m².
   Round 1.5 m to 2 m.
   2 m x 6 m = 12 m²
   12 m² ÷ 4 = 3 m²

   b) Calculate the area to two decimal places. Show your work.

   1.5 m x 6 m = 9 m²

   $$\begin{array}{r} 2.25\ \text{m}^2 \\ 4\overline{)9.00\ \text{m}^2} \\ \underline{8} \\ 1.0 \\ \underline{0.8} \\ 0.20 \\ \underline{0.20} \\ 0.00 \end{array}$$

At-Home Help

When you divide a decimal number by a whole number, apply the same rules for division as when you divide two whole numbers. Any whole number remainder is regrouped to tenths and combined with any tenths. Then any remaining tenths are regrouped to hundredths and combined with any hundredths.

For example:

$$\begin{array}{r} 5.63 \\ 4\overline{)22.52} \\ \underline{20} \\ 2.5 \\ \underline{2.4} \\ 0.12 \\ \underline{0.12} \\ 0.00 \end{array}$$

When 2 ones remain, regroup as 20 tenths and combine with 5 tenths.

When 1 tenth remains, regroup as 10 hundredths and combine with 2 hundredths.

22.52 ÷ 4 to the nearest hundredth is 5.63.

2. Calculate to two decimal places.

   a) 1.98 ÷ 2 — 0.99 **b)** 7.26 ÷ 3 — 2.42

   c) 13.64 ÷ 4 — 3.41 **d)** 5.85 ÷ 5 — 1.17

3. A bulletin board measures 2.35 m by 6 m. It is divided into 3 equal sections. Calculate the area of each section to two decimal places.
   4.70 m²

4. A hula hoop travels 17.04 m after 6 complete turns.

   a) Estimate the circumference of the hula hoop.
   Suggested answer: about 3 m

   b) Calculate the circumference of the hoop to the nearest hundredth of a metre. 2.84 m

   c) How far will the hula hoop travel after 4 complete turns? 11.36 m

Choosing a Calculation Method

Justify your choice of calculation method.

Ms Shishido is making origami swans from a sheet of coloured paper. The paper measures 10.5 cm by 46.5 cm. She divides the area into 6 equal parts. Each part has a length of 10.5 cm.

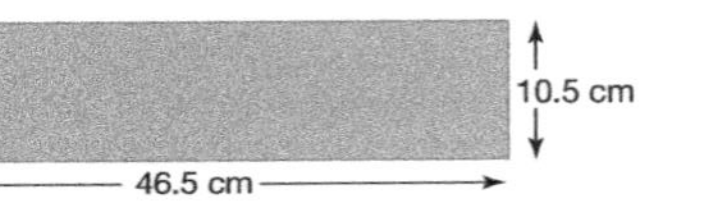

At-Home Help

To solve problems, it is important to choose an appropriate calculation method.

- If the numbers are easy to work with, use mental math.
- If the problem asks "About how many ..." use estimation.
- If the problem asks for an accurate answer and you cannot easily calculate the numbers in your head, then use paper and pencil or a calculator.

1. About how wide is each part? about 8 cm
   To get my answer I used estimation
   because the question asks for an estimate, not an exact answer.

2. How wide is each part to the nearest hundredth of a centimetre? 7.75 cm
   To get my answer I used calculator or paper and pencil because the question requires an accurate answer and it is not easy to calculate 46.5 ÷ 6 in my head.

3. If the coloured paper were divided into 3 equal parts, how wide would each part be? 15.5 cm
   To get my answer I used calculator or paper and pencil because it is not easy to calculate 46.5 ÷ 3 in my head.

4. If 10 swans were made from the coloured paper, what would be the width of each part? 4.65 cm
   To get my answer I used mental math because it is easy to divide 46.5 cm by 10.

Dividing to Compare

 **Use division and other operations to solve problems about money.**

You will need a calculator.

1. Vasco, his father, and his grandfather, who is a senior citizen, tour the zoo regularly by bus. Vasco is in Grade 5.

	Single-fare ticket	Book of 5 tickets
Adult	$3.50	$14.00
Senior and student	$2.50	$9.50
Child (12 and under)	$1.25	$4.50

a) What is the cost difference per ticket between a single-fare ticket and a book of tickets? Show your work.

	Cost per ticket using book of 5 tickets	Savings per ticket
Adult	$14.00 ÷ 5 = $2.80	$3.50 – $2.80 = $0.70
Senior	$9.50 ÷ 5 = $1.90	$2.50 – $1.90 = $0.60
Child	$4.50 ÷ 5 = $0.90	$1.25 – $0.90 = $0.35

b) How much would each person save by using a book of tickets instead of single-fare tickets? Show your work.

(adult) 5 x $0.70 = $3.50, (senior) 5 x $0.60 = $3.00,
(child) 5 x $0.35 = $1.75

2. A package of 3 energy-efficient light bulbs costs $9.87. A package of 5 bulbs costs $14.95.

a) What is the cost difference per light bulb between the two packages? Show your work.

(cost per bulb in package of 3) $9.87 ÷ 3 = $3.29,
(cost per bulb in package of 5) $14.95 ÷ 5 = $2.99
(difference) $3.29 – $2.99 = $0.30

b) If 15 high-efficiency bulbs are purchased, what will be the cost difference between buying them in packages of 3 and packages of 5?

15 x $0.30 = $4.50

At-Home Help

There are two ways to compare costs if you know the cost of a package of items and the cost of an individual item.

- Find the cost per item in the package by dividing the cost by the number of items.
- Multiply the cost of an individual item by the number of items in the package.

For example:

The cost of a package of 5 tennis balls is $3.95 and the cost of one tennis ball is $1.19.

cost of one tennis ball in package = $3.95 ÷ 5
= $0.79
difference = $1.19 − $0.79
= $0.40 per tennis ball

OR

cost of 5 tennis balls = 5 × $1.19
= $5.95
difference = $5.95 − $3.95
= $2.00 per 5 tennis balls

It is more expensive to buy the tennis balls individually.

Calculating the Mean

 **Use division to calculate the mean.**

1. Karen and Fariq play basketball on different teams. Their team scores for last month are shown below.

Karen's team scores	Fariq's team scores
26	37
33	13
17	22
24	

Calculate the mean score for each team.

(Karen) 25, (Fariq) 24

2. Calculate the mean of each set of numbers.

a) 5, 8, 8, 9, 10
8

b) 2, 3, 4, 5, 6
4

c) 120, 130, 342, 376
242

d) 12.4, 11.2, 9.1, 7.7
10.1

3. **a)** Create a set of 5 different numbers where the mean is one of the original numbers.

Suggested answer: 10, 11, 13, 15, 16
(mean) 13

b) Create a set of 3 different numbers where the mean is not one of the original numbers.

Suggested answer: 150, 200, 226
(mean) 192

At-Home Help

The **mean** of a set of numbers is equal to the sum of all the numbers divided by the number of numbers in the set.

For example:

7, 8, 9, 11, 11, 14

sum = 7 + 8 + 9 + 11 + 11 + 14
= 60
mean = 60 ÷ 6
= 10

Page 95

Solve Problems by Working Backward

Use a working backward strategy to solve problems.

1. Keisha delivers advertising flyers. He delivered 16 flyers in his own apartment building. Then he divided the remainder into 3 groups of 27 to deliver in nearby buildings.

   a) How many flyers did Keisha have originally?

   97 flyers

   b) Draw a diagram as in At-Home Help to show how you solved the problem by working backward.

? number of flyers → Subtract 16. → Divide by 3. → Each group has 27 flyers.

? number of flyers ← Add 16. ← Multiply by 3. ← Each group has 27 flyers.

2. Frank collects comic books. He tripled his collection last month. Then his friend gave him 20 more comics. Now he has 68 comics.

   How many comics did Frank have one month ago? Use a working backward strategy. Show your work.

   16 comics

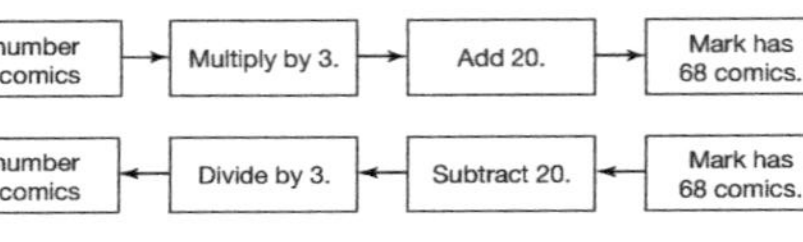

3. A number is multiplied by 8. Then 6.4 is added to the product. The result is 80. What is the original number? 9.2

4. Tickets for a concert were sold during the week. 23 were sold on Monday. 30 were sold on Tuesday. On Wednesday 39 were left. How many tickets were there originally? 92 tickets

At-Home Help

To solve some problems, it is easier to find the answer by working backward.

Start by drawing a diagram to help figure out each operation you need to use.

Remember that multiplication is the opposite operation to division, and subtraction is the opposite operation to addition.

For example:

A number is multiplied by 5. Then 5 is added to it and the result is 40. What is the original number?

? original number. → Multiply by 5. → Add 5. → Result is 40.

? original number. ← Divide by 5. ← Subtract 5. ← Result is 40.

The original number is 7.

Page 96

Test Yourself

Circle the correct answer.

1. A 1.89 L carton of lemonade is shared equally by 6 people. What is the best estimate of each person's share?

   (**A.** 0.3 L) **B.** 0.4 L **C.** 0.5 L **D.** 0.6 L

2. Jason's mother drove to work and back, and nowhere else, each day for 5 days. The odometer showed she had driven 95.3 km. What is the distance from her home to her workplace?

   A. 953 m **B.** 95.30 km (**C.** 9.53 km) **D.** 0.953 km

3. A 45.7 m wide parking lot is divided into 10 parking spaces. What is the width of one parking space?

   A. 457 m **B.** 45.70 m (**C.** 4.57 m) **D.** 0.457 m

4. A 1.2 kg package of trail mix is shared equally by 8 people. What is the mass of each person's share?

   A. 120 g (**B.** 0.15 kg) **C.** 1.5 kg **D.** 1.2 kg

5. An open office space measures 24 m by 3.5 m. It is divided into 8 equal-sized cubicles. What is the area of each cubicle?

   A. 84 m^2 **B.** 84 cm^2 **C.** 105 m^2 (**D.** 10.5 m^2)

6. What methods would you use to do these calculations?

   (i) What is the cost of 10 L of gas?

   (ii) About how much would 25 L of gas cost?

   (iii) How much change would Mr. Kwan receive if he paid $40.00 for 25 L of gas?

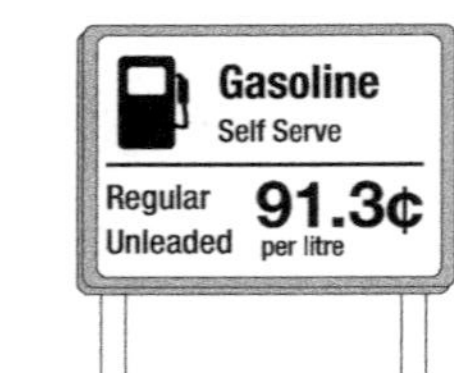

Gasoline
Self Serve
Regular Unleaded
91.3¢
per litre

   A. (i) mental math, (ii) a calculator, (iii) estimation

   (**B.** (i) mental math, (ii) estimation, (iii) a calculator)

   C. (i) estimation, (ii) mental math, (iii) a calculator

   D. (i) a calculator, (ii) estimation, (iii) mental math

Page 97

Test Yourself Page 2

7. A package of 6 containers of yogurt costs $2.94. Individually these containers cost $0.65. What is the cost difference between purchasing the package and purchasing 6 individually?

A. $0.96 (circled) **B.** $0.16 **C.** $1.96 **D.** $0.80

8. High temperatures for a five-day period were recorded.

Temperature (°C)	17.3°C	18.7°C	14.4°C	19.2°C	11.9°C

What is the mean high temperature for this period?

A. 14.4°C **B.** 16.3°C (circled) **C.** 16°C **D.** 17.3°C

9. How would you label these statements?

(i) The mean of a set of numbers must be one of the original numbers.

(ii) The mean of a set of numbers can be one of the original numbers.

(iii) The mean of a set of numbers must lie within the range of the numbers in the set.

A. (i) true, (ii) false, (iii) true **B.** (i) false, (ii) true, (iii) false

C. (i) true, (ii) false, (iii) false **D.** (i) false, (ii) true, (iii) true (circled)

10. A scout group is divided into 6 equal squads. At the last meeting, Squad A had 2 members absent and 7 members present. How many members are in the group altogether?

A. 42 **B.** 30 **C.** 50 **D.** 54 (circled)

11. A case of 4 1 L cartons of juice costs $8.96. Individual cartons cost $2.49. What is the cost difference per carton between a case and 4 individual cartons?

A. $0.25 (circled) **B.** $0.30

C. $0.20 **D.** $0.26

Page 98

Making 3-D Shapes

Draw and build 3-D shapes.

1. **a)** Sketch all the faces of the tent. The base has been drawn for you.

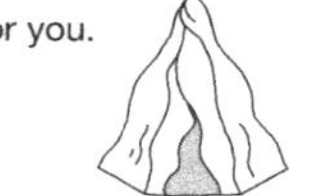

b) What shape is the base? hexagon

c) What shape are the other faces? triangles

d) Use modelling clay to make the 3-D object. Make the base first and then the faces that join at the top vertex.

e) Draw the model starting with the base. Locate the top vertex and join the vertices.

f) What is the shape of the tent? hexagon-based pyramid

2. **a)** Draw the faces of a hexagon-based prism.

b) Draw the model of the prism.

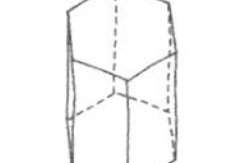

At-Home Help

Steps to draw and build 3-D objects

- Find a model.
- Sketch all the faces.

A pyramid has a base and 3 or more triangular faces.

A prism has a base and top that are congruent, and 3 or more rectangular faces.

- Use modelling clay to make the object. Always start with the base.
- Draw the model. Always start with the base.

top vertex

Page 99

Making Nets

Make nets for 3-D shapes.

1. 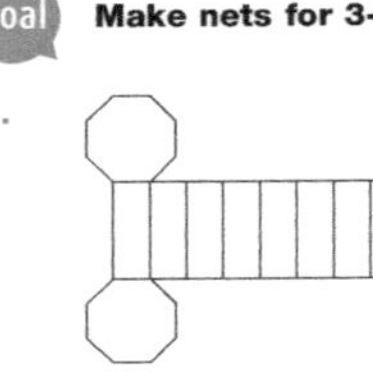

a) Is this the net of a pyramid or a prism? Explain.
It is a prism because there is a top and base that are congruent, and the other faces are rectangles. A pyramid would have a base but no top, and the other faces would be triangles.

b) Name the 3-D object.
octagon-based prism

c) Draw another net for this object.
Suggested answer:

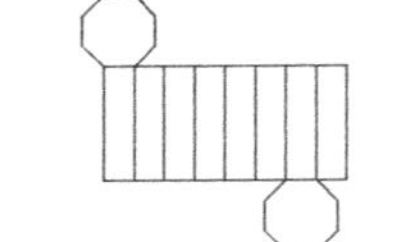

d) Trace it on another piece of paper. Cut it out and fold to check.

2. **a)** Name the 3-D object.
triangle-based pyramid

b) Draw a net for this object.
Suggested answer:

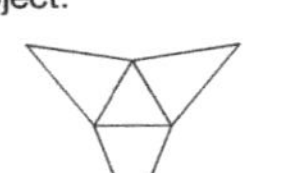

At-Home Help

When you make nets from 3-D objects

- make sure all the faces are traced only once
- make sure the faces are connected in the drawing
- check that the appropriate faces are the same size and shape
- cut out the net and fold to check

This net of a pyramid has triangles attached to the base.

This net of a prism has rectangles all connected. The base and top are congruent, and are attached to opposite sides of the rectangles.

Page 100

Identifying Nets

Match 3-D shapes with their nets.

A B C D 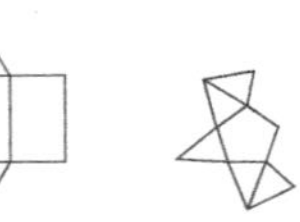

E F G H

a b c d 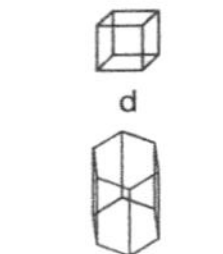

e f g h

At-Home Help

To identify the nets of pyramids and prisms and match them with their 3-D models, ask yourself:

- Does the net have a top and a base that are congruent?
- What shape are the other faces on the net?
- Does the 3-D model have a top and a base that are congruent?
- What shape are the other faces on the 3-D model?

If the net has a base but no top and the other faces are triangles, then it is a pyramid.

If the net has a top and a base that are congruent and the other faces are rectangles, then it is a prism.

1. **a)** Identify the nets of the pyramids. B, D, E, and H

   b) Explain how you know they are nets of pyramids.
   The nets of pyramids have a base but no top, and the other faces are triangles.

2. **a)** Identify the nets of the prisms. A, C, F, and G

   b) Explain how you know they are nets of prisms.
   The nets of prisms have a top and a base that are congruent, and the other faces are rectangles.

3. Match each pyramid with its net. a and E, c and B, e and D, and g and H

4. Match each prism with its net. b and C, d and G, f and F, and h and A

Communicate About Building a Model

Write clear instructions for building a model from a picture.

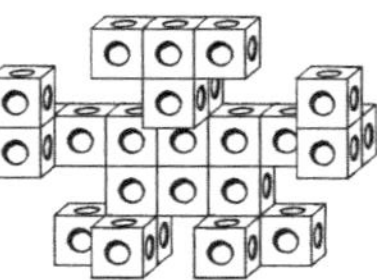

Wendy wrote instructions to make this cube creature.

You will need a whole bunch of cubes.
The head is like a T-shape.
The arms are sticking out, and each arm is 3 cubes.
Each hand is 1 cube, attached to the end of each arm.
The body is flat in the middle.
The legs are short, with 3 cubes each.

At-Home Help

When you communicate about building a model
- give clear instructions using math language
- show all the steps needed to build the model
- give directions in the correct order
- give the right amount of detail for each step
- do not give information that is not useful, such as the colour of the cubes

Communication Checklist

☑ Did you show all the steps?
☑ Did you use the right amount of detail?
☑ Did you use math language?

1. Go over Wendy's instructions. Revise and improve each line if necessary.

   Suggested answer:
   You will need 25 cubes to build the model.
   The head has 3 cubes all connected in a row.
   The neck has 2 cubes connected in a row directly below the head.
   The body has 6 cubes, arranged in 2 rows of 3 cubes each.
   There are 2 arms. Each arm has 2 cubes that are connected, extending from the top row of the body.
   There are 2 hands. Each hand has 2 cubes that are connected, attached to the end of each arm.
   There are 2 feet. Each foot has 2 cubes that are connected, attached below the bottom row of the body.
   There are decorations on both feet. Each foot has 1 cube on the outer side.

2. Check your instructions using the Communication Checklist.

   Suggested answer:
   I showed all the steps.
   I used the right amount of detail.
   I used math language.

3. How can you improve your instructions?

   Suggested answer:
   I can improve my instructions by giving the orientation of the cubes in the neck, hands, and feet.

Measuring and Comparing Capacity

Estimate, measure, and compare capacities, and determine relationships among units.

1. **a)** Choose two cups of different sizes in your home. Label them A and B.

   b) Would you use millilitres or litres to measure the capacity of each cup? Write your choices in the chart and explain your thinking.

	Capacity unit
Cup A	*Suggested answer: mL* *I would use millilitres because the cup is small in size.*
Cup B	*Suggested answer: L* *I would use litres because the cup can easily hold a litre.*

2. Use a big spoon or a soup ladle to compare the capacity of the two cups in Question 1.

   a) Estimate the number of spoonfuls that will fill each cup. Then measure and record the number in the table.

	My estimate: capacity in spoonfuls	Actual capacity in spoonfuls
Cup A	*Suggested answer: 5*	*Suggested answer: 6*
Cup B	*Suggested answer: 9*	*Suggested answer: 10*

   b) Which cup has a larger capacity? Explain how you know.

   (using suggested answer given) Cup B because it can hold 10 spoonfuls while Cup A can hold only 6 spoonfuls.

   c) Describe another method you could use to compare the capacity of the two cups.

   Suggested answer: Fill one of the cups with water. Then pour the water into the other cup. If the water overflows, then the second cup has a smaller capacity. If the water does not fill the cup, then the second cup has a larger capacity.

At-Home Help

The **capacity** of a container refers to how much the container can hold. Capacity can be measured using millilitres or litres.

Compare the capacities of two containers using one of these ways.
- Fill each container with water. Then pour the water into a graduated pitcher to measure the capacity. The container with the larger capacity can hold the most liquid.

- Use a spoon or small cup. Record the number of spoonfuls needed to fill each container. The container with the larger capacity can hold the most spoonfuls.
- Fill one container with water. Then pour the water into the other container. If the water overflows, then the first container has a larger capacity. If the water does not fill the container, then the first container has a smaller capacity.

Page 103

Measuring and Comparing Volume

Goal **Estimate, measure, and compare volumes using cubic centimetres.**

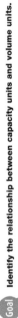

Tanisha's cube creature

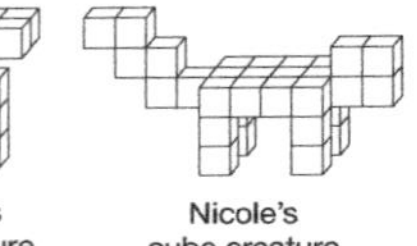

Nicole's cube creature

At-Home Help

Volume is the space taken up by an object.

To measure the volume of a 3-D object made from centimetre cubes, count the total number of cubes using one of these two ways.

- Count the number of cubes in each section. Then find the total number of cubes for all sections.
- Look at the object from above. Count the number of cubes in each column. Then find the total number of cubes for all columns.

The unit for volume is cubic centimetres (cm^3).

Both creatures were made using centimetre linking cubes.

1. **a)** For Tanisha's creature, count and record the number of cubes in each body part.

Body part	Number of cubes
head	2
body	16
2 arms	4 (2 for each arm)
2 hands	2 (1 for each hand)
2 legs	6 (3 for each leg)
2 feet	2 (1 for each foot)

b) What is the volume of Tanisha's creature in cubic centimetres? Show your work.

Volume = total number of cubes
= 2 + 16 + 4 + 2 + 6 + 2
= 32 cm^3

2. **a)** For Nicole's creature, imagine you are looking at the creature from above. Count and record the number of cubes in each column.

0	0	0	0	3	1	1	3	0	0
1	2	2	1	1	1	1	1	2	2
0	0	0	0	3	1	1	3	0	0

b) What is the volume of Nicole's creature in cubic centimetres? Show your work.

Volume = total number of cubes
= 1 + 2 + 2 + 1 + 7 + 3 + 3 + 7 + 2 + 2
= 30 cm^3

Page 104

Relating Capacity Units to Volume

Goal **Identify the relationship between capacity units and volume units.**

A: 16 cm^3

B: 30 cm^3

C: 31 cm^3

D: 22 cm^3

E: 100 cm^3

F: 36 cm^3

At-Home Help

The units of volume and capacity are related.

1 cm^3 = 1 mL

The volume of a 3-D object can be measured using water displacement.

- Record the volume of water in the measuring cup at the start.
- Then put the object under water.
- Record the volume of water with the object in the measuring cup.
- The difference between the 2 volumes is equal to the volume of the object.

For example, the water level went from 400 mL to 430 mL when this object was put under water. So the volume of the object is 30 mL or 30 cm^3.

Models A to F were made using centimetre linking cubes.

1. Find the volume of each model in cubic centimetres. Write your answer below each model.

2. Each of the models A to F was put under water in a measuring cup to measure its volume.

a: before 400 mL, after 422 mL — 22 mL

b: before 400 mL, after 500 mL — 100 mL

c: before 400 mL, after 416 mL — 16 mL

d: before 400 mL, after 430 mL — 30 mL

e: before 400 mL, after 436 mL — 36 mL

f: before 400 mL, after 431 mL — 31 mL

Find the capacity of displaced water in millilitres. Write your answer below each measuring cup.

3. Match each model with the correct measuring cup.

Model	Measuring cup
A	c
B	d
C	f
D	a
E	b
F	e

Page 105

Measuring and Comparing Mass

Estimate, measure, and compare the masses of objects using appropriatenits.

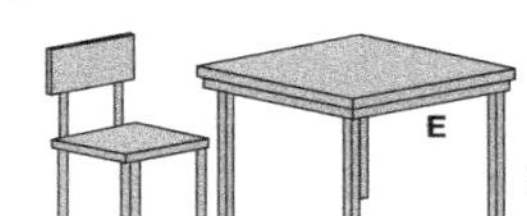

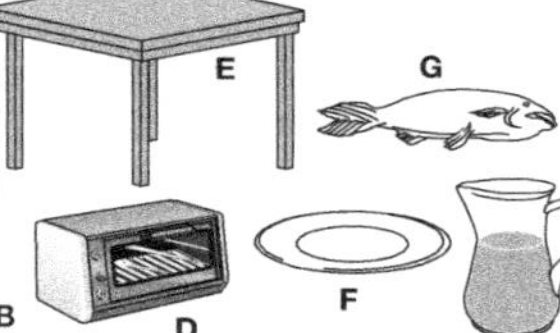

At-Home Help

The mass of most objects we can carry can be measured in grams or kilograms.

1 kg = 1000 g

1. Circle the unit you would use to measure the mass of the objects in the picture.

   A **g**, kg B **g**, kg C g, **kg** D g, **kg**

   E g, **kg** F **g**, kg G g, **kg** H g, **kg**

2. Match the masses below with the objects in the picture. There may be more than one possible answer for some masses.

   a) 7 kg C, D, G b) 30 g A, B

   c) 10 kg C d) 150 g B, F

   e) 4 kg D, G, H f) 35 kg E

   g) 250 g B, F h) 3 kg D, G, H

3. List three objects you can find in your home that would be best measured in grams.

   Suggested answer: spoon, hat, and CD

4. List three objects you can find in your home that would be best measured in kilograms.

   Suggested answer: vacuum cleaner, lawn mower, and TV

Page 106

Using Tonnes

Relate tonnes to kilograms.

At-Home Help

Objects that are big and heavy, such as trucks, cars, or herds of elephants, are measured in metric tonnes.

A **tonne** is a unit used for measuring mass.

1 t = 1000 kg
1 kg = 1000 g

1. Circle the unit you would use to measure the mass of the animals or objects in the picture.

   A kg, **t** B **kg**, t C **kg**, t D kg, **t**

   E **kg**, t F kg, **t** G **kg**, t H kg, **t**

2. Match the masses below with the animals or objects in the picture. There may be more than one possible answer for some masses.

   a) 6 t F, H b) 70 t A

   c) 65 kg G d) 10 t F, H

   e) 45 kg B, E f) 150 kg C

   g) 30 t D h) 40 kg B, E

3. List three other objects that would be best measured in tonnes.

   Suggested answer: garbage truck, fire truck, and ocean liner

Page 107

Test Yourself

Circle the correct answer.

Models

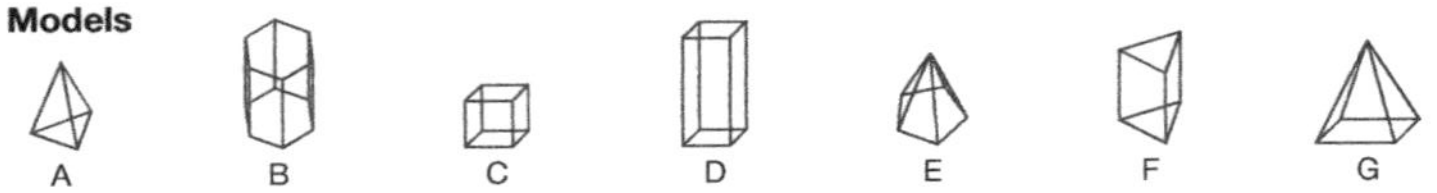

A B C D E F G

Nets

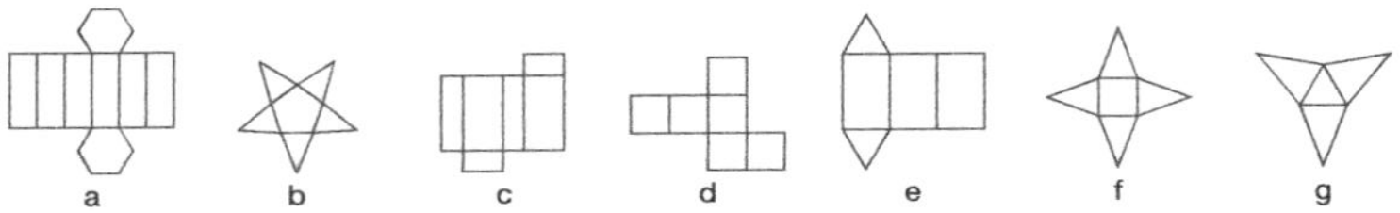

a b c d e f g

Use the pictures to answer Questions 1 to 5.

1. Which picture is the net of a pyramid?
   A. net e **B.** net a **C.** net c **D.** net f (circled)
2. Which net matches with model D?
   A. net b **B.** net g **C.** net d **D.** net c (circled)
3. Which model has no parallel edges?
   A. model B **B.** model G **C.** model E (circled) **D.** model C
4. Which model has 4 faces?
   A. model F **B.** model D **C.** model G **D.** model A (circled)
5. Which model matches with net e?
   A. model A **B.** model F (circled) **C.** model C **D.** model E
6. What is the most likely mass for a school backpack?
   A. 2 g **B.** 2 t **C.** 50 kg **D.** 2 kg (circled)
7. What is the most likely mass for a piano?
   A. 150 t **B.** 150 g **C.** 150 kg (circled) **D.** 15 kg
8. What is the most likely volume for an apple?
   A. 450 cm^3 (circled) **B.** 45 cm^3 **C.** 4500 cm^3 **D.** 4 cm^3
9. How much water would likely be displaced if a pencil were put under water?
   A. 150 mL **B.** 150 L **C.** 15 L **D.** 15 mL (circled)

Page 108

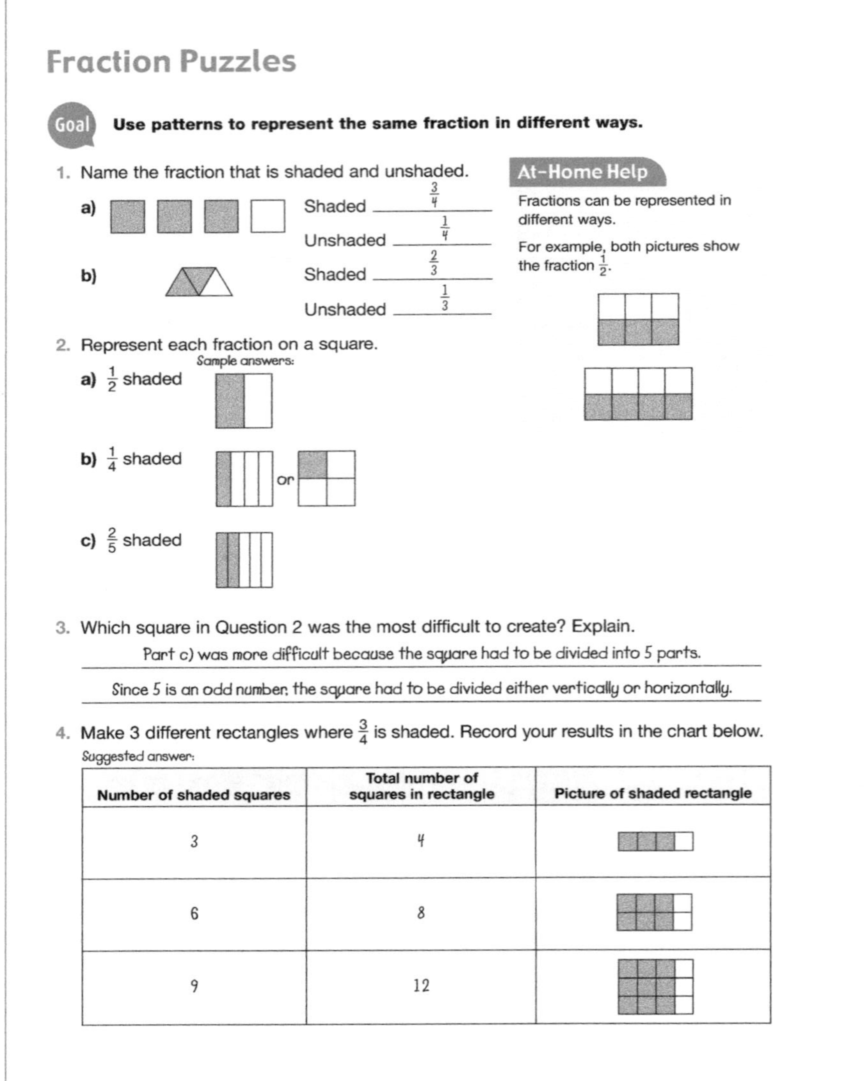

Fraction Puzzles

Goal **Use patterns to represent the same fraction in different ways.**

1. Name the fraction that is shaded and unshaded.
   a) Shaded $\frac{3}{4}$ Unshaded $\frac{1}{4}$
   b) Shaded $\frac{2}{3}$ Unshaded $\frac{1}{3}$

At-Home Help

Fractions can be represented in different ways.

For example, both pictures show the fraction $\frac{1}{2}$.

2. Represent each fraction on a square.
   Sample answers:
   a) $\frac{1}{2}$ shaded
   b) $\frac{1}{4}$ shaded (or)
   c) $\frac{2}{5}$ shaded

3. Which square in Question 2 was the most difficult to create? Explain.
   Part c) was more difficult because the square had to be divided into 5 parts.
   Since 5 is an odd number, the square had to be divided either vertically or horizontally.

4. Make 3 different rectangles where $\frac{3}{4}$ is shaded. Record your results in the chart below.
   Suggested answer:

Number of shaded squares	Total number of squares in rectangle	Picture of shaded rectangle
3	4	
6	8	
9	12	

Page 109

Equivalent Fractions

Goal **Make models of fractions and name equivalent fractions.**

1. Colour each model to show each fraction.
Suggested answers:
   a) $\frac{1}{2}$ ▯ or ▯ **b)** $\frac{2}{3}$ ▯ or ▯
   c) $\frac{4}{8}$ ▯ or ▯ **d)** $\frac{8}{12}$ ▯ or ▯

2. Which fractions in Question 1 are equivalent? Explain how you know.
$\frac{1}{2}$ and $\frac{4}{8}$. The numerator in each of these fractions is exactly half of the denominator.
$\frac{2}{3}$ and $\frac{8}{12}$. Both fractions represent the same amount.

3. Write the fraction to represent the shaded part in each model.
   a) *$\frac{3}{4}$*
   b) 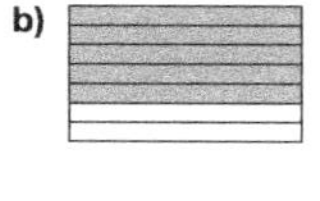 *$\frac{5}{7}$*
   c) *$\frac{6}{8}$*
   d) 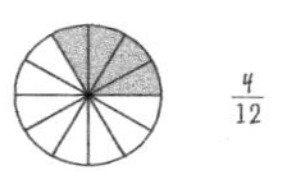 *$\frac{4}{12}$*

4. Sketch a fraction model that shows an equivalent fraction for Parts **c)** and **d)** in Question 3. Write the equivalent fraction.
   c) *Suggested answer:* *$\frac{3}{4}$*
   d) *Suggested answer:* *$\frac{1}{3}$*

At-Home Help

Equivalent fractions are fractions that represent the same part of a whole or the same part of a set.

For example, $\frac{2}{4}$ is equivalent to $\frac{1}{2}$.

$\frac{2}{4} = \frac{1}{2}$

$\frac{2}{4}$ $\frac{1}{2}$

Page 110

Comparing Fractions

Goal **Compare the size of fractions.**

1. Compare. Write > or <. Explain your strategy.
   a) $\frac{3}{8}$ *<* $\frac{5}{8}$ *Suggested answer: Since the denominators are the same, compare the numerators. 5 is greater than 3 so $\frac{5}{8}$ is greater.*

   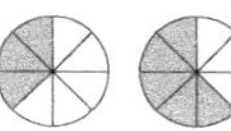

   b) $\frac{4}{5}$ *<* $\frac{19}{20}$ *Suggested answer: Draw a model for each fraction and compare the two models.*

   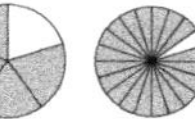
   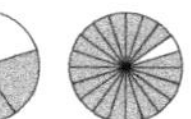

   c) $\frac{4}{6}$ *>* $\frac{5}{9}$ *Suggested answer: Draw a model for each fraction and compare the two models.*

   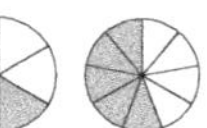
   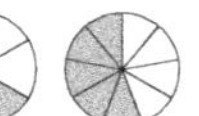

2. **a)** Draw a tablecloth that is $\frac{1}{3}$ red and $\frac{1}{2}$ yellow. Which area is greater? Explain.
$\frac{1}{2}$ is greater than $\frac{1}{3}$. Since the sections of the tablecloth are the same size, count the sections of each colour. 4 sections are red and 6 sections are yellow. So there is more yellow than red.

Suggested answer:

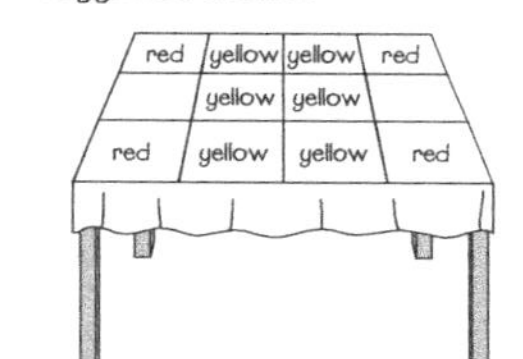

   b) What fraction of the tablecloth is not shaded? Explain.
$\frac{2}{12}$ or $\frac{1}{6}$ is not shaded. Since the sections of the tablecloth are the same size, count the number of unshaded sections.

At-Home Help

Fractions can be compared when the denominators are the same, because the total number of sections and the size of the sections are the same.

For example, to compare $\frac{3}{5}$ and $\frac{4}{5}$, look at the numerators.

$\frac{4}{5}$ is greater than $\frac{3}{5}$.

If the denominators are not the same, model the fractions using a picture. Then compare the pictures.

For example, to compare $\frac{3}{8}$ and $\frac{2}{6}$ use a model.

$\frac{3}{8}$ is greater than $\frac{2}{6}$.

Page 111

Improper Fractions and Mixed Numbers

Goal **Represent and rename improper fractions as mixed numbers.**

1. Draw a picture to represent each improper fraction.

   a) $\frac{14}{4}$ Suggested answer:

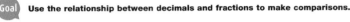

   b) $\frac{15}{10}$ Suggested answer:

   c) $\frac{12}{8}$ Suggested answer:

   d) $\frac{7}{2}$ Suggested answer:

At-Home Help

A **mixed number** is a number made up of a whole number and a fraction.

For example, $1\frac{1}{4}$ is a mixed number.

An **improper fraction** is a fraction with a numerator that is greater than or equal to the denominator.

For example, $\frac{5}{4}$ is an improper fraction.

Mixed numbers can be renamed as improper fractions.

For example, $1\frac{1}{4} = \frac{5}{4}$.

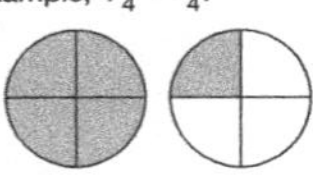
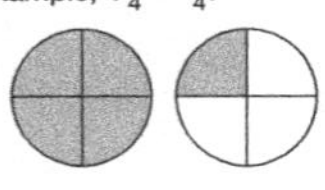

2. Rename each improper fraction in Question 1 as a mixed number.

   a) $\frac{14}{4} =$ $3\frac{2}{4}$ or $3\frac{1}{2}$ b) $\frac{15}{10} =$ $1\frac{5}{10}$ or $1\frac{1}{2}$ c) $\frac{12}{8} =$ $1\frac{4}{8}$ or $1\frac{1}{2}$ d) $\frac{7}{2} =$ $3\frac{1}{2}$

3. Change each mixed number to an improper fraction.

   a) $4\frac{1}{2} =$ $\frac{9}{2}$ b) $3\frac{2}{8} =$ $\frac{26}{8}$ c) $1\frac{3}{5} =$ $\frac{8}{5}$

   d) $2\frac{5}{6} =$ $\frac{17}{6}$ e) $5\frac{5}{10} =$ $\frac{55}{10}$ f) $3\frac{4}{12} =$ $\frac{40}{12}$

4. A hockey tournament for younger children is a total of 4 games. Each game is $\frac{2}{3}$ of an hour long. Use improper fractions and mixed numbers to represent each time. Explain your thinking.

   a) length of 1 tournament

   $\frac{8}{3}$ h or $2\frac{2}{3}$ h. Draw 4 clocks and divide each into thirds. Shade in $\frac{2}{3}$ on each clock. Then count the total number of thirds.

   b) length of 2 tournaments

   $\frac{16}{3}$ h or $5\frac{1}{3}$ h. Multiply the number of thirds counted in Part a) by 2.

Page 112

Relating Fractions to Decimals

Goal **Use the relationship between decimals and fractions to make comparisons.**

You will need a calculator.

1. Calculate.

   a) $6 \div 8 =$ 0.75

   b) $3 \div 20 =$ 0.15

   c) $8 \div 25 =$ 0.32

2. Order these fractions from least to greatest. Use inequality signs.

   $\frac{4}{5}, \frac{9}{50}, 3\frac{3}{25}$ $\frac{9}{50} < \frac{4}{5} < 3\frac{3}{25}$

3. Write decimal equivalents for each fraction in Question 2.

   a) $\frac{4}{5} =$ 0.8 b) $\frac{9}{50} =$ 0.18 c) $3\frac{3}{25} =$ 3.12

4. Order these decimals from greatest to least. Use inequality signs.

   0.20, 1.25, 0.55 1.25 > 0.55 > 0.20

5. Write each decimal in Question 4 as a fraction.

   a) $0.20 =$ $\frac{20}{100}$ or $\frac{1}{5}$ b) $1.25 =$ $1\frac{25}{100}$ or $1\frac{1}{4}$ c) $0.55 =$ $\frac{55}{100}$ or $\frac{11}{20}$

6. Martin won $100 in a bingo game. He shared his prize equally with 8 people in his family.

   a) How much did each person get? Show your work.

   $100 ÷ 8 = $12.50

   b) How would you write this decimal number as a mixed number?

   $\frac{100}{8} = 12\frac{4}{8}$ or $12\frac{1}{2}$

At-Home Help

A **decimal equivalent** is a decimal that represents the same part of a whole or part of a set as a fraction.

For example:

$\frac{1}{4} = \frac{25}{100}$
$= 0.25$

$\frac{5}{100} = 0.05$

Solve Problems by Making Models

Solve fraction problems by making models of the information.

1. Math and reading classes begin at 10:15 a.m. They run for $2\frac{3}{4}$ hours. What time will math and reading finish? Show your work.

   Add 2 h to 10:15 a.m. to get 12:15 p.m. $\frac{3}{4}$ h is the same as 45 min. So add 45 min to 12:15 p.m. to get 1:00 p.m.

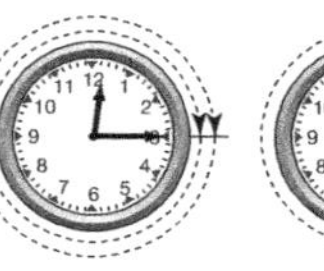

At-Home Help

To solve problems with fractions, start by making a model. You may use counters, shapes, or sketches.

You may need to arrange the counters or shapes into groups that match the fractions in the problem.

Use the arrangement to find the answer.

2. Danielle shares her snack with her friends. She has 16 carrots and 12 strawberries. She gives $\frac{1}{2}$ of her carrots and $\frac{2}{3}$ of her strawberries to her friends.

   a) How many carrots and strawberries does she give away? Show your work.

   Suggested answer: 8 carrots and 8 strawberries

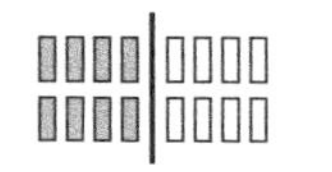

carrots

strawberries

   b) How many carrots and strawberries does she have left for herself? Show your work.

   Suggested answer: (carrots) 16 − 8 = 8
   (strawberries) 12 − 8 = 4

3. Jin fills a container $1\frac{2}{3}$ full while Brad fills a container $\frac{7}{4}$ full. Who has more? How do you know? Show your work.

   Suggested answer: $\frac{7}{4} = 1\frac{3}{4}$ Brad has more.

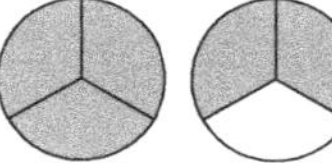

Jin

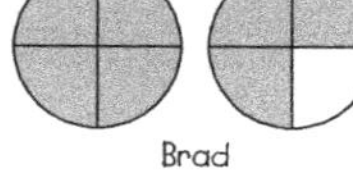

Brad

Ordering Fractions on a Number Line

Use number lines to compare and order fractions.

1. Use a number line to find the greatest fraction.

   $\frac{3}{4}$ $\frac{5}{8}$ $\frac{4}{6}$ — *$\frac{3}{4}$*

2. Order these fractions from least to greatest. Use inequality signs.

   $\frac{3}{4}$ $\frac{3}{8}$ $\frac{5}{6}$ $\frac{1}{3}$ $\frac{8}{9}$ $\frac{1}{2}$

   $\frac{1}{3} < \frac{3}{8} < \frac{1}{2} < \frac{3}{4} < \frac{5}{6} < \frac{8}{9}$

3. Order these fractions from greatest to least. Use inequality signs.

   $\frac{2}{4}$ $\frac{1}{4}$ $\frac{2}{3}$ $\frac{7}{8}$ $\frac{1}{3}$ $\frac{3}{5}$

   $\frac{7}{8} > \frac{2}{3} > \frac{3}{5} > \frac{2}{4} > \frac{1}{3} > \frac{1}{4}$

4. Lise bought different lengths of material to make curtains. She bought $\frac{2}{3}$ of a length of silk, $\frac{5}{7}$ of cotton, and $\frac{4}{5}$ of corduroy. Which material is the greatest length? Show your work.

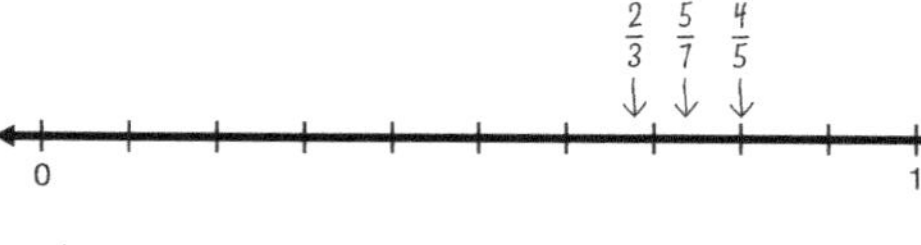

corduroy

At-Home Help

To compare fractions, use a number line to mark the positions of the fractions.

The order of the fractions can be read from the number line.

For example, to order $\frac{3}{4}$, $\frac{2}{3}$, and $\frac{3}{8}$ from least to greatest, use a number line.

The correct order is $\frac{3}{8}$, $\frac{2}{3}$, and $\frac{3}{4}$.

Page 115

Test Yourself

Circle the correct answer.

1. What fraction does *not* represent the shaded part of the picture?
   - A. $\frac{8}{12}$
   - B. $\frac{4}{6}$
   - C. $\frac{6}{12}$ (circled)
   - D. $\frac{2}{3}$
2. What fraction is equivalent to $\frac{4}{5}$?
   - A. $\frac{2}{3}$
   - B. $\frac{8}{12}$
   - C. $\frac{5}{4}$
   - D. $\frac{8}{10}$ (circled)
3. Which shaded rectangle is the same as $\frac{6}{9}$?
   - A.
   - B. (circled)
   - C.
   - D.
4. What fraction is shaded in the picture?
   - A. $\frac{2}{6}$
   - B. $\frac{8}{10}$
   - C. $\frac{2}{3}$ (circled)
   - D. $\frac{4}{8}$
5. What fraction is shaded in the picture?
   - A. $\frac{2}{3}$
   - B. $\frac{3}{6}$
   - C. $\frac{3}{2}$
   - D. $\frac{3}{9}$ (circled)
6. Which fraction is greater than $\frac{5}{9}$?
   - A. $\frac{7}{13}$
   - B. $\frac{6}{10}$ (circled)
   - C. $\frac{3}{7}$
   - D. $\frac{4}{8}$

Page 116

Test Yourself Page 2

7. Which fraction is less than $\frac{8}{10}$?
   - A. $\frac{4}{5}$
   - B. $\frac{8}{9}$
   - C. $\frac{7}{9}$ (circled)
   - D. $\frac{10}{12}$
8. What is $\frac{14}{8}$ as a mixed number?
   - A. $2\frac{6}{8}$
   - B. $2\frac{4}{6}$
   - C. $1\frac{4}{6}$
   - D. $1\frac{6}{8}$ (circled)
9. What is $\frac{17}{13}$ as a mixed number?
   - A. $1\frac{13}{17}$
   - B. $2\frac{4}{17}$
   - C. $1\frac{4}{13}$ (circled)
   - D. $2\frac{4}{13}$
10. What is $2\frac{3}{5}$ as an improper fraction?
    - A. $\frac{13}{5}$ (circled)
    - B. $\frac{10}{5}$
    - C. $\frac{10}{3}$
    - D. $\frac{8}{5}$
11. What is $5\frac{4}{7}$ as an improper fraction?
    - A. $\frac{35}{4}$
    - B. $\frac{54}{7}$
    - C. $\frac{39}{7}$ (circled)
    - D. $\frac{39}{4}$
12. Which decimal represents the part that is shaded?
    - A. 3.5 (circled)
    - B. 5.3
    - C. 3.05
    - D. 5.03
13. What is the decimal equivalent of $\frac{15}{20}$?
    - A. 0.15
    - B. 0.65
    - C. 0.75 (circled)
    - D. 0.55
14. What is $\frac{17}{20}$ as a decimal?
    - A. 0.83
    - B. 0.73
    - C. 0.75
    - D. 0.85 (circled)
15. What is 0.14 as a fraction?
    - A. $\frac{14}{10}$
    - B. $\frac{7}{10}$
    - C. $1\frac{4}{10}$
    - D. $\frac{14}{100}$ (circled)
16. Raj and Milo play on the same soccer team. Each game is 60 min long. Raj plays $\frac{1}{3}$ of a game. Milo plays $\frac{5}{6}$ of a game. How many more minutes does Milo play than Raj?
    - A. 20 min
    - B. 35 min
    - C. 30 min (circled)
    - D. 25 min

Using Probability Language

Goal **Use probability language to describe predictions.**

1. Make a check mark under the probability word that would apply for each sentence. For some sentences, more than one probability word may apply. Explain the reason for your choice.

   a) Today is Wednesday.

   b) It will rain today.

   c) The teacher is in the classroom.

   d) The temperature is 1°C and it might snow.

   e) People go on vacation in the summer.

   f) You can travel to another planet in a rocket.

At-Home Help

Probability words are used to describe how likely it is that an event will happen.

Examples of probability words are
- certain
- likely
- more probable
- less probable
- impossible

	Impossible	Less probable	More probable	Certain	Reason
a)	✓			✓	It depends on day of the week.
b)	✓	✓	✓	✓	It depends on weather forecast today.
c)				✓	My teacher is in the classroom teaching us math.
d)			✓		It usually snows when the temperature is close to 0°C.
e)			✓		Families usually go on vacation in the summer because children are not in school.
f)		✓			No human has landed on another planet yet.

2. Which event from Question 1 did you find most difficult to decide the probability? Explain.

   Suggested answer: Part d) because it may rain or snow if the temperature is 1°C.

3. Give an example of an event that would fit each probability word.

   a) impossible Suggested answer: It snows when the temperature is 20°C.

   b) more probable Suggested answer: I will eat my lunch today.

   c) certain Suggested answer: I am in Grade 5.

   d) less probable Suggested answer: I chew my food 20 times before swallowing.

Predicting Probabilities

Goal **Predict the probability of events and test your predictions.**

Letters	Value of each letter
AEIOU	1
LNRST	2
BCDFGHKMPVWY	3
JQXZ	4

At-Home Help

It is possible to predict the probability of an event by repeating an experiment several times.

The results of the experiment can help you think about why the results happened. You can also use the results to predict the probability of other events that are related.

1. Use the information in the table above. Predict how likely each event is.

   a) picking three letters and getting a value of 12 very unlikely, but possible

   b) picking a 3-point letter before picking a 1-point letter very likely

   c) picking four consonants before picking any vowels likely, but not very likely

2. Test each prediction in Question 1. Explain your results.

   a) Sample answers: I picked 3 letters 10 times. I didn't get a value of 12. The only way to get a value of 12 with three letters is to pick three 4-point letters. This is very unlikely.

   b) It is easier to pick 3-point letters because there are 12 of them. There are only five 1-point letters. In 10 tries, this happened 2 times.

   c) Although there are far fewer vowels than consonants, it is still possible to pick at least 1 vowel because the picking is random. This happened once in 10 times.

3. Write the letters from your first and last name on separate pieces of paper. Place them into the same bag or container. Predict how likely each event is. Test your predictions. Remember to place each letter back into the bag after each draw. Explain what you found out.

   a) on the first draw, picking a vowel instead of a consonant

   Suggested answer: likely, but not very likely

   You are more likely to pick a consonant because most names have fewer vowels than consonants.

   b) on two draws, picking the first letter of your name before any other letter

   Suggested answer: very unlikely, but possible

Page 119

Probabilities as Fractions

Express the likelihood of an event as a fraction.

You rolled two dice 10 times and recorded the sum of the numbers you got on each roll.

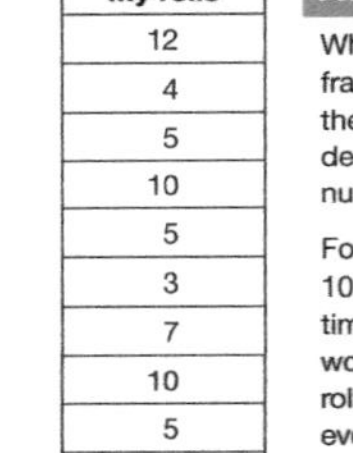

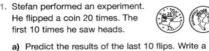

My rolls
12
4
5
10
5
3
7
10
5
9

At-Home Help

When probabilities are written as fractions, the numerator represents the number of likely events, and the denominator represents the total number of events.

For example, if you rolled a die 10 times and you got a 4 three times, the total number of events would be 10, because the die was rolled 10 times. The number of likely events in this case would be 3, because you got a 4 three times. So the probability of you rolling a 4 was $\frac{3}{10}$.

1. Write the probability of each event as a fraction.

a) getting 5 $\frac{3}{10}$

b) getting an even number $\frac{4}{10}$ or $\frac{2}{5}$

c) getting a number below 7 $\frac{5}{10}$ or $\frac{1}{2}$

d) getting a number above 9 $\frac{3}{10}$

2. **a)** Write the names of 6 different sports on separate pieces of paper. Place them in a bag or container.

Suggested answer: cycling, soccer, swimming, basketball, baseball, and hockey

b) What is the probability of choosing a sport beginning with letter S? Carry out an experiment. Pick one sport from the bag and record your results. Repeat the experiment 10 times. Write the probability as a fraction.

Suggested answer: $\frac{2}{10}$

c) Carry out another experiment to find the probability of choosing a sport that has only two syllables. Repeat the experiment 10 times. Write the probability as a fraction.

Suggested answer: $\frac{6}{10}$ or $\frac{3}{5}$

Page 120

Modelling Probability Problems

Conduct probability experiments.

1. Stefan performed an experiment. He flipped a coin 20 times. The first 10 times he saw heads.

a) Predict the results of the last 10 flips. Write a fraction for your prediction. Explain your prediction.

Prediction: *5 heads out of 10 flips*

Fraction: $\frac{5}{10}$ or $\frac{1}{2}$

Reason: *Stefan is just as likely to get a head as a tail.*

b) Now flip a coin 10 times and record your results in the table. Write your results as a fraction.

Flip of coin	Heads	Tails
1	✓	
2		✓
3	✓	
4	✓	
5	✓	
6	✓	
7		✓
8	✓	
9	✓	
10		✓

Suggested answer: (heads) $\frac{7}{10}$, (tails) $\frac{3}{10}$

At-Home Help

It is possible to predict the probability that an event will happen. To test the prediction, you can do an experiment and record the results in a table.

The results of the experiment can be written as fractions to show probabilities.

Sometimes the results do not match the predictions.

For example, there is a 1 in 2 chance of getting heads when flipping a coin. So the predicted probability is $\frac{1}{2}$.

If you flipped the coin 10 times and got heads 6 times, then the probability of getting heads in the experiment was $\frac{6}{10}$.

2. Write the names of girls and boys on small pieces of paper. Make sure there are 8 names in total. Place the names in a bag or container. Conduct 2 experiments for each part. How many names of girls and boys might give you these results?

a) picking a girl's name is more probable

Suggested answer: 5 girls' names and 3 boys' names

b) picking a boy's name is very probable

Suggested answer: 6 boys' names and 2 girls' names

c) picking a girl's name is very improbable but not impossible

Suggested answer: 7 boys' names and 1 girl's name

Page 121

Using Tree Diagrams

Goal **Use tree diagrams to record the outcomes of an experiment.**

1. Play the game Rock, Paper, Scissors 6 times with a partner at home.
   Keep a tally of the results using a tree diagram.

   Suggested answer:

I choose	Partner chooses	Results
Rock	Rock	I tie
	Paper	I partner wins
	Scissors	I I win
Paper	Rock	I I win
	Paper	
	Scissors	
Scissors	Rock	I partner wins
	Paper	I I win
	Scissors	

2. Students choose their pizza slices to eat for lunch. The cost depends upon the type of crust and the number of toppings.

   Crust: thin, thick
   Toppings: pepperoni, mushroom

   a) Draw a tree diagram to show all possible pizza slice combinations.

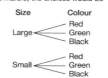

Crust	Toppings
Thin	Pepperoni
	Mushroom
	Pepperoni and mushroom
Thick	Pepperoni
	Mushroom
	Pepperoni and mushroom

   b) How many different types of pizza slices could you buy? 6

   c) Imagine that only one slice is left of each type of pizza, and that you choose a slice by pointing with your eyes closed. Which event is more probable, you choosing a pizza slice with one topping or a slice with two toppings? Record your answer as a fraction. Explain.

   1 topping, $\frac{4}{6}$. There are 6 possible pizzas in total and 4 of them have one topping and 2 have two toppings.

At-Home Help

Tree diagrams are pictures that show all possible combinations for a particular choice.

For example:
A bag has two sizes of marbles. Each size of marble comes in three colours: red, green, and black. There is only one marble of each size and colour. If you were to pick a marble, the choices would be

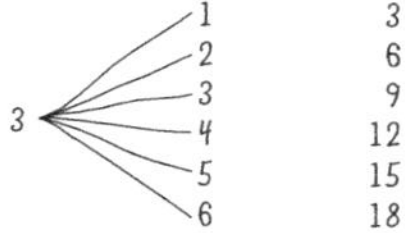

The total number of marbles is 6, and two marbles are red. So the probability of picking a marble that is red is $\frac{2}{6}$.

Page 122

Solve Problems by Considering All Possibilities

Goal **Think about all of the possibilities when solving a problem.**

You roll a die and get a number. Then you roll the die again and multiply the first number by the second number. You get 2 bonus points if you make a correct prediction about the product *before* rolling the die the second time.

1. **a)** You play one game and roll a 4 on the first roll. Use a tree diagram to list all possible products.

First roll	Second roll	Product
4	1	4
	2	8
	3	12
	4	16
	5	20
	6	24

   b) You play another game and roll a 3 on the first roll. Use a tree diagram to list all possible products.

First roll	Second roll	Product
3	1	3
	2	6
	3	9
	4	12
	5	15
	6	18

   c) Based on your tree diagrams, which prediction should you make if you roll 4 on the first roll? Explain.

   Suggested answer: The product will be an even number.

2. Imagine you roll a die 10 times, and record the number you get on each roll. If you were to multiply each number you got by 3, which numbers must you roll to always get a product that is an even number?

   2, 4, or 6

At-Home Help

To solve a probability problem, start by listing all possibilities. It is easier if you organize the possibilities in a tree diagram or chart.

Look at your diagram and decide what predictions are reasonable.

You can test your predictions by doing an experiment.

Page 123

Test Yourself

Circle the correct answer.

1. What is the correct order in which to place these probability words?
   - **A.** certain, less probable, impossible, likely, more probable, unlikely
   - **B.** less probable, more probable, likely, unlikely, certain, impossible
   - **C.** impossible, unlikely, less probable, likely, more probable, certain
   - **D.** certain, likely, more probable, less probable, unlikely, impossible
2. Which event is impossible?
   - **A.** It will rain tomorrow.
   - **B.** In Canada, winter is warmer than summer.
   - **C.** We will have a test in math soon.
   - **D.** The school year ends in June.
3. Which event is certain?
   - **A.** I will go to a movie soon.
   - **B.** I will sleep 8 hours tonight.
   - **C.** Earth orbits around the sun.
   - **D.** All trees will grow this season.
4. Which probability word would best describe this event?

   It will rain 1 out of 7 days this week.

   A. certain **B.** less probable **C.** more probable **D.** impossible
5. Which probability word would best describe this event?

   All students in a class are boys.

   A. certain **B.** less probable **C.** more probable **D.** impossible
6. When Twyla rolled a pair of dice 10 times, these numbers appeared: 10, 6, 9, 10, 5, 3, 6, 4, 6, and 9. What was the probability of Twyla rolling a 6?

   A. $\frac{4}{10}$ **B.** $\frac{4}{6}$ **C.** $\frac{3}{6}$ **D.** $\frac{3}{10}$
7. Look at Question 6. What was the probability of Twyla rolling an even number?

   A. $\frac{6}{10}$ **B.** $\frac{4}{10}$ **C.** $\frac{5}{10}$ **D.** $\frac{7}{10}$

Page 124

Test Yourself Page 2

8. Look at Question 6. What was the probability of Twyla rolling a number below 5?

   A. $\frac{2}{5}$ **B.** $\frac{1}{4}$ **C.** $\frac{2}{10}$ **D.** $\frac{5}{10}$
9. Imagine that all the dessert choices on the menu were written on separate pieces of paper, and these papers were put in a bag. You choose one dessert choice from the bag without looking. What would be the probability of choosing a dessert with chocolate?

   A. $\frac{2}{8}$ **B.** $\frac{3}{8}$ **C.** $\frac{6}{10}$ **D.** $\frac{6}{15}$
10. Which tree diagram represents the dessert choices in Question 9?

A. Type — Flavour
- Cake: Chocolate, Apple, Blueberry
- Ice cream: Vanilla, Chocolate
- Pie: Lemon, Strawberry, Apple

B. Type — Flavour
- Cake: Blueberry, Chocolate, Raspberry
- Ice cream: Vanilla, Chocolate, Blueberry
- Pie: Strawberry, Lemon, Apple

C. Type — Flavour
- Cake: Chocolate, Raspberry
- Ice cream: Vanilla, Chocolate
- Pie: Strawberry, Lemon, Apple

D. Type — Flavour
- Cake: Blueberry, Chocolate, Raspberry
- Ice cream: Vanilla, Chocolate
- Pie: Strawberry, Lemon, Apple

Tiling an Area

Goal **Tile an area using software.**

1. How many congruent shapes will tile this area? Use Geometer's Sketchpad or the grid below.

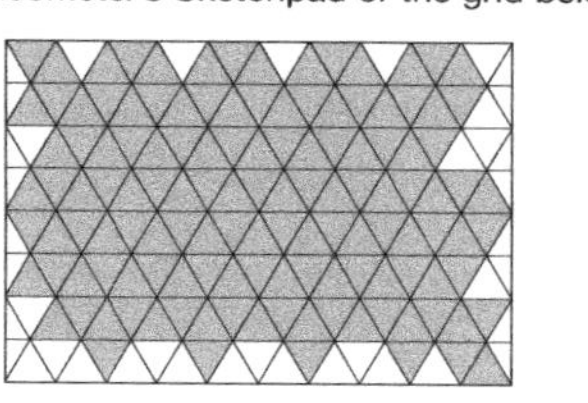

32 congruent shapes

2. Tile the area below with this shape.

Cover as much of the area as possible. Use reflections only and show the lines of reflection on the grid.

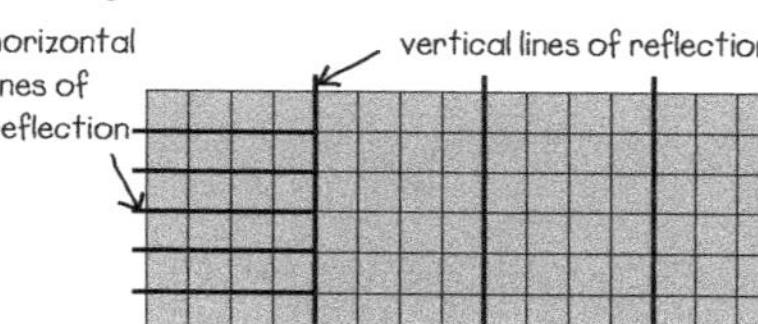

3. How would you move this shape to tile the lightly shaded area below?

Circle the correct answer.

- translate 4 squares left
- (rotate 90° clockwise) [circled]
- translate 2 squares right and 1 square down
- reflect about the horizontal

At-Home Help

Congruent means the same shape and size.

To tile an area, use repeated congruent shapes. There should be no gaps and no overlaps.

line of reflection

A **line of reflection** is a line in which a shape is reflected. Both shapes are identical in size and shape, but one appears flipped.

For example, in the picture above, there is a horizontal line of reflection.

Describing Tiling Patterns

Goal **Describe tiling patterns.**

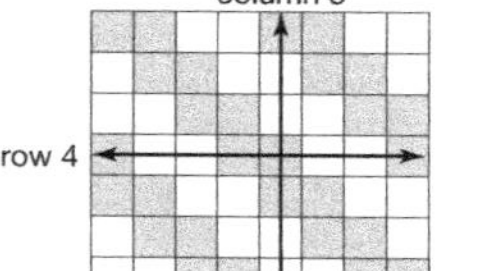
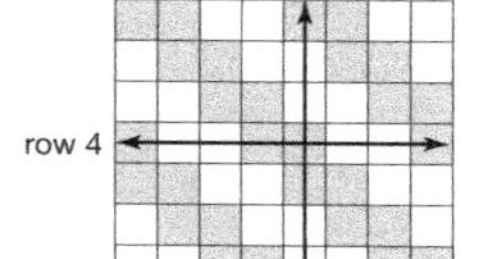

1. Which columns have different pattern rules? How do you know?

Columns 1, 2, 3, and 4 have different pattern rules because either they start with tiles of a different colour or they start with different numbers of tiles of a particular colour. Columns 5, 6, 7, and 8 are identical to columns 1, 2, 3, and 4 respectively.

2. Write a pattern rule for columns 5 and 7. How are the pattern rules the same? How are they different?

(column 5) Start with 1 shaded tile, then 2 white, 2 shaded, and 2 white tiles. (column 7) Start with 1 white tile, then 2 shaded, 2 white, and 2 shaded tiles. Pattern rules are the same in that the tile colour changes based on the same sequence: 1 tile of one colour, 2 tiles of other colour, and so on. Pattern rules are different in that the colours of the tiles in the two columns are reversed (what is white in one column is shaded in the other).

3. Record the number of white and shaded tiles in each column. Use the table below.

Column	White tiles	Shaded tiles
1	4	3
2	3	4
3	3	4
4	4	3
5	4	3
6	3	4
7	3	4
8	4	3

At-Home Help

A **tiling pattern** is a pattern of repeated congruent shapes that fit together with no gaps and no overlaps.

A **pattern rule** describes how you can reproduce a pattern.

For example, the pattern rule for the first column in the picture above is:

Start with 1 white rectangle, then 1 shaded square, 1 white rectangle, and 1 shaded square.

Page 127

Extending Tiling Patterns

 **Write a pattern rule to extend a pattern.**

1. Which pattern rule best describes the first row of this tiling pattern? Circle the correct answer.

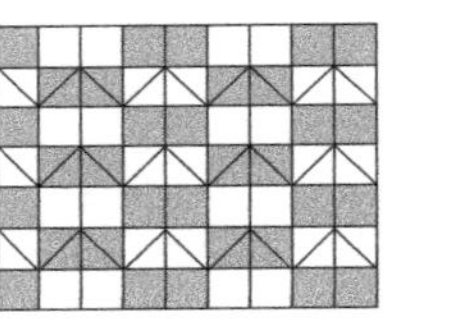

Start with 1 shaded tile, then alternate 1 white tile and 1 shaded tile.

Start with 1 white tile, then alternate 2 shaded tiles and 2 white tiles 4 times.

(Start with 1 shaded tile, then alternate 2 white tiles and 2 shaded tiles 2 times.)

Start with 1 white tile, then alternate 2 shaded tiles and 2 white tiles.

At-Home Help

A **pattern rule** states the starting point of a pattern, a description of the attributes that change, and the number of repetitions.

For example, the pattern rule for the first row is start with 1 shaded tile, then alternate 2 white tiles and 3 shaded tiles 3 times, and end with 2 white tiles.

2. Look at the tiling pattern in Question 1. Write a pattern rule for any column.

Suggested answer: (column 1) Start with 1 shaded tile, then alternate 1 white tile (with a diagonal through top left and bottom right vertices) and 1 shaded tile 3 times.

3. Write a pattern rule for a row on this rug based on the letter F.

Suggested answer: Start with a backward and upside down F. Hold bottom right corner of F down and turn 90° clockwise. Repeat the same turn 2 more times. Repeat this sequence 2 more times.

Page 128

Translating Shapes on Grids

 **Identify the rule for translating a shape.**

1. Which statement best describes this translation? Circle the correct answer.

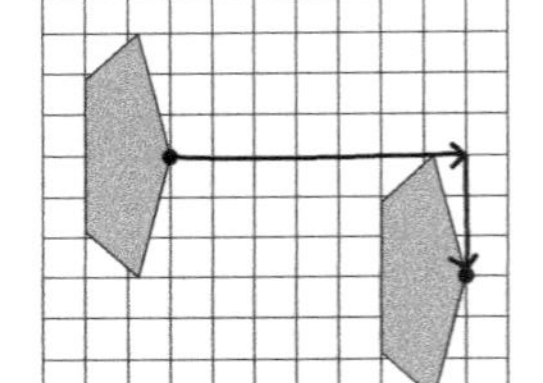

right 6 squares, down 3 squares

left 7 squares, up 4 squares

(right 7 squares, down 3 squares)

right 6 squares, down 2 squares

At-Home Help

A **translation** is a movement in a straight line. It can be left, right, up, or down.

For example, the translation shown is left 3 squares and down 5 squares.

2. Greg wrote rules to describe the translation of a shape. Follow Greg's steps in the box.

Show the result of each translation on the grid.

Start with a T-shape.
Step 1: right 6, down 2
Step 2: left 3, up 2
Step 3: left 3, down 2
Step 4: right 4, up 5
Step 5: up 2
Step 6: left 4

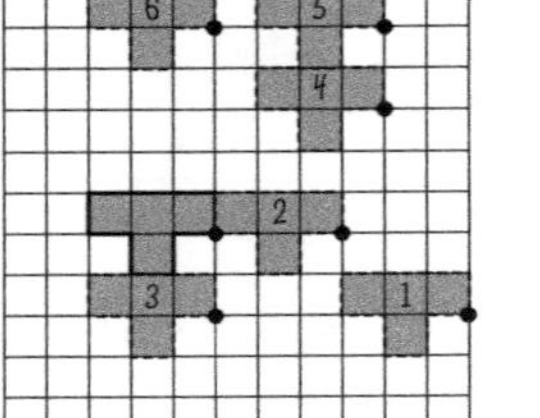

Rotating Shapes

Rotate shapes in a pattern.

You will need a protractor and a ruler.

1. Which rotation rule was used? Circle the correct answer.

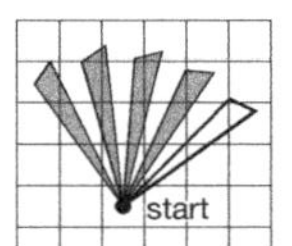

(Rotate 20° counterclockwise 4 times.) — circled

Rotate 25° counterclockwise 4 times.

Rotate 20° counterclockwise 5 times.

Rotate 25° counterclockwise 5 times.

2. Chandra's Rotation Rule
Choose a vertex on the shape to be the centre of rotation. Rotate 25° counterclockwise 10 times.

Draw the logo using the rotation rule. Label the centre of rotation. Label the angle of rotation showing the direction.

3. A shape was rotated to create this logo.

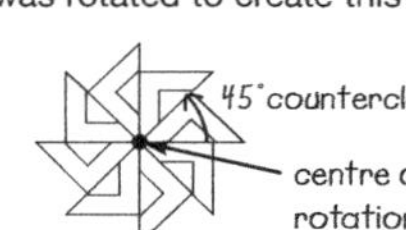

a) Identify the centre of rotation. Label it on the logo.

b) What is the angle of rotation? Label it on the logo. 45°

c) What is a possible direction of each rotation? Label it on the logo.
counterclockwise (or clockwise)

At-Home Help

A **rotation** in 2-D is a turn about a point called the **centre of rotation**. When describing a rotation, remember to include both the angle and direction.

For example, this shape was rotated 90° counterclockwise.

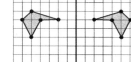

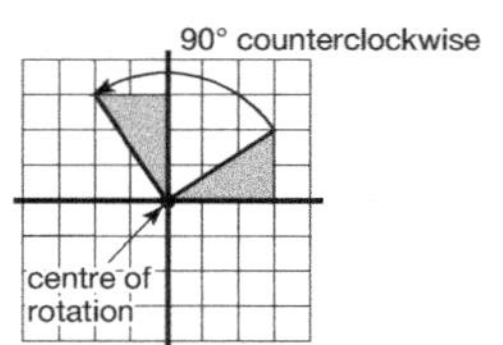

Suggested answer:

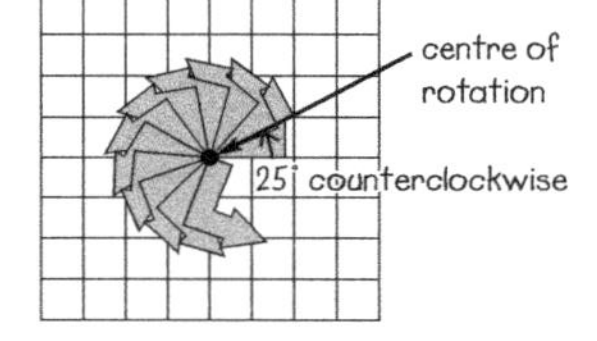

Communicate About Transformations

Describe transformations using math language.

You will need a protractor and a ruler.

1. Name the transformation used to create shapes A, B, and C from the black shape.

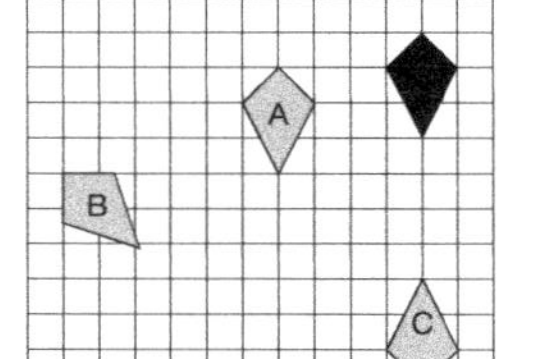

a) shape A translation, left 4 squares and down 1 square

b) shape B rotation, 45° counterclockwise

c) shape C reflection, in line 2 squares below lower vertex

2. Look at the picture in Question 1. What kind of transformation is each student describing? Identify the shape by its letter. Explain how you know.

a) Isabelle: My transformation changed the orientation of the shape.
shape B or shape C
Rotations and reflections change the orientation of a shape.

b) Zev: My transformation changed the position of every point on the shape.
shape A, shape B, or shape C
Translations change the position of every point on a shape but the orientation remains the same.
Rotations and reflections change the position of every point on a shape and change the orientation.

3. a) Copy the diagram on grid paper. Reflect it in the darker line.

b) Describe the effect of the reflection.
Reflections are mirror images of the original shape. Both shapes are congruent but the orientation of the reflection is different from the original.

At-Home Help

Transformations can change the position, orientation, and size of a shape.

Translations and rotations change the position of a shape but not its orientation.

Reflections change both the position and orientation of a shape.

When describing transformations, remember to use the Communication Checklist.

Communication Checklist
- ☑ Did you use math language?
- ☑ Did you include diagrams?
- ☑ Did you show the right amount of detail?

Page 131

Modelling Congruence with Transformations

Show congruence using transformations.

You will need a protractor and a ruler.

1. Circle the congruent shapes. Explain how you know. Use transformation language.

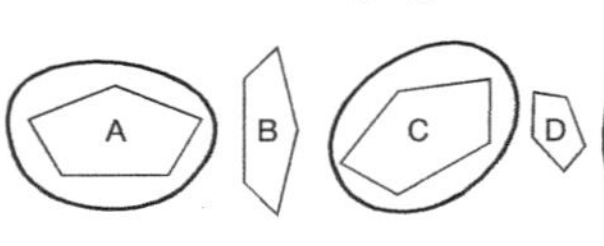

A, C, and E are identical in shape and size, but not in orientation. C and E are rotations of A.

At-Home Help

Congruent means the same shape and size. Congruent shapes may be translated, rotated, or reflected.

For example, all three triangles are congruent.

2.

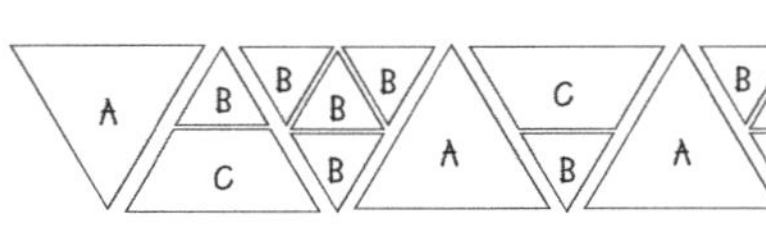

a) Identify all sets of congruent shapes. Use the letters A, B, and C to show shapes that are congruent.

b) Describe the shape in each set.

(set A) large equilateral triangles

(set B) small equilateral triangles

(set C) trapezoids

c) Choose one set of congruent shapes. Describe the transformations you used to show congruence.

(set A) rotation of 180° clockwise (or reflection in a horizontal line); translations to the right

(set B) rotations of 180° clockwise (or reflections in a horizontal or vertical line); translations to the right and down

(set C) rotation of 180° clockwise (or reflection in a horizontal line); translation to the right

Page 132

Exploring Similarity

Identify similar figures using transformations.

You will need a ruler.

1. Two shapes were made using elastics. Why are these shapes similar?

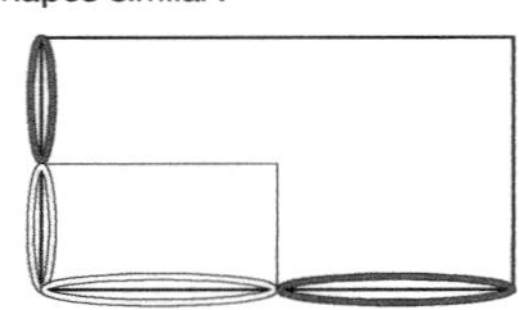

The larger rectangle is twice as big as the smaller rectangle.

At-Home Help

Similar means the same shape but a different size.

For example, both trapezoids are similar.

2. Yvette began to enlarge this triangle using elastics.

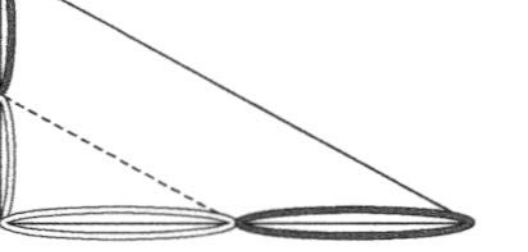

Draw the enlarged similar triangle.

3. What does a smaller similar triangle look like? Draw it.

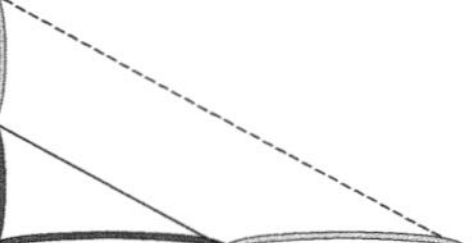

Test Yourself

Circle the correct answer.

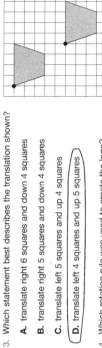

1. How would you move this shape to tile the lightly shaded area below?

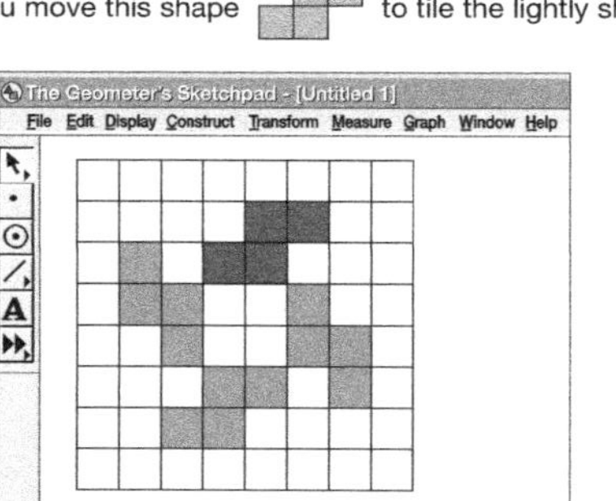

A. translate down 3 squares and left 2 squares
B. rotate 90° clockwise
C. translate right 2 squares and down 3 squares
D. reflect in a horizontal line

2. Which rows have a different pattern rule?

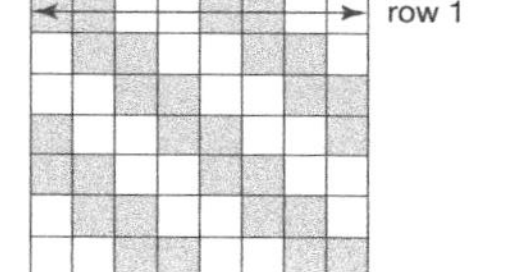

A. rows 1 and 5
B. rows 2 and 6
C. rows 3 and 7
D. rows 4 and 5

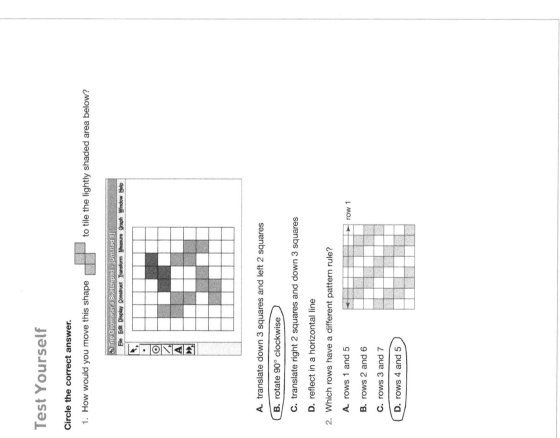

Test Yourself Page 2

3. Which statement best describes the translation shown?

A. translate right 6 squares and down 4 squares
B. translate right 5 squares and down 4 squares
C. translate left 5 squares and up 4 squares
D. translate left 4 squares and up 5 squares

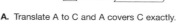

4. Which rotation rule was used to create the logo?

A. Rotate 30° counterclockwise about B 5 times.
B. Rotate 45° counterclockwise about O 7 times.
C. Rotate 45° counterclockwise about A 5 times.
D. Rotate 30° counterclockwise about O 7 times.

5. Which shapes are congruent and how do you know?

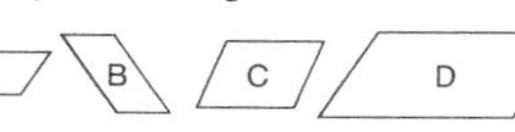

A. Translate A to C and A covers C exactly.
B. Rotate A to B and A covers B exactly.
C. Reflect A to D and A covers D exactly.
D. Translate A to B and A covers B exactly.

6. Look at the picture in Question 5. Which shapes are similar and how do you know?

A. C is twice as large as B.
B. C is twice as tall as A.
C. D is twice as large as A.
D. D is twice as tall as B.

CONGRATULATIONS!

You have completed the Nelson Math Grade 5 Workbook!

Presented to: ________________________________

Date: __________________________

GREAT JOB!

Study Planner

Sunday	Monday	Tuesday	Wednesday	Thursday	Friday	Saturday

Study Topic Checklist

- ☐ Patterns in Mathematics
- ☐ Numeration
- ☐ Data Management
- ☐ Addition and Subtraction
- ☐ Measuring Length and Time
- ☐ Multiplication and Division
- ☐ 2-D Geometry
- ☐ Area and Grids
- ☐ Multiplying Decimals
- ☐ Dividing Decimals
- ☐ 3-D Geometry and 3-D Measurement
- ☐ Fractions
- ☐ Probability
- ☐ Patterns and Motion in Geometry

Notes

____

____

____

____

Goals

____

____

____

____

Multiplication Table

1	1	2	3	4	5	6	7	8	9	10	11	12
1	1	2	3	4	5	6	7	8	9	10	11	12
2	2	4	6	8	10	12	14	16	18	20	22	24
3	3	6	9	12	15	18	21	24	27	30	33	36
4	4	8	12	16	20	24	28	32	36	40	44	48
5	5	10	15	20	25	30	35	40	45	50	55	60
6	6	12	18	24	30	36	42	48	54	60	66	72
7	7	14	21	28	35	42	49	56	63	70	77	84
8	8	16	24	32	40	48	56	64	72	80	88	96
9	9	18	27	36	45	54	63	72	81	90	99	108
10	10	20	30	40	50	60	70	80	90	100	110	120
11	11	22	33	44	55	66	77	88	99	110	121	132
12	12	24	36	48	60	72	84	96	108	120	132	144